THE SCREWTAPE LETTERS

MERE CHRISTIANITY

SURPRISED BY JOY

THE SCREWTAPE LETTERS

MERE CHRISTIANITY

SURPRISED BY JOY

C. S. LEWIS

BOOK-OF-THE-MONTH CLUB
NEW YORK

THE SCREWTAPE LETTERS

TO

J. R. R. TOLKIEN

"The best way to drive out the devil, if he will not yield to texts of Scripture, is to jeer and flout him, for he cannot bear scorn."—*Luther*

"The devill . . the prowde spirite . . cannot endure to be mocked."—*Thomas More*

PREFACE

I HAVE no intention of explaining how the correspondence which I now offer to the public fell into my hands.

There are two equal and opposite errors into which our race can fall about the devils. One is to disbelieve in their existence. The other is to believe, and to feel an excessive and unhealthy interest in them. They themselves are equally pleased by both errors and hail a materialist or a magician with the same delight. The sort of script which is used in this book can be very easily obtained by anyone who has once learned the knack; but ill-disposed or excitable people who might make a bad use of it shall not learn it from me.

Readers are advised to remember that the devil is a liar. Not everything that Screwtape says should be assumed to be true even from his own angle. I have made no attempt to identify any of the human beings mentioned in the letters; but I think it very unlikely that the portraits, say, of Fr. Spike or the patient's mother, are wholly just. There is wishful thinking in Hell as well as on Earth.

In conclusion, I ought to add that no effort has been made to clear up the chronology of

9

the letters. Number XVII appears to have been composed before rationing became serious; but in general the diabolical method of dating seems to bear no relation to terrestrial time and I have not attempted to reproduce it. The history of the European War, except in so far as it happens now and then to impinge upon the spiritual condition of one human being, was obviously of no interest to Screwtape.

C. S. LEWIS

MAGDALEN COLLEGE

July 5, 1941

I

M<small>Y DEAR</small> W<small>ORMWOOD</small>,

I note what you say about guiding
your patient's reading and taking care that he
sees a good deal of his materialist friend. But
are you not being a trifle *naïf*? It sounds as if
you supposed that *argument* was the way to
keep him out of the Enemy's clutches. That
might have been so if he had lived a few
centuries earlier. At that time the humans still
knew pretty well when a thing was proved and
when it was not; and if it was proved they
really believed it. They still connected thinking
with doing and were prepared to alter their
way of life as the result of a chain of reasoning.
But what with the weekly press and other such
weapons we have largely altered that. Your
man has been accustomed, ever since he was a
boy, to have a dozen incompatible philosophies
dancing about together inside his head. He
doesn't think of doctrines as primarily "true"
or "false", but as "academic" or "practical",
"outworn" or "contemporary", "conventional"
or "ruthless". Jargon, not argument, is your
best ally in keeping him from the Church.
Don't waste time trying to make him think

that materialism is *true*! Make him think it is strong, or stark, or courageous—that it is the philosophy of the future. That's the sort of thing he cares about.

The trouble about argument is that it moves the whole struggle onto the Enemy's own ground. He can argue too; whereas in really practical propaganda of the kind I am suggesting He has been shown for centuries to be greatly the inferior of Our Father Below. By the very act of arguing, you awake the patient's reason; and once it is awake, who can foresee the result? Even if a particular train of thought can be twisted so as to end in our favour, you will find that you have been strengthening in your patient the fatal habit of attending to universal issues and withdrawing his attention from the stream of immediate sense experiences. Your business is to fix his attention on the stream. Teach him to call it "real life" and don't let him ask what he means by "real".

Remember, he is not, like you, a pure spirit. Never having been a human (Oh that abominable advantage of the Enemy's!) you don't realise how enslaved they are to the pressure of the ordinary. I once had a patient, a sound atheist, who used to read in the British Museum. One day, as he sat reading, I saw a train of thought in his mind beginning to go the wrong way. The Enemy, of course, was at his elbow in a moment. Before I knew where I was I saw my twenty years' work beginning to totter. If I had lost my head and begun to attempt a defence by argument I should have been undone. But I was not such a fool. I struck instantly at the part of the man which I had best under my control and suggested that it was just about time he had some lunch. The Enemy presumably made the counter-suggestion (you know how one can never *quite* overhear what He says to them?) that this was more important than lunch. At least I think that must have been His line for when I said "Quite. In fact much *too* important to tackle at the end of a morning", the patient brightened up considerably; and by the time I had added "Much better come back after lunch and go into it with a fresh mind", he was already half way to the door. Once he was in the street the battle was won. I showed him a newsboy shouting the midday paper, and a No. 73 bus going past, and before he reached the bottom of the steps I had got into him an unalterable conviction that, whatever odd ideas might come into a man's head when he was shut up alone with his books, a healthy dose of "real life" (by which he meant the bus and the newsboy) was enough to show him that all "that sort of thing" just couldn't be true. He knew he'd had a narrow escape and in later years was fond of talking about "that inarticulate sense for actuality which is our ultimate safeguard against the aberrations of mere logic". He is now safe in Our Father's house.

You begin to see the point? Thanks to processes which we set at work in them centuries ago, they find it all but impossible to believe in the unfamiliar while the familiar is before their eyes. Keep pressing home on him the *ordinariness* of things. Above all, do not attempt to use science (I mean, the real sciences) as a defence against Christianity. .They will positively encourage him to think about realities he can't touch and see. There have been sad cases among the modern physicists. If he must dabble in science, keep him on economics and sociology; don't let him get away from that invaluable "real life". But the best of all is to let him read no science but to give him a grand general idea that he knows it all and that everything he happens to have picked up in casual talk and reading is "the results of modern investigation". Do remember you are there to fuddle him. From the way some of you young fiends talk, anyone would suppose it was our job to *teach*!

Your affectionate uncle
SCREWTAPE

II

MY DEAR WORMWOOD,
I note with grave displeasure that your patient has become a Christian. Do not indulge the hope that you will escape the usual penalties; indeed, in your better moments, I trust you would hardly even wish to do so. In the meantime we must make the best of the situation. There is no need to despair; hundreds of these adult converts have been reclaimed after a brief sojourn in the Enemy's camp and are now with us. All the *habits* of the patient, both mental and bodily, are still in our favour.

One of our great allies at present is the Church itself. Do not misunderstand me. I do not mean the Church as we see her spread out through all time and space and rooted in eternity, terrible as an army with banners. That, I confess, is a spectacle which makes our boldest tempters uneasy. But fortunately it is quite invisible to these humans. All your patient sees is the half-finished, sham Gothic erection on the new building estate. When he goes inside, he sees the local grocer with rather an oily expression on his face bustling up to offer him one shiny little book containing a

15

liturgy which neither of them understands, and one shabby little book containing corrupt texts of a number of religious lyrics, mostly bad, and in very small print. When he gets to his pew and looks round him he sees just that selection of his neighbours whom he has hitherto avoided. You want to lean pretty heavily on those neighbours. Make his mind flit to and fro between an expression like "the body of Christ" and the actual faces in the next pew. It matters very little, of course, what kind of people that next pew really contains. You may know one of them to be a great warrior on the Enemy's side. No matter. Your patient, thanks to Our Father below, is a fool. Provided that any of those neighbours sing out of tune, or have boots that squeak, or double chins, or odd clothes, the patient will quite easily believe that their religion must therefore be somehow ridiculous. At his present stage, you see, he has an idea of "Christians" in his mind which he supposes to be spiritual but which, in fact, is largely pictorial. His mind is full of togas and sandals and armour and bare legs and the mere fact that the other people in church wear modern clothes is a real—though of course an unconscious—difficulty to him. Never let it come to the surface; never let him ask what he expected them to look like. Keep everything hazy in his mind now, and you will have all eternity wherein to amuse yourself by producing in him the peculiar kind of clarity which Hell affords.

Work hard, then, on the disappointment or anticlimax which is certainly coming to the patient during his first few weeks as a churchman. The Enemy allows this disappointment to occur on the threshold of every human endeavour. It occurs when the boy who has been enchanted in the nursery by *Stories from the Odyssey* buckles down to really learning Greek. It occurs when lovers have got married and begin the real task of learning to live together. In every department of life it marks the transition from dreaming aspiration to laborious doing. The Enemy takes this risk because He has a curious fantasy of making all these disgusting little human vermin into what He calls His "free" lovers and servants— "sons" is the word He uses, with His inveterate love of degrading the whole spiritual world by unnatural liaisons with the two-legged animals. Desiring their freedom, He therefore refuses to carry them, by their mere affections and habits, to any of the goals which He sets before them: He leaves them to "do it on their own". And there lies our opportunity. But also, re-

17

member, there lies our danger. If once they get through this initial dryness successfully, they become much less dependent on emotion and therefore much harder to tempt.

I have been writing hitherto on the assumption that the people in the next pew afford no *rational* ground for disappointment. Of course if they do—if the patient knows that the woman with the absurd hat is a fanatical bridge-player or the man with squeaky boots a miser and an extortioner—then your task is so much the easier. All you then have to do is to keep out of his mind the question "If I, being what I am, can consider that I am in some sense a Christian, why should the different vices of those people in the next pew prove that their religion is mere hypocrisy and convention?" You may ask whether it is possible to keep such an obvious thought from occurring even to a human mind. It is, Wormwood, it is! Handle him properly and it simply won't come into his head. He has not been anything like long enough with the Enemy to have any real humility yet. What he says, even on his knees, about his own sinfulness is all parrot talk. At bottom, he still believes he has run up a very favourable credit-balance in the Enemy's ledger by allowing himself to be converted, and thinks that he is showing great humility and condescension in going to church with these "smug", commonplace neighbours at all. Keep him in that state of mind as long as you can.

Your affectionate uncle
SCREWTAPE

III

MY DEAR WORMWOOD,
I am very pleased by what you tell me about this man's relations with his mother. But you must press your advantage. The Enemy will be working from the centre outwards, gradually bringing more and more of the patient's conduct under the new standard, and may reach his behaviour to the old lady at any moment. You want to get in first. Keep in close touch with our colleague Glubose who is in charge of the mother, and build up between you in that house a good settled habit of mutual annoyance; daily pinpricks. The following methods are useful.

1. Keep his mind on the inner life. He thinks his conversion is something *inside* him and his attention is therefore chiefly turned at present to the states of his own mind—or rather to that very expurgated version of them which is all you should allow him to see. Encourage this. Keep his mind off the most elementary duties by directing it to the most advanced and spiritual ones. Aggravate that most useful human characteristic, the horror and neglect of the obvious. You must bring him to a condition in which he

can practise self-examination for an hour without discovering any of those facts about himself which are perfectly clear to anyone who has ever lived in the same house with him or worked in the same office.

2. It is, no doubt, impossible to prevent his praying for his mother, but we have means of rendering the prayers innocuous. Make sure that they are always very "spiritual", that he is always concerned with the state of her soul and never with her rheumatism. Two advantages will follow. In the first place, his attention will be kept on what he regards as her sins, by which, with a little guidance from you, he can be induced to mean any of her actions which are inconvenient or irritating to himself. Thus you can keep rubbing the wounds of the day a little sorer even while he is on his knees; the operation is not at all difficult and you will find it very entertaining. In the second place, since his ideas about her soul will be very crude and often erroneous, he will, in some degree, be praying for an imaginary person, and it will be your task to make that imaginary person daily less and less like the real mother—the sharp-tongued old lady at the breakfast table. In time, you may get the cleavage so wide that no thought or feeling from his prayers for the imagined mother will ever flow over into his treatment of

the real one. I have had patients of my own so well in hand that they could be turned at a moment's notice from impassioned prayer for a wife's or son's "soul" to beating or insulting the real wife or son without a qualm.

3. When two humans have lived together for many years it usually happens that each has tones of voice and expressions of face which are almost unendurably irritating to the other. Work on that. Bring fully into the consciousness of your patient that particular lift of his mother's eyebrows which he learned to dislike in the nursery, and let him think how much he dislikes it. Let him assume that she knows how annoying it is and does it to annoy—if you know your job he will not notice the immense improbability of the assumption. And, of course, never let him suspect that he has tones and looks which similarly annoy her. As he cannot see or hear himself, this is easily managed.

4. In civilised life domestic hatred usually expresses itself by saying things which would appear quite harmless on paper (the *words* are not offensive) but in such a voice, or at such a moment, that they are not far short of a blow in the face. To keep this game up you and Glubose must see to it that each of these two fools has a sort of double standard. Your patient must demand that all his own utterances

are to be taken at their face value and judged simply on the actual words, while at the same time judging all his mother's utterances with the fullest and most over-sensitive interpretation of the tone and the context and the suspected intention. She must be encouraged to do the same to him. Hence from every quarrel they can both go away convinced, or very nearly convinced, that they are quite innocent. You know the kind of thing: "I simply ask her what time dinner will be and she flies into a temper." Once this habit is well established you have the delightful situation of a human saying things with the express purpose of offending and yet having a grievance when offence is taken.

Finally, tell me something about the old lady's religious position. Is she at all jealous of the new factor in her son's life?—at all piqued that he should have learned from others, and so late, what she considers she gave him such good opportunity of learning in childhood? Does she feel he is making a great deal of "fuss" about it —or that he's getting in on very easy terms? Remember the elder brother in the Enemy's story,

Your affectionate uncle

SCREWTAPE

IV

MY DEAR WORMWOOD,
The amateurish suggestions in your last letter warn me that it is high time for me to write to you fully on the painful subject of prayer. You might have spared the comment that my advice about his prayers for his mother "proved singularly unfortunate". That is not the sort of thing that a nephew should write to his uncle—nor a junior tempter to the under-secretary of a department. It also reveals an unpleasant desire to shift responsibility; you must learn to pay for your own blunders.

The best thing, where it is possible, is to keep the patient from the serious intention of praying altogether. When the patient is an adult recently re-converted to the Enemy's party, like your man, this is best done by encouraging him to remember, or to think he remembers, the parrot-like nature of his prayers in childhood. In reaction against that, he may be persuaded to aim at something entirely spontaneous, inward, informal, and unregularised; and what this will actually mean to a beginner will be an effort to produce in himself a vaguely devotional *mood* in which real con-

centration of will and intelligence have no part
One of their poets, Coleridge, has recorded
that he did not pray "with moving lips and
bended knees" but merely "composed his
spirit to love" and indulged "a sense of suppli-
cation". That is exactly the sort of prayer we
want; and since it bears a superficial resemblance
to the prayer of silence as practised by those
who are very far advanced in the Enemy's
service, clever and lazy patients can be taken
in by it for quite a long time. At the very
least, they can be persuaded that the bodily
position makes no difference to their prayers;
for they constantly forget, what you must
always remember, that they are animals and
that whatever their bodies do affects their
souls. It is funny how mortals always picture
us as putting things into their minds: in
reality our best work is done by keeping things
out.

If this fails, you must fall back on a subtler
misdirection of his intention. Whenever they
are attending to the Enemy Himself we are
defeated, but there are ways of preventing
them from doing so. The simplest is to turn
their gaze away from Him towards themselves.
Keep them watching their own minds and
trying to produce *feelings* there by the action
of their own wills. When they meant to ask

Him for charity, let them, instead, start trying to manufacture charitable feelings for themselves and not notice that this is what they are doing. When they meant to pray for courage, let them really be trying to feel brave. When they say they are praying for forgiveness, let them be trying to feel forgiven. Teach them to estimate the value of each prayer by their success in producing the desired feeling; and never let them suspect how much success or failure of that kind depends on whether they are well or ill, fresh or tired, at the moment.

But of course the Enemy will not meantime be idle. Wherever there is prayer, there is danger of His own immediate action. He is cynically indifferent to the dignity of His position, and ours, as pure spirits, and to human animals on their knees He pours out self-knowledge in a quite shameless fashion. But even if He defeats your first attempt at misdirection, we have a subtler weapon. The humans do not start from that direct perception of Him which we, unhappily, cannot avoid. They have never known that ghastly luminosity, that stabbing and searing glare which makes the background of permanent pain to our lives. If you look into your patient's mind when he is praying, you will not find *that*. If you examine the object to which he is attending, you will find that it is a composite object containing many quite ridiculous ingredients. There will be images derived from pictures of the Enemy as He appeared during the discreditable episode known as the Incarnation: there will be vaguer—perhaps quite savage and puerile—images associated with the other two Persons. There will even be some of his own reverence (and of bodily sensations accompanying it) objectified and attributed to the object revered. I have known cases where what the patient called his "God" was actually *located*—up and to the left at the corner of the bedroom ceiling, or inside his own head, or in a crucifix on the wall. But whatever the nature of the composite object, you must keep him praying to *it*—to the thing that he has made, not to the Person who has made him. You may even encourage him to attach great importance to the correction and improvement of his composite object, and to keeping it steadily before his imagination during the whole prayer. For if he ever comes to make the distinction, if ever he consciously directs his prayers "Not to what I think thou art but to what thou knowest thyself to be", our situation is, for the moment, desperate. Once all his thoughts and images have been flung

27

aside or, if retained, retained with a full recognition of their merely subjective nature, and the man trusts himself to the completely real, external, invisible Presence, there with him in the room and never knowable by him as he is known by it—why, then it is that the incalculable may occur. In avoiding this situation—this real nakedness of the soul in prayer—you will be helped by the fact that the humans themselves do not desire it as much as they suppose. There's such a thing as getting more than they bargained for!

Your affectionate uncle
SCREWTAPE

V

MY DEAR WORMWOOD,
It is a little bit disappointing to expect a detailed report on your work and to receive instead such a vague rhapsody as your last letter. You say you are "delirious with joy" because the European humans have started another of their wars. I see very well what has happened to you. You are not delirious; you are only drunk. Reading between the lines in your very unbalanced account of the patient's sleepless night, I can reconstruct your state of mind fairly accurately. For the first time in your career you have tasted that wine which is the reward of all our labours—the anguish and bewilderment of a human soul—and it has gone to your head. I can hardly blame you. I do not expect old heads on young shoulders. Did the patient respond to some of your terror-pictures of the future? Did you work in some good self-pitying glances at the happy past?—some fine thrills in the pit of his stomach, were there? You played your violin prettily did you? Well, well, it's all very natural. But do remember, Wormwood, that duty comes before pleasure. If any present

self-indulgence on your part leads to the ultimate loss of the prey, you will be left eternally thirsting for that draught of which you are now so much enjoying your first sip. If, on the other hand, by steady and cool-headed application here and now you can finally secure his soul, he will then be yours forever—a brim-full living chalice of despair and horror and astonishment which you can raise to your lips as often as you please. So do not allow any temporary excitement to distract you from the real business of undermining faith and preventing the formation of virtues. Give me without fail in your next letter a full account of the patient's reactions to the war, so that we can consider whether you are likely to do more good by making him an extreme patriot or an ardent pacifist. There are all sorts of possibilities. In the meantime, I must warn you not to hope too much from a war.

Of course a war is entertaining. The immediate fear and suffering of the humans is a legitimate and pleasing refreshment for our myriads of toiling workers. But what permanent good does it do us unless we make use of it for bringing souls to Our Father Below? When I see the temporal suffering of humans who finally escape us, I feel as if I had been allowed

to taste the first course of a rich banquet and
then denied the rest. It is worse than not to
have tasted it at all. The Enemy, true to His
barbarous methods of warfare, allows us to see
the short misery of His favourites only to
tantalise and torment us—to mock the incessant
hunger which, during this present phase of the
great conflict, His blockade is admittedly im-
posing. Let us therefore think rather how to
use, than how to enjoy, this European war.
For it has certain tendencies inherent in it
which are, in themselves, by no means in our
favour. We may hope for a good deal of cruelty
and unchastity. But, if we are not careful, we
shall see thousands turning in this tribulation
to the Enemy, while tens of thousands who do
not go so far as that will nevertheless have
their attention diverted from themselves to
values and causes which they believe to be
higher than the self. I know that the Enemy
disapproves many of these causes. But that is
where He is so unfair. He often makes prizes
of humans who have given their lives for
causes He thinks bad on the monstrously
sophistical ground that the humans thought
them good and were following the best they
knew. Consider too what undesirable deaths
occur in wartime. Men are killed in places
where they knew they might be killed and to

which they go, if they are at all of the Enemy's party, prepared. How much better for us if *all* humans died in costly nursing homes amid doctors who lie, nurses who lie, friends who lie, as we have trained them, promising life to the dying, encouraging the belief that sickness excuses every indulgence, and even, if our workers know their job, withholding all suggestion of a priest lest it should betray to the sick man his true condition! And how disastrous for us is the continual remembrance of death which war enforces. One of our best weapons, contented worldliness, is rendered useless. In wartime not even a human can believe that he is going to live forever.

I know that Scabtree and others have seen in wars a great opportunity for attacks on faith, but I think that view was exaggerated. The Enemy's human partisans have all been plainly told by Him that suffering is an essential part of what He calls Redemption; so that a faith which is destroyed by a war or a pestilence cannot really have been worth the trouble of destroying. I am speaking now of diffused suffering over a long period such as the war will produce. Of course, at the precise moment of terror, bereavement, or physical pain, you may catch your man when his reason is temporarily suspended. But even then, if he applies to Enemy headquarters, I have found that the post is nearly always defended,

Your affectionate uncle

SCREWTAPE

VI

M^Y DEAR WORMWOOD,
I am delighted to hear that your
patient's age and profession make it possible,
but by no means certain, that he will be called
up for military service. We want him to be
in the maximum uncertainty, so that his mind
will be filled with contradictory pictures of the
future, every one of which arouses hope or
fear. There is nothing like suspense and
anxiety for barricading a human's mind against
the Enemy. He wants men to be concerned
with what they do; our business is to keep
them thinking about what will happen to them.

Your patient will, of course, have picked up
the notion that he must submit with patience
to the Enemy's will. What the Enemy means
by this is primarily that he should accept with
patience the tribulation which has actually been
dealt out to him—the present anxiety and
suspense. It is about *this* that he is to say "Thy
will be done", and for the daily task of bearing
this that the daily bread will be provided. It is
your business to see that the patient never
thinks of the present fear as his appointed
cross but only of the things he is afraid of.

Let him regard them as his crosses: let him forget that, since they are incompatible, they cannot all happen to him, and let him try to practise fortitude and patience to them all in advance. For real resignation, at the same moment, to a dozen different and hypothetical fates, is almost impossible, and the Enemy does not greatly assist those who are trying to attain it: resignation to present and actual suffering, even where that suffering consists of fear, is far easier and is usually helped by this direct action.

An important spiritual law is here involved. I have explained that you can weaken his prayers by diverting his attention from the Enemy Himself to his own states of mind about the Enemy. On the other hand fear becomes easier to master when the patient's mind is diverted from the thing feared to the fear itself, considered as a present and undesirable state of his own mind; and when he regards the fear as his appointed cross he will inevitably think of it as a state of mind. One can therefore formulate the general rule; in all activities of mind which favour our cause, encourage the patient to be un-selfconscious and to concentrate on the object, but in all activities favourable to the Enemy bend his mind back on itself. Let an insult or a woman's body so fix his attention outward that he does not reflect "I am now entering into the state called Anger—or the state called Lust". Contrariwise let the reflection "My feelings are now growing more devout, or more charitable" so fix his attention inward that he no longer looks beyond himself to see our Enemy or his own neighbours.

As regards his more general attitude to the war, you must not rely too much on those feelings of hatred which the humans are so fond of discussing in Christian, or anti-Christian, periodicals. In his anguish, the patient can, of course, be encouraged to revenge himself by some vindictive feelings directed towards the German leaders, and that is good so far as it goes. But it is usually a sort of melodramatic or mythical hatred directed against imaginary scapegoats. He has never met these people in real life—they are lay figures modelled on what he gets from newspapers. The results of such fanciful hatred are often most disappointing, and of all humans the English are in this respect the most deplorable milksops. They are creatures of that miserable sort who loudly proclaim that torture is too good for their enemies and then give tea and cigarettes to the first wounded German pilot who turns up at the back door.

Do what you will, there is going to be some benevolence, as well as some malice, in your patient's soul. The great thing is to direct the malice to his immediate neighbours whom he meets every day and to thrust his benevolence out to the remote circumference, to people he does not know. The malice thus becomes wholly real and the benevolence largely imaginary. There is no good at all in inflaming his hatred of Germans if, at the same time, a pernicious habit of charity is growing up between him and his mother, his employer, and the man he meets in the train. Think of your man as a series of concentric circles, his will being the innermost, his intellect coming next, and finally his fantasy. You can hardly hope, at once, to exclude from all the circles everything that smells of the Enemy: but you must keep on shoving all the virtues outward till they are finally located in the circle of fantasy, and all the desirable qualities inward into the Will. It is only in so far as they reach the will and are there embodied in habits that the virtues are really fatal to us. (I don't, of course, mean what the patient mistakes for his will, the conscious fume and fret of resolutions and clenched teeth, but the real centre, what the Enemy calls the Heart.) All sorts of virtues painted in the fantasy or approved by the intellect or even, in some measure, loved and admired, will not keep a man from our Father's house: indeed they may make him more amusing when he gets there,

Your affectionate uncle

SCREWTAPE

VII

My dear Wormwood,

I wonder you should ask me whether it is essential to keep the patient in ignorance of your own existence. That question, at least for the present phase of the struggle, has been answered for us by the High Command. Our policy, for the moment, is to conceal ourselves. Of course this has not always been so. We are really faced with a cruel dilemma. When the humans disbelieve in our existence we lose all the pleasing results of direct terrorism and we make no magicians. On the other hand, when they believe in us, we cannot make them materialists and sceptics. At least, not yet. I have great hopes that we shall learn in due time how to emotionalise and mythologise their science to such an extent that what is, in effect, a belief in us, (though not under that name) will creep in while the human mind remains closed to belief in the Enemy. The "Life Force", the worship of sex, and some aspects of Psychoanalysis, may here prove useful. If once we can produce our perfect work—the Materialist Magician, the man, not using, but veritably worshipping, what he vaguely calls

"Forces" while denying the existence of "spirits"—then the end of the war will be in sight. But in the meantime we must obey our orders. I do not think you will have much difficulty in keeping the patient in the dark. The fact that "devils" are predominantly *comic* figures in the modern imagination will help you. If any faint suspicion of your existence begins to arise in his mind, suggest to him a picture of something in red tights, and persuade him that since he cannot believe in that (it is an old textbook method of confusing them) he therefore cannot believe in you.

I had not forgotten my promise to consider whether we should make the patient an extreme patriot or an extreme pacifist. All extremes, except extreme devotion to the Enemy, are to be encouraged. Not always, of course, but at this period. Some ages are lukewarm and complacent, and then it is our business to soothe them yet faster asleep. Other ages, of which the present is one, are unbalanced and prone to faction, and it is our business to inflame them. Any small coterie, bound together by some interest which other men dislike or ignore, tends to develop inside itself a hothouse mutual admiration, and towards the outer world, a great deal of pride and hatred which is entertained without shame because the

"Cause" is its sponsor and it is thought to be impersonal. Even when the little group exists originally for the Enemy's own purposes, this remains true. We want the Church to be small not only that fewer men may know the Enemy but also that those who do may acquire the uneasy intensity and the defensive self-righteousness of a secret society or a clique. The Church herself is, of course, heavily defended and we have never yet quite succeeded in giving her *all* the characteristics of a faction; but subordinate factions within her have often produced admirable results, from the parties of Paul and of Apollos at Corinth down to the High and Low parties in the Church of England.

If your patient can be induced to become a conscientious objector he will automatically find himself one of a small, vocal, organised, and unpopular society, and the effects of this, on one so new to Christianity, will almost certainly be good. But only *almost* certainly. Has he had serious doubts about the lawfulness of serving in a just war before this present war began? Is he a man of great physical courage— so great that he will have no half-conscious misgivings about the real motives of his pacifism? Can he, when nearest to honesty (no human is ever *very* near), feel fully convinced that he is actuated wholly by the desire to obey the

Enemy? If he is that sort of man, his pacifism will probably not do us much good, and the Enemy will probably protect him from the usual consequences of belonging to a sect. Your best plan, in that case, would be to attempt a sudden, confused, emotional crisis from which he might emerge as an uneasy convert to patriotism. Such things can often be managed. But if he is the man I take him to be, try Pacifism.

Whichever he adopts, your main task will be the same. Let him begin by treating the Patriotism or the Pacifism as a part of his religion. Then let him, under the influence of partisan spirit, come to regard it as the most important part. Then quietly and gradually nurse him on to the stage at which the religion becomes merely part of the "cause", in which Christianity is valued chiefly because of the excellent arguments it can produce in favour of the British war-effort or of Pacifism. The attitude which you want to guard against is that in which temporal affairs are treated primarily as material for obedience. Once you have made the World an end, and faith a means, you have almost won your man, and it makes very little difference what kind of worldly end he is pursuing. Provided that meetings, pamphlets, policies, movements, causes, and crusades, matter more to him than prayers and sacraments and charity, he is ours—and the more "religious" (on those terms) the more securely ours. I could show you a pretty cageful down here,

Your affectionate uncle
SCREWTAPE

VIII

M^Y DEAR WORMWOOD,

So you "have great hopes that the patient's religious phase is dying away", have you? I always thought the Training College had gone to pieces since they put old Slubgob at the head of it, and now I am sure. Has no one ever told you about the law of Undulation?

Humans are amphibians—half spirit and half animal. (The Enemy's determination to produce such a revolting hybrid was one of the things that determined Our Father to withdraw his support from Him.) As spirits they belong to the eternal world, but as animals they inhabit time. This means that while their spirit can be directed to an eternal object, their bodies, passions, and imaginations are in continual change, for to be in time means to change. Their nearest approach to constancy, therefore, is undulation—the repeated return to a level from which they repeatedly fall back, a series of troughs and peaks. If you had watched your patient carefully you would have seen this undulation in every department of his life— his interest in his work, his affection for his friends, his physical appetites, all go up and down. As long as he lives on earth periods of emotional and bodily richness and liveliness will alternate with periods of numbness and poverty. The dryness and dulness through which your patient is now going are not, as you fondly suppose, your workmanship; they are merely a natural phenomenon which will do us no good unless you make a good use of it.

To decide what the best use of it is, you must ask what use the Enemy wants to make of it, and then do the opposite. Now it may surprise you to learn that in His efforts to get permanent possession of a soul, He relies on the troughs even more than on the peaks; some of His special favourites have gone through longer and deeper troughs than anyone else. The reason is this. To us a human is primarily food; our aim is the absorption of its will into ours, the increase of our own area of selfhood at its expense. But the obedience which the Enemy demands of men is quite a different thing. One must face the fact that all the talk about His love for men, and His service being perfect freedom, is not (as one would gladly believe) mere propaganda, but an appalling truth. He really *does* want to fill the universe with a lot of loathsome little replicas of Himself—creatures whose life, on its miniature scale, will be qualitatively like His own, not because He has absorbed them but because their wills freely conform to His. We want cattle who can finally become food; He wants servants who can finally become sons. We want to suck in, He wants to give out. We are empty and would be filled; He is full and flows over. Our war aim is a world in which Our Father Below has drawn all other beings into himself: the Enemy wants a world full of beings united to Him but still distinct.

And that is where the troughs come in. You must have often wondered why the Enemy does not make more use of His power to be sensibly present to human souls in any degree He chooses and at any moment. But you now see that the Irresistible and the Indisputable are the two weapons which the very nature of His scheme forbids Him to use. Merely to over-ride a human will (as His felt presence in any but the faintest and most mitigated degree would certainly do) would be for Him useless. He cannot ravish. He can only woo. For His ignoble idea is to eat the cake and have it; the creatures are to be one with Him, but yet themselves; merely to cancel them, or assimilate them, will not serve. He is prepared to do a little over-riding at the beginning. He will set them off with communications of His presence which, though faint, seem great to them, with emotional sweetness, and easy conquest over temptation. But He never allows this state of affairs to last long. Sooner or later He withdraws, if not in fact, at least from their conscious experience, all those supports and incentives. He leaves the creature to stand up on its own legs—to carry out from the will alone duties which have lost all relish. It is during such trough periods, much more than during the peak periods, that it is growing into the sort of creature He wants it to be. Hence the prayers offered in the state of dryness are those which please Him best. We can drag our patients along by continual tempting, because we design them only for the table, and the more their will is interfered with the better. He cannot "tempt" to virtue as we do to vice. He wants them to learn to walk and must therefore take away His hand; and if only the will to walk is really there He is pleased even with their stumbles. Do not be deceived, Wormwood. Our cause is never more in danger than when a human, no longer desiring, but still intending, to do our Enemy's will, looks round upon a universe from which every trace of Him seems to have vanished, and asks why he has been forsaken, and still obeys.

But of course the troughs afford opportunities to our side also. Next week I will give you some hints on how to exploit them,

Your affectionate uncle

SCREWTAPE

IX

M<small>Y DEAR</small> W<small>ORMWOOD</small>,

I hope my last letter has convinced you that the trough of dulness or "dryness" through which your patient is going at present will not, of itself, give you his soul, but needs to be properly exploited. What forms the exploitation should take I will now consider.

In the first place I have always found that the Trough periods of the human undulation provide excellent opportunity for all sensual temptations, particularly those of sex. This may surprise you, because, of course, there is more physical energy, and therefore more potential appetite, at the Peak periods; but you must remember that the powers of resistance are then also at their highest. The health and spirits which you want to use in producing lust can also, alas, be very easily used for work or play or thought or innocuous merriment. The attack has a much better chance of success when the man's whole inner world is drab and cold and empty. And it is also to be noted that the Trough sexuality is subtly different in quality from that of the Peak—much less likely to lead to the milk and water phenomenon which the humans call "being in love", much more easily drawn into perversions, much less contaminated by those generous and imaginative and even spiritual concomitants which often render human sexuality so disappointing. It is the same with other desires of the flesh. You are much more likely to make your man a sound drunkard by pressing drink on him as an anodyne when he is dull and weary than by encouraging him to use it as a means of merriment among his friends when he is happy and expansive. Never forget that when we are dealing with any pleasure in its healthy and normal and satisfying form, we are, in a sense, on the Enemy's ground. I know we have won many a soul through pleasure. All the same, it is His invention, not ours. He made the pleasures: all our research so far has not enabled us to produce one. All we can do is to encourage the humans to take the pleasures which our Enemy has produced, at times, or in ways, or in degrees, which He has forbidden. Hence we always try to work away from the natural condition of any pleasure to that in which it is least natural, least redolent of its Maker, and least pleasurable. An ever increasing craving for an ever diminishing pleasure is the formula. It is more certain; and it's better *style*. To get the man's soul and give him *nothing* in return—that is what really gladdens our Father's heart. And the troughs are the time for beginning the process.

But there is an even better way of exploiting the Trough; I mean through the patient's own thoughts about it. As always, the first step is to keep knowledge out of his mind. Do not let him suspect the law of undulation. Let him assume that the first ardours of his conversion might have been expected to last, and ought to have lasted, forever, and that his present dryness is an equally permanent condition. Having once got this misconception well fixed in his head, you may then proceed in various ways. It all depends on whether your man is of the desponding type who can be tempted to despair, or of the wishful-thinking type who can be assured that all is well. The former type is getting rare among the humans. If your patient should happen to belong to it, everything is easy. You have only got to keep him out of the way of experienced Christians (an easy task now-a-days), to direct his attention to the appropriate passages in scripture, and then to set him to work on the desperate design of recovering his old feelings by sheer will-power, and the game is ours. If he is of the more hopeful type, your job is to make him acquiesce in the present low temperature of his spirit and gradually become content with it, persuading himself that it is not so low after all. In a week or two you will be making him doubt whether the first days of his Christianity were not, perhaps, a little excessive. Talk to him about "moderation in all things". If you can once get him to the point of thinking that "religion is all very well up to a point", you can feel quite happy about his soul. A moderated religion is as good for us as no religion at all—and more amusing.

Another possibility is that of direct attack on his faith. When you have caused him to assume that the trough is permanent, can you not persuade him that "his religious phase" is just going to die away like all his previous phases? Of course there is no conceivable way of getting by reason from the proposition "I am losing interest in this" to the proposition "This is false". But, as I said before, it is jargon, not reason, you must rely on. The mere word *phase* will very likely do the trick. I assume that the creature has been through several of them before—they all have—and that he always feels superior and patronising to the ones he has emerged from, not because he has really criticised them but simply because they are in the past. (You keep him well fed on hazy ideas of Progress and Development and the Historical Point of View, I trust, and give him lots of modern Biographies to read? The people in them are always emerging from Phases, aren't they?)

You see the idea? Keep his mind off the plain antithesis between True and False. Nice shadowy expressions—"It was a phase"—"I've been through all that"—and don't forget the blessed word "Adolescent",

Your affectionate uncle

SCREWTAPE

X

MY DEAR WORMWOOD,

I was delighted to hear from Trip-tweeze that your patient has made some very desirable new acquaintances and that you seem to have used this event in a really promising manner. I gather that the middle-aged married couple who called at his office are just the sort of people we want him to know—rich, smart, superficially intellectual, and brightly sceptical about everything in the world. I gather they are even vaguely pacifist, not on moral grounds but from an ingrained habit of belittling anything that concerns the great mass of their fellow men and from a dash of purely fashionable and literary communism. This is excellent. And you seem to have made good use of all his social, sexual, and intellectual vanity. Tell me more. Did he commit himself deeply? I don't mean in words. There is a subtle play of looks and tones and laughs by which a mortal can imply that he is of the same party as those to whom he is speaking. That is the kind of betrayal you should specially encourage, because the man does not fully realise it himself; and by the time he does you will have made withdrawal difficult.

No doubt he must very soon realise that his own faith is in direct opposition to the assumptions on which all the conversation of his new friends is based. I don't think that matters much provided that you can persuade him to postpone any open acknowledgment of the fact, and this, with the aid of shame, pride, modesty and vanity, will be easy to do. As long as the postponement lasts he will be in a false position. He will be silent when he ought to speak and laugh when he ought to be silent. He will assume, at first only by his manner, but presently by his words, all sorts of cynical and sceptical attitudes which are not really his. But if you play him well, they may become his. All mortals tend to turn into the thing they are pretending to be. This is elementary. The real question is how to prepare for the Enemy's counter attack.

The first thing is to delay as long as possible the moment at which he realises this new pleasure as a temptation. Since the Enemy's servants have been preaching about "the World" as one of the great standard temptations for two thousand years, this might seem difficult to do. But fortunately they have said very little about it for the last few decades. In modern Christian writings, though I see much (indeed more than I like) about Mammon, I see few of the old warnings about Worldly Vanities, the Choice of Friends, and the Value of Time. All that, your patient would probably classify as "Puritanism"—and may I remark in passing that the value we have given to that word is one of the really solid triumphs of the last hundred years? By it we rescue annually thousands of humans from temperance, chastity, and sobriety of life.

Sooner or later, however, the real nature of his new friends must become clear to him, and then your tactics must depend on the patient's intelligence. If he is a big enough fool you can get him to realise the character of the friends only while they are absent; their presence can be made to sweep away all criticism. If this succeeds, he can be induced to live, as I have known many humans live, for quite long periods, two parallel lives; he will not only appear to be, but actually be, a different man in each of the circles he frequents. Failing this, there is a subtler and more entertaining method. He can be made to take a positive pleasure in the perception that the two sides of his life are inconsistent. This is done by exploiting his vanity. He can be taught to enjoy kneeling beside the grocer on Sunday just because he remembers that the grocer could not possibly understand the urbane and mocking world which he inhabited on Saturday evening; and contrariwise, to enjoy the bawdy and blasphemy over the coffee with these admirable friends all the more because he is aware of a "deeper", "spiritual" world within him which they cannot understand. You see the idea—the worldly friends touch him on one side and the grocer on the other, and he is the complete, balanced, complex man who sees round them all. Thus, while being permanently treacherous to at least two sets of people, he will feel, instead of shame, a continual undercurrent of self-satisfaction. Finally, if all else fails, you can persuade him, in defiance of conscience, to continue the new acquaintance on the ground that he is, in some unspecified way, doing these people "good" by the mere fact of drinking their cocktails and laughing at their jokes, and that to cease to do so would be "priggish", "intolerant", and (of course) "Puritanical".

Meanwhile you will of course take the obvious precaution of seeing that this new development induces him to spend more than he can afford and to neglect his work and his mother. Her jealousy, and alarm, and his increasing evasiveness or rudeness, will be invaluable for the aggravation of the domestic tension,

Your affectionate uncle

SCREWTAPE

XI

My dear Wormwood,

Everything is clearly going very well. I am specially glad to hear that the two new friends have now made him acquainted with their whole set. All these, as I find from the record office, are thoroughly reliable people; steady, consistent scoffers and worldlings who without any spectacular crimes are progressing quietly and comfortably towards our Father's house. You speak of their being great laughers. I trust this does not mean that you are under the impression that laughter as such is always in our favour. The point is worth some attention.

I divide the causes of human laughter into Joy, Fun, the Joke Proper, and Flippancy. You will see the first among friends and lovers reunited on the eve of a holiday. Among adults some pretext in the way of Jokes is usually provided, but the facility with which the smallest witticisms produce laughter at such a time shows that they are not the real cause. What that real cause is we do not know. Something like it is expressed in much of that detestable art which the humans call Music, and something like it occurs in Heaven—a meaningless acceleration in the rhythm of celestial experience, quite opaque to us. Laughter of this kind does us no good and should always be discouraged. Besides, the phenomenon is of itself disgusting and a direct insult to the realism, dignity, and austerity of Hell.

Fun is closely related to Joy—a sort of emotional froth arising from the play instinct. It is very little use to us. It can sometimes be used, of course, to divert humans from something else which the Enemy would like them to be feeling or doing: but in itself it has wholly undesirable tendencies; it promotes charity, courage, contentment, and many other evils.

The Joke Proper, which turns on sudden perception of incongruity, is a much more promising field. I am not thinking primarily of indecent or bawdy humour, which, though much relied upon by second-rate tempters, is often disappointing in its results. The truth is that humans are pretty clearly divided on this matter into two classes. There are some to whom "no passion is as serious as lust" and for whom an indecent story ceases to produce lasciviousness precisely in so far as it becomes funny: there are others in whom laughter and lust are excited at the same moment and by the same things. The first sort joke about sex because it gives rise to many incongruities: the second cultivate incongruities because they afford a pretext for talking about sex. If your man is of the first type, bawdy humour will not help you—I shall never forget the hours which I wasted (hours to me of unbearable tedium) with one of my early patients in bars and smoking-rooms before I learned this rule. Find out which group the patient belongs to— and see that he does *not* find out.

The real use of Jokes or Humour is in quite a different direction, and it is specially promising among the English who take their "sense of humour" so seriously that a deficiency in this sense is almost the only deficiency at which they feel shame. Humour is for them the all-consoling and (mark this) the all-excusing, grace of life. Hence it is invaluable as a means of destroying shame. If a man simply lets others pay for him, he is "mean"; if he boasts of it in a jocular manner and twits his fellows with having been scored off, he is no longer "mean" but a comical fellow. Mere cowardice is shameful; cowardice boasted of with humorous exaggerations and grotesque gestures can be passed off as funny. Cruelty is shameful— unless the cruel man can represent it as a practical joke. A thousand bawdy, or even blasphemous, jokes do not help towards a man's damnation so much as his discovery that almost anything he wants to do can be done, not only without the disapproval but with the admiration of his fellows, if only it can get itself treated as a Joke. And this temptation can be almost entirely hidden from your patient by that English seriousness about Humour. Any suggestion that there might be too much of it can be represented to him as "Puritanical" or as betraying a "lack of humour".

But flippancy is the best of all. In the first place it is very economical. Only a clever human can make a real Joke about virtue, or indeed about anything else; any of them can be trained to talk *as if* virtue were funny. Among flippant people the Joke is always assumed to have been made. No one actually makes it; but every serious subject is discussed in a manner which implies that they have already found a ridiculous side to it. If prolonged, the habit of Flippancy builds up around a man the finest armour-plating against the Enemy that I know, and it is quite free from the dangers inherent in the other sources of laughter. It is a thousand miles away from joy: it deadens, instead of sharpening, the intellect; and it excites no affection between those who practice it,

Your affectionate uncle
SCREWTAPE

XII

M<small>Y DEAR</small> W<small>ORMWOOD</small>,
     Obviously you are making excellent
progress. My only fear is lest in attempting to
hurry the patient you awaken him to a sense
of his real position. For you and I, who see
that position as it really is, must never forget
how totally different it ought to appear to
him. We know that we have introduced a
change of direction in his course which is
already carrying him out of his orbit around
the Enemy; but he must be made to imagine
that all the choices which have effected this
change of course are trivial and revocable. He
must not be allowed to suspect that he is now,
however slowly, heading right away from the
sun on a line which will carry him into the
cold and dark of utmost space.

For this reason I am almost glad to hear
that he is still a churchgoer and a communicant.
I know there are dangers in this; but anything
is better than that he should realise the break
he has made with the first months of his
Christian life. As long as he retains externally
the habits of a Christian he can still be made
to think of himself as one who has adopted a

61

few new friends and amusements but whose spiritual state is much the same as it was six weeks ago. And while he thinks that, we do not have to contend with the explicit repentance of a definite, fully recognised, sin, but only with his vague, though uneasy, feeling that he hasn't been doing very well lately.

This dim uneasiness needs careful handling. If it gets too strong it may wake him up and spoil the whole game. On the other hand, if you suppress it entirely—which, by the by, the Enemy will probably not allow you to do— we lose an element in the situation which can be turned to good account. If such a feeling is allowed to live, but not allowed to become irresistible and flower into real repentance, it has one invaluable tendency. It increases the patient's reluctance to think about the Enemy. All humans at nearly all times have some such reluctance; but when thinking of Him involves facing and intensifying a whole vague cloud of half-conscious guilt, this reluctance is increased tenfold. They hate every idea that suggests Him, just as men in financial embarrassment hate the very sight of a pass-book. In this state your patient will not omit, but he will increasingly dislike, his religious duties. He will think about them as little as he feels he decently can beforehand, and forget them as soon as possible when they are over. A few weeks ago you had to *tempt* him to unreality and inattention in his prayers: but now you will find him opening his arms to you and almost begging you to distract his purpose and benumb his heart. He will *want* his prayers to be unreal, for he will dread nothing so much as effective contact with the Enemy. His aim will be to let sleeping worms lie.

As this condition becomes more fully established, you will be gradually freed from the tiresome business of providing Pleasures as temptations. As the uneasiness and his reluctance to face it cut him off more and more from all real happiness, and as habit renders the pleasures of vanity and excitement and flippancy at once less pleasant and harder to forgo (for that is what habit fortunately does to a pleasure) you will find that anything or nothing is sufficient to attract his wandering attention. You no longer need a good book, which he really likes, to keep him from his prayers or his work or his sleep; a column of advertisements in yesterday's paper will do. You can make him waste his time not only in conversation he enjoys with people whom he likes, but in conversations with those he cares nothing about on subjects that bore him. You can make him do nothing at all for long periods.

You can keep him up late at night, not roistering, but staring at a dead fire in a cold room. All the healthy and outgoing activities which we want him to avoid can be inhibited and *nothing* given in return, so that at last he may say, as one of my own patients said on his arrival down here, "I now see that I spent most of my life in doing *neither* what I ought *nor* what I liked". The Christians describe the Enemy as one "without whom Nothing is strong". And Nothing is very strong: strong enough to steal away a man's best years not in sweet sins but in a dreary flickering of the mind over it knows not what and knows not why, in the gratification of curiosities so feeble that the man is only half aware of them, in drumming of fingers and kicking of heels, in whistling tunes that he does not like, or in the long, dim labyrinth of reveries that have not even lust or ambition to give them a relish, but which, once chance association has started them, the creature is too weak and fuddled to shake off.

You will say that these are very small sins; and doubtless, like all young tempters, you are anxious to be able to report spectacular wickedness. But do remember, the only thing that matters is the extent to which you separate the man from the Enemy. It does not matter how small the sins are provided that their cumulative effect is to edge the man away from the Light and out into the Nothing. Murder is no better than cards if cards can do the trick. Indeed the safest road to Hell is the gradual one—the gentle slope, soft underfoot, without sudden turnings, without milestones, without signposts,

Your affectionate uncle

SCREWTAPE

XIII

M<small>Y DEAR</small> W<small>ORMWOOD</small>,
     It seems to me that you take a great
many pages to tell a very simple story. The
long and the short of it is that you have let
the man slip through your fingers. The situation is very grave, and I really see no reason
why I should try to shield you from the
consequences or your inefficiency. A repentance
and renewal of what the other side call "grace"
on the scale which you describe is a defeat of
the first order. It amounts to a second conversion—and probably on a deeper level than the
first.

As you ought to have known, the asphyxi-
ating cloud which prevented your attacking the
patient on his walk back from the old mill, is
a well-known phenomenon. It is the Enemy's
most barbarous weapon, and generally appears
when He is directly present to the patient
under certain modes not yet fully classified.
Some humans are permanently surrounded by
it and therefore inaccessible to us.

And now for your blunders. On your own
showing you first of all allowed the patient to
read a book he really enjoyed, because he

enjoyed it and not in order to make clever remarks about it to his new friends. In the second place, you allowed him to walk down to the old mill and have tea there—a walk through country he really likes, and taken alone. In other words you allowed him two real positive Pleasures. Were you so ignorant as not to see the danger of this? The characteristic of Pains and Pleasures is that they are unmistakably real, and therefore, as far as they go, give the man who feels them a touchstone of reality. Thus if you had been trying to damn your man by the Romantic method—by making him a kind of Childe Harold or Werther submerged in self-pity for imaginary distresses —you would try to protect him at all costs from any real pain; because, of course, five minutes' genuine toothache would reveal the romantic sorrows for the nonsense they were and unmask your whole strategem. But you were trying to damn your patient by the World, that is by palming off vanity, bustle, irony, and expensive tedium as pleasures. How can you have failed to see that a *real* pleasure was the last thing you ought to have let him meet? Didn't you foresee that it would just kill by contrast all the trumpery which you have been so laboriously teaching him to value? And that the sort of pleasure which the book and the walk gave him was the most dangerous of all? That it would peel off from his sensibility the kind of crust you have been forming on it, and make him feel that he was coming home, recovering himself? As a preliminary to detaching him from the Enemy, you wanted to detach him from himself, and had made some progress in doing so. Now, all that is undone.

Of course I know that the Enemy also wants to detach men from themselves, but in a different way. Remember always, that He really likes the little vermin, and sets an absurd value on the distinctness of every one of them. When He talks of their losing their selves, He only means abandoning the clamour of self-will; once they have done that, He really gives them back all their personality, and boasts (I am afraid, sincerely) that when they are wholly His they will be more themselves than ever. Hence, while He is delighted to see them sacrificing even their innocent wills to His, He hates to see them drifting away from their own nature for any other reason. And we should always encourage them to do so. The deepest likings and impulses of any man are the raw material, the starting-point, with which the Enemy has furnished him. To get him away from those is therefore always a point gained; even in things indifferent it is always desirable to substitute the standards of the World, or convention, or fashion, for a human's own real likings and dislikings. I myself would carry this very far. I would make it a rule to eradicate from my patient any strong personal taste which is not actually a sin, even if it is something quite trivial such as a fondness for county cricket or collecting stamps or drinking cocoa. Such things, I grant you, have nothing of virtue in them; but there is a sort of innocence and humility and self-forgetfulness about them which I distrust. The man who truly and disinterestedly enjoys any one thing in the world, for its own sake, and without caring twopence what other people say about it, is by that very fact fore-armed against some of our subtlest modes of attack. You should always try to make the patient abandon the people or food or books he really likes in favour of the "best" people, the "right" food, the "impoi-tant" books. I have known a human defended from strong temptations to social ambition by a still stronger taste for tripe and onions.

It remains to consider how we can retrieve this disaster. The great thing is to prevent his doing anything. As long as he does not convert it into action, it does not matter how much he thinks about this new repentance. Let the little brute wallow in it. Let him, if he has any bent that way, write a book about it; that is often an excellent way of sterilising the seeds which the Enemy plants in a human soul. Let him do anything but act. No amount of piety in his imagination and affections will harm us if we can keep it out of his will. As one of the humans has said, active habits are strengthened by repetition but passive ones are weakened. The more often he feels without acting, the less he will be able ever to act, and, in the long run, the less he will be able to feel,

Your affectionate uncle
SCREWTAPE

XIV

M<small>Y DEAR</small> W<small>ORMWOOD</small>,

The most alarming thing in your last account of the patient is that he is making none of those confident resolutions which marked his original conversion. No more lavish promises of perpetual virtue, I gather; not even the expectation of an endowment of "grace" for life, but only a hope for the daily and hourly pittance to meet the daily and hourly temptation! This is very bad.

I see only one thing to do at the moment. Your patient has become humble; have you drawn his attention to the fact? All virtues are less formidable to us once the man is aware that he has them, but this is specially true of humility. Catch him at the moment when he is really poor in spirit and smuggle into his mind the gratifying reflection, "By jove! I'm being humble", and almost immediately pride—pride at his own humility—will appear. If he awakes to the danger and tries to smother this new form of pride, make him proud of his attempt—and so on, through as many stages as you please. But don't try this too long, for fear you awake his sense of humour and proportion, in which case he will merely laugh at you and go to bed.

But there are other profitable ways of fixing his attention on the virtue of Humility. By this virtue, as by all the others, our Enemy wants to turn the man's attention away from self to Him, and to the man's neighbours. All the abjection and self-hatred are designed, in the long run, solely for this end; unless they attain this end they do us little harm; and they may even do us good if they keep the man concerned with himself, and, above all, if self-contempt can be made the starting-point for contempt of other selves, and thus for gloom, cynicism, and cruelty.

You must therefore conceal from the patient the true end of Humility. Let him think of it not as self-forgetfulness but as a certain kind of opinion (namely, a low opinion) of his own talents and character. Some talents, I gather, he really has. Fix in his mind the idea that humility consists in trying to believe those talents to be less valuable than he believes them to be. No doubt they *are* in fact less valuable than he believes, but that is not the point. The great thing is to make him value an opinion for some quality other than truth, thus introducing an element of dishonesty and make-believe into the heart of what otherwise threatens to become a virtue. By this method thousands of humans have been brought to think that humility means pretty women trying to believe they are ugly and clever men trying to believe they are fools. And since what they are trying to believe may, in some cases, be manifest nonsense, they cannot succeed in believing it and we have the chance of keeping their minds endlessly revolving on themselves in an effort to achieve the impossible. To anticipate the Enemy's strategy, we must consider His aims. The Enemy wants to bring the man to a state of mind in which he could design the best cathedral in the world, and know it to be the best, and rejoice in the fact, without being any more (or less) or otherwise glad at having done it than he would be if it had been done by another. The Enemy wants him, in the end, to be so free from any bias in his own favour that he can rejoice in his own talents as frankly and gratefully as in his neighbour's talents—or in a sunrise, an elephant, or a waterfall. He wants each man, in the long run, to be able to recognise all creatures (even himself) as glorious and excellent things. He wants to kill their animal self-love as soon as possible; but it is His long-term policy, I fear, to restore to them a new kind of self-love—a charity and gratitude for all selves, including their own; when they have really learned to love their neighbours as themselves, they will be allowed to love themselves as their neighbours. For we must never forget what is the most repellent and inexplicable trait in our Enemy; He *really* loves the hairless bipeds He has created and always gives back to them with His right hand what He has taken away with His left.

His whole effort, therefore, will be to get the man's mind off the subject of his own value altogether. He would rather the man thought himself a great architect or a great poet and then forgot about it, than that he should spend much time and pains trying to think himself a bad one. Your efforts to instil either vainglory or false modesty into the patient will therefore be met from the Enemy's side with the obvious reminder that a man is not usually called upon to have an opinion of his own talents at all, since he can very well go on improving them to the best of his ability without deciding on his own precise niche in the temple of Fame. You must try to exclude this reminder from the patient's consciousness at all costs. The Enemy will also try to render real in the patient's mind a doctrine which they all profess but find it difficult to bring home to their feelings—the doctrine that they did not create themselves, that their talents were given them, and that they might as well be proud of the colour of their hair. But always and by all methods the Enemy's aim will be to get the patient's mind off such questions, and yours will be to fix it on them. Even of his sins the Enemy does not want him to think too much: once they are repented, the sooner the man turns his attention outward, the better the Enemy is pleased,

Your affectionate uncle
SCREWTAPE

75

XV

MY DEAR WORMWOOD,
I had noticed, of course, that the humans were having a lull in their European war—what they naïvely call "*The War*"!—and am not surprised that there is a corresponding lull in the patient's anxieties. Do we want to encourage this, or to keep him worried? Tortured fear and stupid confidence are both desirable states of mind. Our choice between them raises important questions.

The humans live in time but our Enemy destines them to eternity. He therefore, I believe, wants them to attend chiefly to two things, to eternity itself, and to that point of time which they call the Present. For the Present is the point at which time touches eternity. Of the present moment, and of it only, humans have an experience analogous to the experience which our Enemy has of reality as a whole; in it alone freedom and actuality are offered them. He would therefore have them continually concerned either with eternity (which means being concerned with Him) or with the Present—either meditating on their eternal union with, or separation from, Himself, or else obeying the present voice of conscience, bearing the present cross, receiving the present grace, giving thanks for the present pleasure.

Our business is to get them away from the eternal, and from the Present. With this in view, we sometimes tempt a human (say a widow or a scholar) to live in the Past. But this is of limited value, for they have some real knowledge of the past and it has a determinate nature and, to that extent, resembles eternity. It is far better to make them live in the Future. Biological necessity makes all their passions point in that direction already, so that thought about the Future inflames hope and fear. Also, it is unknown to them, so that in making them think about it we make them think of unrealities. In a word, the Future is, of all things, the thing *least like* eternity. It is the most completely temporal part of time—for the Past is frozen and no longer flows, and the Present is all lit up with eternal rays. Hence the encouragement we have given to all those schemes of thought such as Creative Evolution, Scientific Humanism, or Communism, which fix men's affections on the Future, on the very core of temporality. Hence nearly all vices are rooted in the future. Gratitude looks to the past and love to the present; fear, avarice, lust, and ambition look ahead. Do not think lust an exception. When the present pleasure arrives, the sin (which alone interests us) is already over. The pleasure is just the part of the process which we regret and would exclude if we could do so without losing the sin; it is the part contributed by the Enemy, and therefore experienced in a Present. The sin, which is our contribution, looked forward.

To be sure, the Enemy wants men to think of the Future too—just so much as is necessary for *now* planning the acts of justice or charity which will probably be their duty tomorrow. The duty of planning the morrow's work is *today's* duty; though its material is borrowed from the future, the duty, like all duties, is in the Present. This is not straw splitting. He does not want men to give the Future their hearts, to place their treasure in it. We do. His ideal is a man who, having worked all day for the good of posterity (if that is his vocation), washes his mind of the whole subject, commits the issue to Heaven, and returns at once to the patience or gratitude demanded by the moment that is passing over him. But we want a man hag-ridden by the Future—haunted by visions of an imminent heaven or hell upon earth—ready to break the Enemy's commands in the present if by so doing we make him think he can attain the one or avert the other—dependent for his faith on the success or failure of schemes whose end he will not live to see. We want a whole race perpetually in pursuit of the rainbow's end, never honest, nor kind, nor happy *now*, but always using as mere fuel wherewith to heap the altar of the future every real gift which is offered them in the Present.

It follows then, in general, and other things being equal, that it is better for your patient to be filled with anxiety or hope (it doesn't much matter which) about this war than for him to be living in the present. But the phrase "living in the present" is ambiguous. It may describe a process which is really just as much concerned with the Future as anxiety itself. Your man may be untroubled about the Future, not because he is concerned with the Present, but because he has persuaded himself that the Future is going to be agreeable. As long as that is the real course of his tranquillity, his tranquillity will do us good, because it is only piling up more disappointment, and therefore more impatience, for him when his false hopes are dashed. If, on the other hand, he is aware that horrors may be in store for him and is praying for the virtues, wherewith to meet them, and meanwhile concerning himself with the Present because there, and there alone, all duty, all grace, all knowledge, and all pleasure dwell, his state is very undesirable and should be attacked at once. Here again, our Philological Arm has done good work; try the word "complacency" on him. But, of course, it is most likely that he is "living in the Present" for none of these reasons but simply because his health is good and he is enjoying his work. The phenomenon would then be merely natural. All the same, I should break it up if I were you. No natural phenomenon is really in our favour. And anyway, why *should* the creature be happy?

Your affectionate uncle

SCREWTAPE

XVI

M<small>Y DEAR</small> W<small>ORMWOOD</small>,
You mentioned casually in your last
letter that the patient has continued to attend
one church, and one only, since he was converted, and that he is not wholly pleased with
it. May I ask what you are about? Why have
I no report on the causes of his fidelity to the
parish church? Do you realise that unless it is
due to indifference it is a very bad thing?
Surely you know that if a man can't be cured
of churchgoing, the next best thing is to send
him all over the neighbourhood looking for the
church that "suits" him until he becomes a
taster or connoisseur of churches.

The reasons are obvious. In the first place
the parochial organisation should always be
attacked, because, being a unity of place and
not of likings, it brings people of different
classes and psychology together in the kind of
unity the Enemy desires. The congregational
principle, on the other hand, makes each church
into a kind of club, and finally, if all goes well,
into a coterie or faction. In the second place,
the search for a "suitable" church makes the
man a critic where the Enemy wants him to be

a pupil. What He wants of the layman in church is an attitude which may, indeed, be critical in the sense of rejecting what is false or unhelpful, but which is wholly uncritical in the sense that it does not appraise—does not waste time in thinking about what it rejects, but lays itself open in uncommenting, humble receptivity to any nourishment that is going. (You see how grovelling, how unspiritual, how irredeemably vulgar He is!) This attitude, especially during sermons, creates the condition (most hostile to our whole policy) in which platitudes can become really audible to a human soul. There is hardly any sermon, or any book, which may not be dangerous to us if it is received in this temper. So pray bestir yourself and send this fool the round of the neighbouring churches as soon as possible. Your record up to date has not given us much satisfaction.

The two churches nearest to him, I have looked up in the office. Both have certain claims. At the first of these the Vicar is a man who has been so long engaged in watering down the faith to make it easier for a supposedly incredulous and hard-headed congregation that it is now he who shocks his parishioners with his unbelief, not *vice versa*. He has undermined many a soul's Christianity. His conduct of the services is also admirable. In order to spare the laity all "difficulties" he has deserted both the lectionary and the appointed psalms and now, without noticing it, revolves endlessly round the little treadmill of his fifteen favourite psalms and twenty favourite lessons. We are thus safe from the danger that any truth not already familiar to him and to his flock should ever reach them through Scripture. But perhaps your patient is not quite silly enough for this church—or not yet?

At the other church we have Fr. Spike. The humans are often puzzled to understand the range of his opinions—why he is one day almost a Communist and the next not far from some kind of theocratic Fascism—one day a scholastic, and the next prepared to deny human reason altogether—one day immersed in politics, and, the day after, declaring that all states of this world are *equally* "under judgment". We, of course, see the connecting link, which is Hatred. The man cannot bring himself to preach anything which is not calculated to shock, grieve, puzzle, or humiliate his parents and their friends. A sermon which such people could accept would be to him as insipid as a poem which they could scan. There is also a promising streak of dishonesty in him; we are teaching him to say "The teaching of the Church is" when he really means "I'm almost sure I read recently in Maritain or someone of that sort". But I must warn you that he has one fatal defect: he really believes. And this may yet mar all.

But there is one good point which both these churches have in common—they are both party churches. I think I warned you before that if your patient can't be kept out of the Church, he ought at least to be violently attached to some party within it. I don't mean on really doctrinal issues; about those, the more lukewarm he is the better. And it isn't the doctrines on which we chiefly depend for producing malice. The real fun is working up hatred between those who *say* "mass" and those who *say* "holy communion" when neither party could possibly state the difference between, say, Hooker's doctrine and Thomas Aquinas', in any form which would hold water for five minutes. And all the purely indifferent things—candles and clothes and what not—are an admirable ground for our activities. We have quite removed from men's minds what that pestilent fellow Paul used to teach about food and other unessentials—namely, that the human without scruples should always give in to the human with scruples. You would think they could not fail to see the application. You would expect to find the "low" churchman genuflecting and crossing himself lest the weak conscience of his "high" brother should be moved to irreverence, and the "high" one refraining from these exercises lest he should betray his "low" brother into idolatry. And so it would have been but for our ceaseless labour. Without that the variety of usage within the Church of England might have become a positive hotbed of charity and humility,

Your affectionate uncle
SCREWTAPE

XVII

MY DEAR WORMWOOD,

The contemptuous way in which you spoke of gluttony as a means of catching souls, in your last letter, only shows your ignorance. One of the great achievements of the last hundred years has been to deaden the human conscience on that subject, so that by now you will hardly find a sermon preached or a conscience troubled about it in the whole length and breadth of Europe. This has largely been effected by concentrating all our efforts on gluttony of Delicacy, not gluttony of Excess. Your patient's mother, as I learn from the dossier and you might have learned from Glubose, is a good example. She would be astonished—one day, I hope, *will* be—to learn that her whole life is enslaved to this kind of sensuality, which is quite concealed from her by the fact that the quantities involved are small. But what do quantities matter, provided we can use a human belly and palate to produce querulousness, impatience, uncharitableness, and self-concern? Glubose has this old woman well in hand. She is a positive terror to hostesses and servants. She is always turning from what

86

has been offered her to say with a demure little sigh and a smile "Oh please, please . .. *all* I want is a cup of tea, weak but not too weak, and the teeniest weeniest bit of really crisp toast". You see? Because what she wants is smaller and less costly than what has been set before her, she never recognises as gluttony her determination to get what she wants, however troublesome it may be to others. At the very moment of indulging her appetite she believes that she is practising temperance. In a crowded restaurant she gives a little scream at the plate which some overworked waitress has set before her and says, "Oh, that's far, far too much! Take it away and bring me about a quarter of it". If challenged, she would say she was doing this to avoid waste; in reality she does it because the particular shade of delicacy to which we have enslaved her is offended by the sight of more food than she happens to want.

The real value of the quiet, unobtrusive work which Glubose has been doing for years on this old woman can be gauged by the way in which her belly now dominates her whole life. The woman is in what may be called the "All-I-want" state of mind. *All* she wants is a cup of tea properly made, or an egg properly boiled, or a slice of bread properly toasted. But she never finds any servant or any friend

who can do these simple things "properly"—
because her "properly" conceals an insatiable
demand for the exact, and almost impossible,
palatal pleasures which she imagines she remembers from the past; a past described by
her as "the days when you could get good
servants" but known to us as the days when
her senses were more easily pleased and she
had pleasures of other kinds which made her
less dependent on those of the table. Meanwhile, the daily disappointment produces daily
ill temper: cooks give notice and friendships
are cooled. If ever the Enemy introduces into
her mind a faint suspicion that she is too
interested in food, Glubose counters it by
suggesting to her that she doesn't mind what
she eats herself but "does like to have things
nice for her boy". In fact, of course, her greed
has been one of the chief sources of his domestic
discomfort for many years.

Now your patient is his mother's son. While
working your hardest, quite rightly, on other
fronts, you must not neglect a little quiet
infiltration in respect of gluttony. Being a male,
he is not so likely to be caught by the "*All* I
want" camouflage. Males are best turned into
gluttons with the help of their vanity. They
ought to be made to think themselves very
knowing about food, to pique themselves on

having found the only restaurant in the town where steaks are really "properly" cooked. What begins as vanity can then be gradually turned into habit. But, however you approach it, the great thing is to bring him into the state in which the denial of any one indulgence—it matters not which, champagne or tea, *sole colbert* or cigarettes—"puts him out", for then his charity, justice, and obedience are all at your mercy.

Mere excess in food is much less valuable than delicacy. Its chief use is as a kind of artillery preparation for attacks on chastity. On that, as on every other subject, keep your man in a condition of false spirituality. Never let him notice the medical aspect. Keep him wondering what pride or lack of faith has delivered him into your hands when a simple enquiry into what he has been eating or drinking for the last twenty-four hours would show him whence your ammunition comes and thus enable him by a very little abstinence to imperil your lines of communication. If he *must* think of the medical side of chastity, feed him the grand lie which we have made the English humans believe, that physical exercise in excess and consequent fatigue are specially favourable to this virtue. How they can believe this, in face of the notorious lustfulness of sailors and soldiers, may well be asked. But we used the schoolmasters to put the story about—men who were really interested in chastity as an excuse for games and therefore recommended games as an aid to chastity. But this whole business is too large to deal with at the tail-end of a letter,

Your affectionate uncle

SCREWTAPE

XVIII

M<small>Y</small> DEAR W<small>ORMWOOD</small>,
   Even under Slubgob you must have
learned at college the routine technique of
sexual temptation, and since, for us spirits, this
whole subject is one of considerable tedium
(though necessary as part of our training) I
will pass it over. But on the larger issues
involved I think you have a good deal to
learn.

The Enemy's demand on humans takes the
form of a dilemma; *either* complete abstinence
or unmitigated monogamy. Ever since our
Father's first great victory, we have rendered
the former very difficult to them. The latter,
for the last few centuries, we have been closing
up as a way of escape. We have done this
through the poets and novelists by persuading
the humans that a curious, and usually short-
lived, experience which they call "being in
love" is the only respectable ground for
marriage; that marriage can, and ought to,
render this excitement permanent; and that a
marriage which does not do so is no longer
binding. This idea is our parody of an idea
that came from the Enemy.

The whole philosophy of Hell rests on recognition of the axiom that one thing is not another thing, and, specially, that one self is not another self. My good is my good and your good is yours. What one gains another loses. Even an inanimate object is what it is by excluding all other objects from the space it occupies; if it expands, it does so by thrusting other objects aside or by absorbing them. A self does the same. With beasts the absorption takes the form of eating; for us, it means the sucking of will and freedom out of a weaker self into a stronger. "To be" *means* "to be in competition".

Now the Enemy's philosophy is nothing more nor less than one continued attempt to evade this very obvious truth. He aims at a contradiction. Things are to be many, yet somehow also one. The good of one self is to be the good of another. This impossibility He calls *love*, and this same monotonous panacea can be detected under all He does and even all He is—or claims to be. Thus He is not content, even Himself, to be a sheer arithmetical unity; He claims to be three as well as one, in order that this nonsense about Love may find a foothold in His own nature. At the other end of the scale, He introduces into matter that obscene invention the organism, in which the parts are perverted from their natural destiny of competition and made to co-operate.

His real motive for fixing on sex as the method of reproduction among humans is only too apparent from the use He has made of it. Sex might have been, from our point of view, quite innocent. It might have been merely one more mode in which a stronger self preyed upon a weaker—as it is, indeed, among the spiders where the bride concludes her nuptials by eating her groom. But in the humans the Enemy has gratuitously associated affection between the parties with sexual desire. He has also made the offspring dependent on the parents and given the parents an impulse to support it—thus producing the Family, which is like the organism, only worse; for the members are more distinct, yet also united in a more conscious and responsible way. The whole thing, in fact, turns out to be simply one more device for dragging in Love.

Now comes the joke. The Enemy described a married couple as "one flesh". He did not say "a happily married couple" or "a couple who married because they were in love", but you can make the humans ignore that. You can also make them forget that the man they call Paul did not confine it to *married* couples. Mere copulation, for him, makes "one flesh".

You can thus get the humans to accept as rhetorical eulogies of "being in love" what were in fact plain descriptions of the real significance of sexual intercourse. The truth is that wherever a man lies with a woman, there, whether they like it or not, a transcendental relation is set up between them which must be eternally enjoyed or eternally endured. From the true statement that this transcendental relation was intended to produce, and, if obediently entered into, too often *will* produce, affection and the family, humans can be made to infer the false belief that the blend of affection, fear, and desire which they call "being in love" is the only thing that makes marriage either happy or holy. The error is easy to produce because "being in love" does very often, in Western Europe, precede marriages which are made in obedience to the Enemy's designs, that is, with the intention of fidelity, fertility and good will; just as religious emotion very often, but not always, attends conversion. In other words, the humans are to be encouraged to regard as the basis for marriage a highly-coloured and distorted version of something the Enemy really promises as its result. Two advantages follow. In the first place, humans who have not the gift of continence can be deterred from seeking marriage as a solution because they do not find themselves "in love", and, thanks to us, the idea of marrying with any other motive seems to them low and cynical. Yes, they think that. They regard the intention of loyalty to a partnership for mutual help, for the preservation of chastity, and for the transmission of life, as something lower than a storm of emotion. (Don't neglect to make your man think the marriage-service very offensive.) In the second place any sexual infatuation whatever, so long as it intends marriage, will be regarded as "love", and "love" will be held to excuse a man from all the guilt, and to protect him from all the consequences, of marrying a heathen, a fool, or a wanton. But more of this in my next,

Your affectionate uncle

SCREWTAPE

XIX

MY DEAR WORMWOOD,
I have been thinking very hard about the question in your last letter. If, as I have clearly shown, all selves are by their very nature in competition, and therefore the Enemy's idea of Love is a contradiction in terms, what becomes of my reiterated warning that He really loves the human vermin and really desires their freedom and continued existence? I hope, my dear boy, you have not shown my letters to anyone. Not that it matters of course. Anyone would see that the appearance of heresy into which I have fallen is purely accidental. By the way, I hope you understood, too, that some apparently uncomplimentary references to Slubgob were purely jocular. I really have the highest respect for him. And, of course, some things I said about not shielding you from the authorities were not seriously meant. You can trust me to look after your interests. But do keep everything under lock and key.

The truth is I slipped by mere carelessness into saying that the Enemy really loves the humans. That, of course, is an impossibility.

He is one being, they are distinct from Him. Their good cannot be His. All His talk about Love must be a disguise for something else— He must have some *real* motive for creating them and taking so much trouble about them. The reason one comes to talk as if He really had this impossible Love is our utter failure to find out that real motive. What does He stand to make out of them? That is the insoluble question. I do not see that it can do any harm to tell you that this very problem was a chief cause of Our Father's quarrel with the Enemy. When the creation of man was first mooted and when, even at that stage, the Enemy freely confessed that he foresaw a certain episode about a cross, Our Father very naturally sought an interview and asked for an explanation. The Enemy gave no reply except to produce the cock-and-bull story about disinterested love which He has been circulating ever since. This Our Father naturally could not accept. He implored the Enemy to lay His cards on the table, and gave Him every opportunity. He admitted that he felt a real anxiety to know the secret; the Enemy replied "I wish with all my heart that you did". It was, I imagine, at this stage in the interview that Our Father's disgust at such an unprovoked lack of confidence caused him to remove himself an infinite distance from the Presence with a suddenness which has given rise to the ridiculous enemy story that he was forcibly thrown out of Heaven. Since then, we have begun to see why our Oppressor was so secretive. His throne depends on the secret. Members of His faction have frequently admitted that if ever we came to understand what He means by Love, the war would be over and we should re-enter Heaven. And there lies the great task. We know that He cannot really love: nobody can: it doesn't make sense. If we could only find out what He is *really* up to! Hypothesis after hypothesis has been tried, and still we can't find out. Yet we must never lose hope; more and more complicated theories, fuller and fuller collections of data, richer rewards for researchers who make progress, more and more terrible punishments for those who fail—all this, pursued and accelerated to the very end of time, cannot, surely, fail to succeed.

You complain that my last letter does not make it clear whether I regard *being in love* as a desirable state for a human or not. But really, Wormwood, that is the sort of question one expects *them* to ask! Leave them to discuss whether "Love", or patriotism, or celibacy, or candles on altars, or teetotalism, or education, are "good" or "bad". Can't you see there's no answer? Nothing matters at all except the tendency of a given state of mind, in given circumstances, to move a particular patient at a particular moment nearer to the Enemy or nearer to us. Thus it would be quite a good thing to make the patient decide that "love" is "good" or "bad". If he is an arrogant man with a contempt for the body really based on delicacy but mistaken by him for purity—and one who takes pleasure in flouting what most of his fellows approve—by all means let him decide against love. Instil into him an over-weening asceticism and then, when you have separated his sexuality from all that might humanise it, weigh in on him with it in some much more brutal and cynical form. If, on the other hand, he is an emotional, gullible man, feed him on minor poets and fifth-rate novelists of the old school until you have made him believe that "Love" is both irresistible and somehow intrinsically meritorious. This belief is not much help, I grant you, in producing casual unchastity; but it is an incomparable recipe for prolonged, "noble", romantic, tragic adulteries, ending, if all goes well, in murders and suicides. Failing that, it can be used to steer the patient into a useful marriage. For marriage, though the Enemy's invention, has its uses. There must be several young women in your patient's neighbourhood who would render the Christian life intensely difficult to him if only you could persuade him to marry one of them. Please send me a report on this when you next write. In the meantime, get it quite clear in your own mind that this state of *falling in love* is not, in itself, necessarily favourable either to us or to the other side. It is simply an occasion which we and the Enemy are both trying to exploit. Like most of the other things which humans are excited about, such as health and sickness, age and youth, or war and peace, it is, from the point of view of the spiritual life, mainly raw material,

Your affectionate uncle
SCREWTAPE

MY DEAR WORMWOOD,
I note with great displeasure that the Enemy has, for the time being, put a forcible end to your direct attacks on the patient's chastity. You ought to have known that He always does in the end, and you ought to have stopped before you reached that stage. For as things are, your man has now discovered the dangerous truth that these attacks don't last forever; consequently you cannot use again what is, after all, our best weapon—the belief of ignorant humans, that there is no hope of getting rid of us except by yielding. I suppose you've tried persuading him that chastity is unhealthy?

I haven't yet got a report from you on young women in the neighbourhood. I should like it at once, for if we can't use his sexuality to make him unchaste we must try to use it for the promotion of a desirable marriage. In the meantime I would like to give you some hint about the type of woman—I mean the physical type—which he should be encouraged to fall in love with if "falling in love" is the best we can manage.

In a rough and ready way, of course, this question is decided for us by spirits far deeper down in the Lowerarchy than you and I. It is the business of these great masters to produce in every age a general misdirection of what may be called sexual "taste". This they do by working through the small circle of popular artists, dressmakers, actresses and advertisers who determine the fashionable type. The aim is to guide each sex away from those members of the other with whom spiritually helpful, happy, and fertile marriages are most likely. Thus we have now for many centuries triumphed over nature to the extent of making certain secondary characteristics of the male (such as the beard) disagreeable to nearly all the females—and there is more in that than you might suppose. As regards the male taste we have varied a good deal. At one time we have directed it to the statuesque and aristocratic type of beauty, mixing men's vanity with their desires and encouraging the race to breed chiefly from the most arrogant and prodigal women. At another, we have selected an exaggeratedly feminine type, faint and languishing, so that folly and cowardice, and all the general falseness and littleness of mind which go with them, shall be at a premium. At present we are on the opposite tack. The age of jazz has succeeded the age of the waltz, and we now teach men to like women whose bodies are scarcely distinguishable from those of boys. Since this is a kind of beauty even more transitory than most, we thus aggravate the female's chronic horror of growing old (with many excellent results) and render her less willing and less able to bear children. And that is not all. We have engineered a great increase in the licence which society allows to the representation of the apparent nude (not the real nude) in art, and its exhibition on the stage or the bathing beach. It is all a fake, of course; the figures in the popular art are falsely drawn; the real women in bathing suits or tights are actually pinched in and propped up to make them appear firmer and more slender and more boyish than nature allows a full-grown woman to be. Yet at the same time, the modern world is taught to believe that it is being "frank" and "healthy" and getting back to nature. As a result we are more and more directing the desires of men to something which does not exist—making the rôle of the eye in sexuality more and more important and at the same time making its demands more and more impossible. What follows you can easily forecast!

That is the general strategy of the moment. But inside that framework you will still find it possible to encourage your patient's desires in one of two directions. You will find, if you look carefully into any human's heart, that he is haunted by at least two imaginary women— a terrestrial and an infernal Venus, and that his desire differs qualitatively according to its object. There is one type for which his desire is such as to be naturally amenable to the Enemy—readily mixed with charity, readily obedient to marriage, coloured all through with that golden light of reverence and naturalness which we detest; there is another type which he desires brutally, and desires to desire brutally, a type best used to draw him away from marriage altogether but which, even within marriage, he would tend to treat as a slave, an idol, or an accomplice. His love for the first might involve what the Enemy calls evil, but only accidentally; the man would wish that she was not someone else's wife and be sorry that he could not love her lawfully. But in the second type, the felt evil is what he wants; it is that "tang" in the flavour which he is after. In the face, it is the visible animality, or sulkiness, or craft, or cruelty which he likes, and in the body, something quite different from what he ordinarily calls Beauty, something he may even, in a sane hour, describe as ugliness, but which, by our art, can be made to play on the raw nerve of his private obsession.

The real use of the infernal Venus is, no doubt, as prostitute or mistress. But if your man is a Christian, and if he has been well trained in nonsense about irresistible and all-excusing "Love", he can often be induced to marry her. And that is very well worth bringing about. You will have failed as regards fornication and solitary vice; but there are other, and more indirect, methods of using a man's sexuality to his undoing. And, by the way, they are not only efficient, but delightful; the unhappiness produced is of a very lasting and exquisite kind,

Your affectionate uncle
SCREWTAPE

XXI

M<small>Y DEAR</small> W<small>ORMWOOD</small>,

Yes. A period of sexual temptation is an excellent time for working in a subordinate attack on the patient's peevishness. It may even be the main attack, as long as he thinks it the subordinate one. But here, as in everything else, the way must be prepared for your moral assault by darkening his intellect.

Men are not angered by mere misfortune but by misfortune conceived as injury. And the sense of injury depends on the feeling that a legitimate claim has been denied. The more claims on life, therefore, that your patient can be induced to make, the more often he will feel injured and, as a result, ill-tempered. Now you will have noticed that nothing throws him into a passion so easily as to find a tract of time which he reckoned on having at his own disposal unexpectedly taken from him. It is the unexpected visitor (when he looked forward to a quiet evening), or the friend's talkative wife (turning up when he looked forward to a *tête-à-tête* with the friend), that throw him out of gear. Now he is not yet so uncharitable or slothful that these small demands on his courtesy are *in themselves* too much for it. They anger him because he regards his time as his own and feels that it is being stolen. You must therefore zealously guard in his mind the curious assumption "My time is my own". Let him have the feeling that he starts each day as the lawful possessor of twenty-four hours. Let him feel as a grievous tax that portion of this property which he has to make over to his employers, and as a generous donation that further portion which he allows to religious duties. But what he must never be permitted to doubt is that the total from which these deductions have been made was, in some mysterious sense, his own personal birthright.

You have here a delicate task. The assumption which you want him to go on making is so absurd that, if once it is questioned, even we cannot find a shred of argument in its defence. The man can neither make, nor retain, one moment of time; it all comes to him by pure gift; he might as well regard the sun and moon as his chattels. He is also, in theory, committed to a total service of the Enemy; and if the Enemy appeared to him in bodily form and demanded that total service for even one day, he would not refuse. He would be greatly relieved if that one day involved nothing harder than listening to the conversation of a foolish woman; and he would be relieved almost to the pitch of disappointment if for one half-hour in that day the Enemy said "Now you may go and amuse yourself". Now if he thinks about his assumption for a moment, even he is bound to realise that he is actually in this situation every day. When I speak of preserving this assumption in his mind, therefore, the last thing I mean you to do is to furnish him with arguments in its defence. There aren't any. Your task is purely negative. Don't let his thoughts come anywhere near it. Wrap a darkness about it, and in the centre of that darkness let his sense of ownership-in-Time lie silent, uninspected, and operative.

The sense of ownership in general is always to be encouraged. The humans are always putting up claims to ownership which sound equally funny in Heaven and in Hell and we must keep them doing so. Much of the modern resistance to chastity comes from men's belief that they "own" their bodies—those vast and perilous estates, pulsating with the energy that made the worlds, in which they find themselves without their consent and from which they are ejected at the pleasure of Another! It is as if a royal child whom his father has placed, for love's sake, in titular command of some great province, under the real rule of wise counsellors, should come to fancy he really owns the cities, the forests, and the corn, in the same way as he owns the bricks on the nursery floor.

We produce this sense of ownership not only by pride but by confusion. We teach them not to notice the different senses of the possessive pronoun—the finely graded differences that run from "my boots" through "my dog", "my servant", "my wife", "my father", "my master" and "my country", to "my God". They can be taught to reduce all these senses to that of "my boots", the "my" of ownership. Even in the nursery a child can be taught to mean by "my Teddy-bear" *not* the old imagined recipient of affection to whom it stands in a special relation (for that is what the Enemy will teach them to mean if we are not careful) but "the bear I can pull to pieces if I like". And at the other end of the scale, we have taught men to say "My God" in a sense not really very different from "My boots", meaning "The God on whom I have a claim for my distinguished services and whom I exploit from the pulpit—the God I have done a corner in".

And all the time the joke is that the word "Mine" in its fully possessive sense cannot be uttered by a human being about anything. In the long run either Our Father or the Enemy will say "Mine" of each thing that exists, and specially of each man. They will find out in the end, never fear, to whom their time, their souls, and their bodies really belong—certainly not to *them*, whatever happens. At present the Enemy says "Mine" of everything on the pedantic, legalistic ground that He made it: Our Father hopes in the end to say "Mine" of all things on the more realistic and dynamic ground of conquest,

Your affectionate uncle

SCREWTAPE

XXII

MY DEAR WORMWOOD,
    So! Your man is in love—and in the worst kind he could possibly have fallen into—and with a girl who does not even appear in the report you sent me. You may be interested to learn that the little misunderstanding with the Secret Police which you tried to raise about some unguarded expressions in one of my letters has been tided over. If you were reckoning on that to secure my good offices, you will find yourself mistaken. You shall pay for that as well as for your other blunders. Meanwhile I enclose a little booklet, just issued, on the new House of Correction for Incompetent Tempters. It is profusely illustrated and you will not find a dull page in it.

I have looked up this girl's dossier and am horrified at what I find. Not only a Christian but such a Christian—a vile, sneaking, simpering, demure, monosyllabic, mouse-like, watery, insignificant, virginal, bread-and-butter miss. The little brute. She makes me vomit. She stinks and scalds through the very pages of the dossier. It drives me mad, the way the world has worsened. We'd have had her to the arena

111

in the old days. That's what her sort is made for. Not that she'd do much good there, either. A two-faced little cheat (I know the sort) who looks as if she'd faint at the sight of blood and then dies with a smile. A cheat every way. Looks as if butter wouldn't melt in her mouth and yet has a satirical wit. The sort of creature who'd find *ME* funny! Filthy insipid little prude—and yet ready to fall into this booby's arms like any other breeding animal. Why doesn't the Enemy blast her for it, if He's so moonstruck by virginity—instead of looking on there, grinning?

He's a hedonist at heart. All those fasts and vigils and stakes and crosses are only a façade. Or only like foam on the sea shore. Out at sea, out in His sea, there is pleasure, and more pleasure. He makes no secret of it; at His right hand are "pleasures for evermore". Ugh! I don't think He has the least inkling of that high and austere mystery to which we rise in the Miserific Vision. He's vulgar, Wormwood. He has a bourgeois mind. He has filled His world full of pleasures. There are things for humans to do all day long without His minding in the least—sleeping, washing, eating, drinking, making love, playing, praying, working. Everything has to be *twisted* before it's any use to us. We fight under cruel disadvantages.

Nothing is naturally on our side. (Not that that excuses *you*. I'll settle with you presently. You have always hated me and been insolent when you dared.)

Then, of course, he gets to know this woman's family and whole circle. Could you not see that the very house she lives in is one that he ought never to have entered? The whole place reeks of that deadly odour. The very gardener, though he has only been there five years, is beginning to acquire it. Even guests, after a week-end visit, carry some of the smell away with them. The dog and the cat are tainted with it. And a house full of the impenetrable mystery. We are certain (it is a matter of first principles) that each member of the family must in some way be making capital out of the others—but we can't find out how. They guard as jealously as the Enemy Himself the secret of what really lies behind this pretence of disinterested love. The whole house and garden is one vast obscenity. It bears a sickening resemblance to the description one human writer made of Heaven; "the regions where there is only life and therefore all that is not music is silence".

Music and silence—how I detest them both! How thankful we should be that ever since our Father entered Hell—though longer ago than humans, reckoning in light years, could express—no square inch of infernal space and no moment of infernal time has been surrendered to either of those abominable forces, but all has been occupied by Noise—Noise, the grand dynamism, the audible expression of all that is exultant, ruthless, and virile—Noise which alone defends us from silly qualms, despairing scruples, and impossible desires. We will make the whole universe a noise in the end. We have already made great strides in this direction as regards the Earth. The melodies and silences of Heaven will be shouted down in the end. But I admit we are not yet loud enough, or anything like it. Research is in progress. Meanwhile *you*, disgusting little——

[*Here the MS. breaks off and is resumed in a different hand.*]

In the heat of composition I find that I have inadvertently allowed myself to assume the form of a large centipede. I am accordingly dictating the rest to my secretary. Now that the transformation is complete I recognise it as a periodical phenomenon. Some rumour of it has reached the humans and a distorted account of it appears in the poet Milton, with the ridiculous addition that such changes of shape are a "punishment" imposed on us by the Enemy. A more modern writer—someone with a name like Pshaw—has, however, grasped the truth. Transformation proceeds from within and is a glorious manifestation of that Life Force which Our Father would worship if he worshipped anything but himself. In my present form I feel even more anxious to see you, to unite you to myself in an indissoluble embrace,

(Signed) TOADPIPE

For his Abysmal Sublimity Under Secretary
Screwtape, T.E., B.S., etc.

XXIII

M^Y DEAR WORMWOOD,
Through this girl and her disgusting
family the patient is now getting to know more
Christians every day, and very intelligent
Christians too. For a long time it will be quite
impossible to *remove* spirituality from his life.
Very well then; we must *corrupt* it. No doubt
you have often practised transforming yourself
into an angel of light as a parade-ground
exercise. Now is the time to do it in the face
of the Enemy. The World and the Flesh have
failed us; a third Power remains. And success
of this third kind is the most glorious of all.
A spoiled saint, a Pharisee, an inquisitor, or a
magician, makes better sport in Hell than a
mere common tyrant or debauchee.

Looking round your patient's new friends I
find that the best point of attack would be the
border-line between theology and politics.
Several of his new friends are very much alive
to the social implications of their religion. That,
in itself, is a bad thing; but good can be made
out of it.

You will find that a good many Christian-
political writers think that Christianity began

going wrong, and departing from the doctrine
of its Founder, at a very early stage. Now this
idea must be used by us to encourage once
again the conception of a "historical Jesus" to
be found by clearing away later "accretions and
perversions" and then to be contrasted with
the whole Christian tradition. In the last
generation we promoted the construction of
such a "historical Jesus" on liberal and humani-
tarian lines; we are now putting forward a new
"historical Jesus" on Marxian, catastrophic,
and revolutionary lines. The advantages of
these constructions, which we intend to change
every thirty years or so, are manifold. In the
first place they all tend to direct men's devotion
to something which does not exist, for each
"historical Jesus" is unhistorical. The docu-
ments say what they say and cannot be added
to; each new "historical Jesus" therefore has
to be got out of them by suppression at one
point and exaggeration at another, and by
that sort of guessing (*brilliant* is the adjective
we teach humans to apply to it) on which no
one would risk ten shillings in ordinary life,
but which is enough to produce a crop of new
Napoleons, new Shakespeares, and new Swifts,
in every publisher's autumn list. In the second
place, all such constructions place the importance of their Historical Jesus in some peculiar

theory He is supposed to have promulgated. He has to be a "great man" in the modern sense of the word—one standing at the terminus of some centrifugal and unbalanced line of thought—a crank vending a panacea. We thus distract men's minds from Who He is, and what He did. We first make Him solely a teacher, and then conceal the very substantial agreement between His teachings and those of all other great moral teachers. For humans must not be allowed to notice that all great moralists are sent by the Enemy not to inform men but to remind them, to restate the primeval moral platitudes against our continual conceal-ment of them. We make the Sophists: He raises up a Socrates to answer them. Our third aim is, by these constructions, to destroy the devotional life. For the real presence of the Enemy, otherwise experienced by men in prayer and sacrament, we substitute a merely probable, remote, shadowy, and uncouth figure, one who spoke a strange language and died a long time ago. Such an object cannot in fact be worshipped. Instead of the Creator adored by its creature, you soon have merely a leader acclaimed by a partisan, and finally a distin-guished character approved by a judicious historian. And fourthly, besides being un-historical in the Jesus it depicts, religion of this kind is false to history in another sense. No nation, and few individuals, are really brought into the Enemy's camp by the historical study of the biography of Jesus, simply as biography. Indeed materials for a full biography have been withheld from men. The earliest converts were converted by a single historical fact (the Resurrection) and a single theological doctrine (the Redemption) operating on a sense of sin which they already had—and sin, not against some new fancy-dress law produced as a novelty by a "great man", but against the old, platitudinous, universal moral law which they had been taught by their nurses and mothers. The "Gospels" come later and were written not to make Christians but to edify Christians already made.

The "Historical Jesus" then, however dangerous he may seem to be to us at some particular point, is always to be encouraged. About the general connection between Christianity and politics, our position is more delicate. Certainly we do not want men to allow their Christianity to flow over into their political life, for the establishment of anything like a really just society would be a major disaster. On the other hand we do want, and want very much, to make men treat Christianity as a means; preferably, of course, as a means to their own advancement, but, failing that, as a means to anything—even to social justice. The thing to do is to get a man at first to value social justice as a thing which the Enemy demands, and then work him on to the stage at which he values Christianity because it may produce social justice. For the Enemy will not be used as a convenience. Men or nations who think they can revive the Faith in order to make a good society might just as well think they can use the stairs of Heaven as a short cut to the nearest chemist's shop. Fortunately it is quite easy to coax humans round this little corner. Only today I have found a passage in a Christian writer where he recommends his own version of Christianity on the ground that "only such a faith can outlast the death of old cultures and the birth of new civilisations". You see the little rift? "Believe this, not because it is true, but for some other reason." That's the game,

Your affectionate uncle

SCREWTAPE

XXIV

MY DEAR WORMWOOD,
I have been in correspondence with Slumtrimpet who is in charge of your patient's young woman, and begin to see the chink in her armour. It is an unobtrusive little vice which she shares with nearly all women who have grown up in an intelligent circle united by a clearly defined belief; and it consists in a quite untroubled assumption that the outsiders who do not share this belief are really too stupid and ridiculous. The males, who habitually meet these outsiders, do not feel that way; their confidence, if they are confident, is of a different kind. Hers, which she supposes to be due to Faith, is in reality largely due to the mere colour she has taken from her surroundings. It is not, in fact, very different from the conviction she would have felt at the age of ten that the kind of fish-knives used in her father's house were the proper or normal or "real" kind, while those of the neighbouring families were "not real fish-knives" at all. Now the element of ignorance and naïvety in all this is so large, and the element of spiritual pride so small, that it gives us little hope of the girl

herself. But have you thought of how it can be made to influence your own patient?

It is always the novice who exaggerates. The man who has risen in society is over-refined, the young scholar is pedantic. In this new circle your patient is a novice. He is there daily meeting Christian life of a quality he never before imagined and seeing it all through an enchanted glass because he is in love. He is anxious (indeed the Enemy commands him) to imitate this quality. Can you get him to imitate this *defect* in his mistress and to exaggerate it until what was venial in her becomes in him the strongest and most beautiful of the vices—Spiritual Pride?

The conditions seem ideally favourable. The new circle in which he finds himself is one of which he is tempted to be proud for many reasons other than its Christianity. It is a better educated, more intelligent, more agreeable society than any he has yet encountered. He is also under some degree of illusion as to his own place in it. Under the influence of "love" he may still think himself unworthy of the girl, but he is rapidly ceasing to think himself unworthy of the others. He has no notion how much in him is forgiven because they are charitable and made the best of because he is now one of the family. He does not dream how much of his conversation, how many of his opinions, are recognised by them all as mere echoes of their own. Still less does he suspect how much of the delight he takes in these people is due to the erotic enchantment which the girl, for him, spreads over all her surroundings. He thinks that he likes their talk and way of life because of some congruity between their spiritual state and his, when in fact they are so far beyond him that if he were not in love he would be merely puzzled and repelled by much which he now accepts. He is like a dog which should imagine it understood fire-arms because its hunting instinct and love for its master enable it to enjoy a day's shooting!

Here is your chance. While the Enemy, by means of sexual love and of some very agreeable people far advanced in His service, is drawing the young barbarian up to levels he could never otherwise have reached, you must make him feel that he is finding his *own* level—that these people are "his sort" and that, coming among them, he has come home. When he turns from them to other society he will find it dull; partly because almost any society within his reach is, in fact, much less entertaining, but still more because he will miss the enchantment of the young woman. You must teach him to mistake this contrast between the circle that delights and the circle that bores him for the contrast between Christians and unbelievers. He must be made to feel (he'd better not put it into words) "how different we Christians are"; and by "we Christians" he must really, but unknowingly, mean "my set"; and by "my set" he must mean not "The people who, in their charity and humility, have accepted me", but "The people with whom I associate by right".

Success here depends on confusing him. If you try to make him explicitly and professedly proud of being a Christian, you will probably fail; the Enemy's warnings are too well known. If, on the other hand, you let the idea of "we Christians" drop out altogether and merely make him complacent about "his set", you will produce not true spiritual pride but mere social vanity which, by comparison, is a trumpery, puny little sin. What you want is to keep a sly self-congratulation mixing with all his thoughts and never allow him to raise the question "What, precisely, am I congratulating myself *about*?" The idea of belonging to an inner ring, of being in a secret, is very sweet to him. Play on that nerve. Teach him, using the influence of this girl when she is silliest, to adopt an air of *amusement* at the things the unbelievers say. Some theories which he may meet in modern Christian circles may here prove helpful;

theories, I mean, that place the hope of society in some inner ring of "clerks", some trained minority of theocrats. It is no affair of yours whether those theories are true or false; the great thing is to make Christianity a mystery religion in which he feels himself one of the initiates.

Pray do not fill your letters with rubbish about this European War. Its final issue is, no doubt, important, but that is a matter for the High Command. I am not in the least interested in knowing how many people in England have been killed by bombs. In what state of mind they died, I can learn from the office at this end. That they were going to die sometime, I knew already. Please keep your mind on your work,

Your affectionate uncle

SCREWTAPE

XXV

M<small>Y DEAR</small> W<small>ORMWOOD</small>,
The real trouble about the set your
patient is living in is that it is *merely* Christian.
They all have individual interests, of course,
but the bond remains mere Christianity. What
we want, if men become Christians at all, is to
keep them in the state of mind I call "Christianity And". You know—Christianity and the
Crisis, Christianity and the New Psychology,
Christianity and the New Order, Christianity
and Faith Healing, Christianity and Psychical
Research, Christianity and Vegetarianism,
Christianity and Spelling Reform. If they must
be Christians let them at least be Christians
with a difference. Substitute for the faith itself
some Fashion with a Christian colouring. Work
on their horror of the Same Old Thing.

The horror of the Same Old Thing is one of
the most valuable passions we have produced
in the human heart—an endless source of
heresies in religion, folly in counsel, infidelity
in marriage, and inconstancy in friendship.
The humans live in time, and experience reality
successively. To experience much of it, therefore, they must experience many different

things; in other words, they must experience change. And since they need change, the Enemy (being a hedonist at heart) has made change pleasurable to them, just as He has made eating pleasurable. But since He does not wish them to make change, any more than eating, an end in itself, He has balanced the love of change in them by a love of permanence. He has contrived to gratify both tastes together in the very world He has made, by that union of change and permanence which we call Rhythm. He gives them the seasons, each season different yet every year the same, so that spring is always felt as a novelty yet always as the recurrence of an immemorial theme. He gives them in His Church a spiritual year; they change from a fast to a feast, but it is the same feast as before.

Now just as we pick out and exaggerate the pleasure of eating to produce gluttony, so we pick out this natural pleasantness of change and twist it into a demand for absolute novelty. This demand is entirely our workmanship. If we neglect our duty, men will be not only contented but transported by the mixed novelty and familiarity of snowdrops *this* January, sunrise *this* morning, plum pudding *this* Christmas. Children, until we have taught them better, will be perfectly happy with a seasonal round of games in which conkers succeed hopscotch as regularly as autumn follows summer. Only by our incessant efforts is the demand for infinite, or unrhythmical, change kept up.

This demand is valuable in various ways. In the first place it diminishes pleasure while increasing desire. The pleasure of novelty is by its very nature more subject than any other to the law of diminishing returns. And continued novelty costs money, so that the desire for it spells avarice or unhappiness or both. And again, the more rapacious this desire, the sooner it must eat up all the innocent sources of pleasure and pass on to those the Enemy forbids. Thus by inflaming the horror of the Same Old Thing we have recently made the Arts, for example, less dangerous to us than perhaps, they have ever been, "low-brow" and "high-brow" artists alike being now daily drawn into fresh, and still fresh, excesses of lasciviousness, unreason, cruelty, and pride. Finally, the desire for novelty is indispensable if we are to produce Fashions or Vogues.

The use of Fashions in thought is to distract the attention of men from their real dangers. We direct the fashionable outcry of each generation against those vices of which it is least in danger and fix its approval on the virtue nearest to that vice which we are trying to make endemic. The game is to have them all running about with fire extinguishers whenever there is a flood, and all crowding to that side of the boat which is already nearly gunwale under. Thus we make it fashionable to expose the dangers of enthusiasm at the very moment when they are all really becoming worldly and lukewarm; a century later, when we are really making them all Byronic and drunk with emotion, the fashionable outcry is directed against the dangers of the mere "understanding". Cruel ages are put on their guard against Sentimentality, feckless and idle ones against Respectability, lecherous ones against Puritanism; and whenever all men are really hastening to be slaves or tyrants we make Liberalism the prime bogey.

But the greatest triumph of all is to elevate this horror of the Same Old Thing into a philosophy so that nonsense in the intellect may reinforce corruption in the will. It is here that the general Evolutionary or Historical character of modern European thought (partly our work) comes in so useful. The Enemy loves platitudes. Of a proposed course of action He wants men, so far as I can see, to ask very simple questions; is it righteous? is it prudent? is it possible? Now if we can keep men asking "Is it in accordance with the general movement of our time? Is it progressive or reactionary? Is this the way that History is going?" they will neglect the relevant questions. And the questions they *do* ask are, of course, unanswerable; for they do not know the future, and what the future will be depends very largely on just those choices which they now invoke the future to help them to make. As a result, while their minds are buzzing in this vacuum, we have the better chance to slip in and bend them to the action *we* have decided on. And great work has already been done. Once they knew that some changes were for the better, and others for the worse, and others again indifferent. We have largely removed this knowledge. For the descriptive adjective "unchanged" we have substituted the emotional adjective "stagnant". We have trained them to think of the Future as a promised land which favoured heroes attain—not as something which everyone reaches at the rate of sixty minutes an hour, whatever he does, whoever he is,

Your affectionate uncle

SCREWTAPE

XXVI

M^{Y DEAR WORMWOOD,}

Yes; courtship is the time for sowing those seeds which will grow up ten years later into domestic hatred. The enchantment of unsatisfied desire produces results which the humans can be made to mistake for the results of charity. Avail yourself of the ambiguity in the word "Love": let them think they have solved by Love problems they have in fact only waived or postponed under the influence of the enchantment. While it lasts you have your chance to foment the problems in secret and render them chronic.

The grand problem is that of "unselfishness". Note, once again, the admirable work of our Philological Arm in substituting the negative unselfishness for the Enemy's positive Charity. Thanks to this you can, from the very outset, teach a man to surrender benefits not that others may be happy in having them but that he may be unselfish in forgoing them. That is a great point gained. Another great help, where the parties concerned are male and female, is the divergence of view about Unselfishness which we have built up between the sexes. A woman means by Unselfishness chiefly taking trouble for others; a man means not giving trouble to others. As a result, a woman who is quite far gone in the Enemy's service will make a nuisance of herself on a larger scale than any man except those whom Our Father has dominated completely; and, conversely, a man will live long in the Enemy's camp before he undertakes as much spontaneous work to please others as a quite ordinary woman may do every day. Thus while the woman thinks of doing good offices and the man of respecting other people's rights, each sex, without any obvious unreason, can and does regard the other as radically selfish.

On top of these confusions you can now introduce a few more. The erotic enchantment produces a mutual complaisance in which each is *really* pleased to give in to the wishes of the other. They also know that the Enemy demands of them a degree of charity which, if attained, would result in similar actions. You must make them establish as a Law for their whole married life that degree of mutual self-sacrifice which is at present sprouting naturally out of the enchantment, but which, when the enchantment dies away, they will not have charity enough to enable them to perform. They will not see the trap, since they are under the double blindness of mistaking sexual excitement for charity and of thinking that the excitement will last.

When once a sort of official, legal, or nominal Unselfishness has been established as a rule—a rule for the keeping of which their emotional resources have died away and their spiritual resources have not yet grown—the most delightful results follow. In discussing any joint action, it becomes obligatory that A should argue in favour of B's supposed wishes and against his own, while B does the opposite. It is often impossible to find out either party's real wishes; with luck, they end by doing something that neither wants, while each feels a glow of self-righteousness and harbours a secret claim to preferential treatment for the unselfishness shown and a secret grudge against the other for the ease with which the sacrifice has been accepted. Later on you can venture on what may be called the Generous Conflict Illusion. This game is best played with more than two players, in a family with grown-up children for example. Something quite trivial, like having tea in the garden, is proposed. One member takes care to make it quite clear (though not in so many words) that he would rather not but is, of course, prepared to do so out of "Unselfishness". The others instantly withdraw their proposal, ostensibly through their "Unselfishness", but really because they don't want to be used as a sort of lay figure on which the first speaker practices petty altruisms. But he is not going to be done out of his debauch of Unselfishness either. He insists on doing "what the others want". They insist on doing what he wants. Passions are roused. Soon someone is saying "Very well then, I won't have any tea at all!", and a real quarrel ensues with bitter resentment on both sides. You see how it is done? If each side had been frankly contending for its own real wish, they would all have kept within the bounds of reason and courtesy; but just because the contention is reversed and each side is fighting the other side's battle, all the bitterness which really flows from thwarted self-righteousness and obstinacy and the accumulated grudges of the last ten years is concealed from them by the nominal or official "Unselfishness" of what they are doing or, at least, held to be excused by it. Each side is, indeed, quite alive to the cheap quality of the adversary's Unselfishness and of the false position into which he is trying to force them; but each manages to feel blameless and ill-used itself, with no more dishonesty than comes natural to a human.

A sensible human once said, "If people knew

how much ill-feeling Unselfishness occasions, it would not be so often recommended from the pulpit"; and again, "She's the sort of woman who lives for others—you can always tell the others by their hunted expression". All this can be begun even in the period of courtship. A little *real* selfishness on your patient's part is often of less value in the long run, for securing his soul, than the first beginnings of that elaborate and self-consciousness unselfishness which may one day blossom into the sort of thing I have described. Some degree of mutual falseness, some surprise that the girl does not always notice just how Unselfish he is being, can be smuggled in already. Cherish these things, and, above all, don't let the young fools notice them. If they notice them they will be on the road to discovering that "love" is not enough, that charity is needed and not yet achieved and that no external law can supply its place. I wish Slumtrimpet could do something about undermining that young woman's sense of the ridiculous,

Your affectionate uncle
SCREWTAPE

XXVII

M<small>Y DEAR</small> W<small>ORMWOOD</small>,

You seem to be doing very little good at present. The use of his "love" to distract his mind from the Enemy is, of course, obvious, but you reveal what poor use you are making of it when you say that the whole question of distraction and the wandering mind has now become one of the chief subjects of his prayers. That means you have largely failed. When this, or any other distraction, crosses his mind you ought to encourage him to thrust it away by sheer will power and to try to continue the normal prayer as if nothing had happened; once he accepts the distraction as his present problem and lays *that* before the Enemy and makes it the main theme of his prayers and his endeavours, then, so far from doing good, you have done harm. Anything, even a sin, which has the total effect of moving him close up to the Enemy, makes against us in the long run.

A promising line is the following. Now that he is in love, a new idea of *earthly* happiness has arisen in his mind: and hence a new urgency in his purely petitionary prayers—about this war and other such matters. Now is the time for raising intellectual difficulties about prayer of that sort. False spirituality is always to be encouraged. On the seemingly pious ground that "praise and communion with God is the true prayer", humans can often be lured into direct disobedience to the Enemy who (in His usual flat, commonplace, uninteresting way) has definitely told them to pray for their daily bread and the recovery of their sick. You will, of course, conceal from him the fact that the prayer for daily bread, interpreted in a "spiritual sense", is really just as crudely petitionary as it is in any other sense.

But since your patient has contracted the terrible habit of obedience, he will probably continue such "crude" prayers whatever you do. But you can worry him with the haunting suspicion that the practice is absurd and can have no objective result. Don't forget to use the "heads I win, tails you lose" argument. If the thing he prays for doesn't happen, then that is one more proof that petitionary prayers don't work; if it does happen, he will, of course, be able to see some of the physical causes which led up to it, and "therefore it would have happened anyway", and thus a granted prayer becomes just as good a proof as a denied one that prayers are ineffective.

You, being a spirit, will find it difficult to

understand how he gets into this confusion. But you must remember that he takes Time for an ultimate reality. He supposes that the Enemy, like himself, sees some things as present, remembers others as past, and anticipates others as future; or even if he believes that the Enemy does not see things that way, yet, in his heart of hearts, he regards this as a peculiarity of the Enemy's mode of perception— he doesn't really think (though he would say he did) that things as the Enemy sees them are things as they are! If you tried to explain to him that men's prayers today are one of the innumerable co-ordinates with which the Enemy harmonises the weather of tomorrow, he would reply that then the Enemy always knew men were going to make those prayers and, if so, they did not pray freely but were predestined to do so. And he would add that the weather on a given day can be traced back through its causes to the original creation of matter itself— so that the whole thing, both on the human and on the material side, is given "from the word go". What he ought to say, of course, is obvious to us; that the problem of adapting the particular weather to the particular prayers is merely the appearance, at two points in his temporal mode of perception, of the total problem of adapting the whole spiritual universe to the whole corporeal universe; that creation in its entirety operates at every point of space and time, or rather that their kind of consciousness forces them to encounter the whole, self-consistent creative act as a series of successive events. *Why* that creative act leaves room for their free will is the problem of problems, the secret behind the Enemy's nonsense about "Love". *How* it does so is no problem at all; for the Enemy does not *foresee* the humans making their free contributions in a future, but *sees* them doing so in His unbounded Now. And obviously to watch a man doing something is not to make him do it.

It may be replied that some meddlesome human writers, notably Boethius, have let this secret out. But in the intellectual climate which we have at last succeeded in producing throughout Western Europe, you needn't bother about that. Only the learned read old books and we have now so dealt with the learned that they are of all men the least likely to acquire wisdom by doing so. We have done this by inculcating The Historical Point of View. The Historical Point of View, put briefly, means that when a learned man is presented with any statement in an ancient author, the one question he never asks is whether it is true. He asks who influenced the ancient writer, and how far the statement is consistent with what he said in other books, and what phase in the writer's development, or in the general history of thought, it illustrates, and how it affected later writers, and how often it has been misunderstood (specially by the learned man's own colleagues) and what the general course of criticism on it has been for the last ten years, and what is the "present state of the question". To regard the ancient writer as a possible source of knowledge—to anticipate that what he said could possibly modify your thoughts or your behaviour—this would be rejected as unutterably simple-minded. And since we cannot deceive the whole human race all the time, it is most important thus to cut every generation off from all others; for where learning makes a free commerce between the ages there is always the danger that the characteristic errors of one may be corrected by the characteristic truths of another. But thanks be to our Father and the Historical Point of View, great scholars are now as little nourished by the past as the most ignorant mechanic who holds that "history is bunk",

Your affectionate uncle
SCREWTAPE

XXVIII

MY DEAR WORMWOOD,
When I told you not to fill your letters
with rubbish about the war, I meant, of course,
that I did not want to have your rather infantile
rhapsodies about the death of men and the
destruction of cities. In so far as the war really
concerns the spiritual state of the patient, I
naturally want full reports. And on this aspect
you seem singularly obtuse. Thus you tell me
with glee that there is reason to expect heavy
air raids on the town where the creature lives.
This is a crying example of something I have
complained about already—your readiness to
forget the main point in your immediate enjoyment of human suffering. Do you not know
that bombs kill men? Or do you not realise
that the patient's death, at this moment, is
precisely what we want to avoid? He has
escaped the worldly friends with whom you
tried to entangle him; he has "fallen in love"
with a very Christian woman and is temporarily
immune from your attacks on his chastity; and
the various methods of corrupting his spiritual
life which we have been trying are so far
unsuccessful. At the present moment, as the

full impact of the war draws nearer and his worldly hopes take a proportionately lower place in his mind, full of his defence work, full of the girl, forced to attend to his neighbours more than he has ever done before and liking it more than he expected, "taken out of himself" as the humans say, and daily increasing in conscious dependence on the Enemy, he will almost certainly be lost to us if he is killed tonight. This is so obvious that I am ashamed to write it. I sometimes wonder if you young fiends are not kept out on temptation-duty too long at a time—if you are not in some danger of becoming infected by the sentiments and values of the humans among whom you work. They, of course, do tend to regard death as the prime evil and survival as the greatest good. But that is because we have taught them to do so. Do not let us be infected by our own propaganda. I know it seems strange that your chief aim at the moment should be the very same thing for which the patient's lover and his mother are praying—namely his bodily safety. But so it is; you should be guarding him like the apple of your eye. If he dies now, you lose him. If he survives the war, there is always hope. The Enemy has guarded him from you through the first great wave of temptations. But, if only he can be kept alive, you have time itself for your ally. The long, dull monotonous years of middle-aged prosperity or middle-aged adversity are excellent campaigning weather. You see, it is so hard for these creatures to *persevere*. The routine of adversity, the gradual decay of youthful loves and youthful hopes, the quiet despair (hardly felt as pain) of ever overcoming the chronic temptations with which we have again and again defeated them, the drabness which we create in their lives and the inarticulate resentment with which we teach them to respond to it—all this provides admirable opportunities of wearing out a soul by attrition. If, on the other hand, the middle years prove prosperous, our position is even stronger. Prosperity knits a man to the World. He feels that he is "finding his place in it", while really it is finding its place in him. His increasing reputation, his widening circle of acquaintances, his sense of importance, the growing pressure of absorbing and agreeable work, build up in him a sense of being really at home in earth which is just what we want. You will notice that the young are generally less unwilling to die than the middle-aged and the old.

The truth is that the Enemy, having oddly destined these mere animals to life in His own eternal world, has guarded them pretty effectively from the danger of feeling at home anywhere else. That is why we must often wish long life to our patients; seventy years is not a day too much for the difficult task of unravelling their souls from Heaven and building up a firm attachment to the earth. While they are young we find them always shooting off at a tangent. Even if we contrive to keep them ignorant of explicit religion, the incalculable winds of fantasy and music and poetry— the mere face of a girl, the song of a bird, or the sight of a horizon—are always blowing our whole structure away. They *will* not apply themselves steadily to worldly advancement, prudent connections, and the policy of safety first. So inveterate is their appetite for Heaven that our best method, at this stage, of attaching them to earth is to make them believe that earth can be turned into Heaven at some future date by politics or eugenics or "science" or psychology, or what not. Real worldliness is a work of time—assisted, of course, by pride, for we teach them to describe the creeping death as good sense or Maturity or Experience. *Experience*, in the peculiar sense we teach them to give it, is, by the bye, a most useful word. A great human philosopher nearly let our secret out when he said that where Virtue is concerned "Experience is the mother of illusion"; but thanks to a change in Fashion, and also, of course, to the Historical Point of View, we have largely rendered his book innocuous.

How valuable time is to us may be gauged by the fact that the Enemy allows us so little of it. The majority of the human race dies in infancy; of the survivors, a good many die in youth. It is obvious that to Him human birth is important chiefly as the qualification for human death, and death solely as the gate to that other kind of life. We are allowed to work only on a selected minority of the race, for what humans call a 'normal life" is the exception. Apparently He wants some—but only a very few—of the human animals with which He is peopling Heaven to have had the experience of resisting us through an earthly life of sixty or seventy years. Well, there is our opportunity. The smaller it is, the better we must use it. Whatever you do, keep your patient as safe as you possibly can,

Your affectionate uncle
SCREWTAPE

XXIX

M<small>Y</small> DEAR W<small>ORMWOOD</small>,
    Now that it is certain the German humans will bombard your patient's town and that his duties will keep him in the thick of the danger, we must consider our policy. Are we to aim at cowardice—or at courage, with consequent pride—or at hatred of the Germans?

Well, I am afraid it is no good trying to make him brave. Our research department has not yet discovered (though success is hourly expected) how to produce *any* virtue. This is a serious handicap. To be greatly and effectively wicked a man needs some virtue. What would Attila have been without his courage, or Shylock without self-denial as regards the flesh? But as we cannot supply these qualities ourselves, we can only use them as supplied by the Enemy—and this means leaving Him a kind of foothold in those men whom, otherwise, we have made most securely our own. A very unsatisfactory arrangement, but, I trust, we shall one day learn to do better.

Hatred we can manage. The tension of human nerves during noise, danger, and fatigue, makes them prone to any violent emotion and

146

it is only a question of guiding this suscepti-
bility into the right channels. If conscience
resists, muddle him. Let him say that he feels
hatred not on his own behalf but on that of
the women and children, and that a Christian
is told to forgive his own, not other people's
enemies. In other words let him consider himself sufficiently identified with the women and
children to feel hatred on their behalf, but *not*
sufficiently identified to regard their enemies as
his own and therefore proper objects of forgiveness.

But hatred is best combined with Fear.
Cowardice, alone of all the vices, is purely
painful—horrible to anticipate, horrible to feel,
horrible to remember; Hatred has its pleasures.
It is therefore often the *compensation* by which
a frightened man reimburses himself for the
miseries of Fear. The more he fears, the more
he will hate. And Hatred is also a great anodyne
for shame. To make a deep wound in his
charity, you should therefore first defeat his
courage.

Now this is a ticklish business. We have
made men proud of most vices, but not of
cowardice. Whenever we have almost succeeded
in doing so, the Enemy permits a war or an
earthquake or some other calamity, and at
once courage becomes so obviously lovely and

147

important even in human eyes that all our work is undone, and there is still at least one vice of which they feel genuine shame. The danger of inducing cowardice in our patients, therefore, is lest we produce real self-knowledge and self-loathing with consequent repentance and humility. And in fact, in the last war, thousands of humans, by discovering their own cowardice, discovered the whole moral world for the first time. In peace we can make many of them ignore good and evil entirely; in danger, the issue is forced upon them in a guise to which even we cannot blind them. There is here a cruel dilemma before us. If we promoted justice and charity among men, we should be playing directly into the Enemy's hands; but if we guide them to the opposite behaviour, this sooner or later produces (for He permits it to produce) a war or a revolution, and the un-disguisable issue of cowardice or courage awakes thousands of men from moral stupor.

This, indeed, is probably one of the Enemy's motives for creating a dangerous world—a world in which moral issues really come to the point. He sees as well as you do that courage is not simply *one* of the virtues, but the form of every virtue at the testing point, which means, at the point of highest reality. A chastity or honesty, or mercy, which yields to danger will be chaste or honest or merciful only on conditions. Pilate was merciful till it became risky.

It is therefore possible to lose as much as we gain by making your man a coward; he may learn too much about himself! There is, of course, always the chance, not of chloroforming the shame, but of aggravating it and producing Despair. This would be a great triumph. It would show that he had believed in, and accepted, the Enemy's forgiveness of his other sins only because he himself did not fully feel their sinfulness—that in respect of the one vice which he really understands in its full depth of dishonour he cannot seek, nor credit, the Mercy. But I fear you have already let him get too far in the Enemy's school, and he knows that Despair is a greater sin than any of the sins which provoke it.

As to the actual technique of temptations to cowardice, not much need be said. The main point is that precautions have a tendency to increase fear. The precautions publicly enjoined on your patient, however, soon become a matter of routine and this effect disappears. What you must do is to keep running in his mind (side by side with the conscious intention of doing his duty) the vague idea of all sorts of things he can do or not do, *inside* the framework of the duty, which seem to make him a little safer. Get his mind off the simple rule ("I've got to stay here and do so-and-so") into a series of imaginary life lines ("If A happened—though I very much hope it won't—I could do B—and if the worst came to the worst, I could always do C"). Superstitions, if not recognised as such, can be awakened. The point is to keep him feeling that he has *something*, other than the Enemy and courage the Enemy supplies, *to fall back on*, so that what was intended to be a total commitment to duty becomes honeycombed all through with little unconscious reservations. By building up a series of imaginary expedients to prevent "the worst coming to the worst" you may produce, at that level of his will which he is not aware of, a determination that the worst *shall not* come to the worst. Then, at the moment of real terror, rush it out into his nerves and muscles and you may get the fatal act done before he knows what you're about. For remember, the *act* of cowardice is all that matters; the emotion of fear is, in itself, no sin and, though we enjoy it, does us no good,

Your affectionate uncle
SCREWTAPE

XXX

MY DEAR WORMWOOD,
I sometimes wonder whether you think you have been sent into the world for your own amusement. I gather, not from your miserably inadequate report but from that of the Infernal Police, that the patient's behaviour during the first raid has been the worst possible. He has been very frightened and thinks himself a great coward and therefore feels no pride; but he has done everything his duty demanded and perhaps a bit more. Against this disaster all you can produce on the credit side is a burst of ill temper with a dog that tripped him up, some excessive cigarette smoking, and the forgetting of a prayer. What is the use of whining to me about your difficulties? If you are proceeding on the Enemy's idea of "justice" and suggesting that your opportunities and intentions should be taken into account, then I am not sure that a charge of heresy does not lie against you. At any rate, you will soon find that the justice of Hell is purely realistic, and concerned only with results. Bring us back food, or be food yourself.

The only constructive passage in your letter

is where you say that you still expect good results from the patient's fatigue. That is well enough. But it won't fall into your hands. Fatigue *can* produce extreme gentleness, and quiet of mind, and even something like vision. If you have often seen men led by it into anger, malice and impatience, that is because those men have had efficient tempters. The paradoxical thing is that moderate fatigue is a better soil for peevishness than absolute exhaustion. This depends partly on physical causes, but partly on something else. It is not fatigue simply as such that produces the anger, but unexpected demands on a man already tired. Whatever men expect they soon come to think they have a right to: the sense of disappointment can, with very little skill on our part, be turned into a sense of injury. It is after men have given in to the irremediable, after they have despaired of relief and ceased to think even a half-hour ahead, that the dangers of humbled and gentle weariness begin. To produce the best results from the patient's fatigue, therefore, you must feed him with false hopes. Put into his mind plausible reasons for believing that the air-raid will not be repeated. Keep him comforting himself with the thought of how much he will enjoy his bed next night. Exaggerate the weariness by making him think it will soon be over; for men usually feel that a strain could have been endured no longer at the very moment when it is ending, or when they think it is ending. In this, as in the problem of cowardice, the thing to avoid is the total commitment. Whatever he *says*, let his inner resolution be not to bear whatever comes to him, but to bear it "for a reasonable period"— and let the reasonable period be shorter than the trial is likely to last. It need not be *much* shorter; in attacks on patience, chastity, and fortitude, the fun is to make the man yield just when (had he but known it) relief was almost in sight.

I do not know whether he is likely to meet the girl under conditions of strain or not. If he does, make full use of the fact that up to a certain point, fatigue makes women talk more and men talk less. Much secret resentment, even between lovers, can be raised from this.

Probably the scenes he is now witnessing will not provide material for an *intellectual* attack on his faith—your previous failures have put that out of your power. But there is a sort of attack on the emotions which can still be tried. It turns on making him *feel*, when first he sees human remains plastered on a wall, that this is "what the world is *really* like" and that all his religion has been a fantasy. You will notice that we have got them completely fogged about the meaning of 'the word "real". They tell each other, of some great spiritual experience, "All that *really* happened was that you heard some music in a lighted building"; here "Real" means the bare physical facts, separated from the other elements in the experience they actually had. On the other hand, they will also say "It's all very well discussing that high dive as you sit here in an armchair, but wait till you get up there and see what it's *really* like": here "real" is being used in the opposite sense to mean, not the physical facts (which they know already while discussing the matter in armchairs) but the emotional effect those facts will have on a human consciousness. Either application of the word could be defended; but our business is to keep the two going at once so that the emotional value of the word "real" can be placed now on one side of the account, now on the other, as it happens to suit us. The general rule which we have now pretty well established among them is that in all experiences which can make them happier or better only the physical facts are "Real" while the spiritual elements are "subjective"; in all experiences which can discourage or corrupt them the spiritual elements are the main reality and to ignore them is to be an escapist. Thus in birth the blood and pain are "real", the rejoicing a mere subjective point of view; in death, the terror and ugliness reveal what death "really means". The hatefulness of a hated person is "real"—in hatred you see men as they are, you are disillusioned; but the loveliness of a loved person is merely a subjective haze concealing a "real" core of sexual appetite or economic association. Wars and poverty are "really" horrible; peace and plenty are mere physical facts about which men happen to have certain sentiments. The creatures are always accusing one another of wanting "to eat the cake and have it"; but thanks to our labours they are more often in the predicament of paying for the cake and not eating it. Your patient, properly handled, will have no difficulty in regarding his emotion at the sight of human entrails as a revelation of Reality and his emotion at the sight of happy children or fair weather as mere sentiment,

Your affectionate uncle
SCREWTAPE

XXXI

M Y DEAR, MY VERY DEAR, WORMWOOD, MY POPPET, MY PIGSNIE,

How mistakenly now that all is lost you come whimpering to ask me whether the terms of affection in which I address you meant nothing from the beginning. Far from it! Rest assured, my love for you and your love for me are as like as two peas. I have always desired you, as you (pitiful fool) desired me. The difference is that I am the stronger. I think they will give you to me now; or a bit of you. Love you? Why, yes. As dainty a morsel as ever I grew fat on.

You have let a soul slip through your fingers. The howl of sharpened famine for that loss re-echoes at this moment through all the levels of the Kingdom of Noise down to the very Throne itself. It makes me mad to think of it. How well I know what happened at the instant when they snatched him from you! There was a sudden clearing of his eyes (was there not?) as he saw you for the first time, and recognised the part you had had in him and knew that you had it no longer. Just think (and let it be the beginning of your agony) what he felt at

156

that moment; as if a scab had fallen from an old sore, as if he were emerging from a hideous, shell-like tetter, as if he shuffled off for good and all a defiled, wet, clinging garment. By Hell, it is misery enough to see them in their mortal days taking off dirtied and uncomfortable clothes and splashing in hot water and giving little grunts of pleasure—stretching their eased limbs. What, then, of this final stripping, this complete cleansing?

The more one thinks about it, the worse it becomes. He got through so easily! No gradual misgivings, no doctor's sentence, no nursing home, no operating theatre, no false hopes of life; sheer, instantaneous liberation. One moment it seemed to be all our world; the scream of bombs, the fall of houses, the stink and taste of high explosive on the lips and in the lungs, the feet burning with weariness, the heart cold with horrors, the brain reeling, the legs aching; next moment all this was gone, gone like a bad dream, never again to be of any account. Defeated, out-manœuvred fool! Did you mark how naturally—as if he'd been born for it— the earth-born vermin entered the new life? How all his doubts became, in the twinkling of an eye, ridiculous? I know what the creature was saying to itself! "Yes. Of course. It always was like this. All horrors have followed the same course, getting worse and worse and forcing you into a kind of bottle-neck till, at the very moment when you thought you must be crushed, behold! you were out of the narrows and all was suddenly well. The extraction hurt more and more and then the tooth was out. The dream became a nightmare and then you woke. You die and die and then you are beyond death. How could I ever have doubted it?"

As he saw you, he also saw Them. I know how it was. You reeled back dizzy and blinded, more hurt by them than he had ever been by bombs. The degradation of it!—that this thing of earth and slime could stand upright and converse with spirits before whom you, a spirit, could only cower. Perhaps you had hoped that the awe and strangeness of it would dash his joy. But that is the cursed thing; the gods are strange to mortal eyes, and yet they are not strange. He had no faintest conception till that very hour of how they would look, and even doubted their existence. But when he saw them he knew that he had always known them and realised what part each one of them had played at many an hour in his life when he had supposed himself alone, so that now he could say to them, one by one, not "Who *are* you?" but "So it was *you* all the time". All that they were and said at this meeting woke memories. The dim consciousness of friends about him which had haunted his solitudes from infancy was now at last explained; that central music in every pure experience which had always just evaded memory was now at last recovered. Recognition made him free of their company almost before the limbs of his corpse became quiet. Only you were left outside.

He saw not only Them; he saw Him. This animal, this thing begotten in a bed, could look on Him. What is blinding, suffocating fire to you, is now cool light to him, is clarity itself, and wears the form of a Man. You would like, if you could, to interpret the patient's prostration in the Presence, his self-abhorrence and utter knowledge of his sins (yes, Wormwood, a clearer knowledge even than yours) on the analogy of your own choking and paralysing sensations when you encounter the deadly air that breathes from the heart of Heaven. But it's all nonsense. Pains he may still have to encounter, but they *embrace* those pains. They would not barter them for any earthly pleasure. All the delights of sense, or heart, or intellect, with which you could once have tempted him, even the delights of virtue itself, now seem to him in comparison but as the half nauseous attractions of a raddled harlot would seem to a man who hears that his true beloved whom he has loved all his life and whom he had believed to be dead is alive and even now at his door. He is caught up into that world where pain and pleasure take on transfinite values and all our arithmetic is dismayed. Once more, the inexplicable meets us. Next to the curse of useless tempters like yourself the greatest curse upon us is the failure of our Intelligence Department. If only we could find out what He is really up to! Alas, alas, that knowledge, in itself so hateful and mawkish a thing, should yet be necessary for Power! Sometimes I am almost in despair. All that sustains me is the conviction that our Realism, our rejection (in the face of all temptations) of all silly nonsense and claptrap, *must* win in the end. Meanwhile, I have you to settle with. Most truly do I sign myself

Your increasingly and ravenously
affectionate uncle
SCREWTAPE

MERE CHRISTIANITY

A revised and enlarged edition, with a new introduction,
of the three books, *The Case for Christianity,*
Christian Behavior, and *Beyond Personality*

PREFACE

The contents of this book were first given on the air, and then published in three separate parts as *The Case for Christianity* (1943),* *Christian Behaviour* (1943), and *Beyond Personality* (1945). In the printed versions I made a few additions to what I had said at the microphone, but otherwise left the text much as it had been. A "talk" on the radio should, I think, be as like real talk as possible, and should not sound like an essay being read aloud. In my talks I had therefore used all the contractions and colloquialisms I ordinarily use in conversation. In the printed version I reproduced this, putting *don't* and *we've* for *do not* and *we have.* And wherever, in the talks, I had made the importance of a word clear by the emphasis of my voice, I printed it in italics. I am now inclined to think that this was a mistake—an undesirable hybrid between the art of speaking and the art of writing. A talker ought to use variations of voice for emphasis because his medium naturally lends itself to that method: but a writer ought not to use italics for the same purpose. He has his own, different, means of bringing out the key words and ought to use them. In this edition I have expanded the contractions and replaced most of the italics by recasting the sentences in which they occurred : but without altering, I hope, the "popular" or "familiar" tone which I had all along intended. I have also added and deleted where I thought I understood any part of my subject better now than ten years ago or where I knew that the original version had been misunderstood by others.

The reader should be warned that I offer no help to anyone who is hesitating between two Christian "denominations." You

* Published in England under the title *Broadcast Talks.*

will not learn from me whether you ought to become an Anglican, a Methodist, a Presbyterian, or a Roman Catholic. This omission is intentional (even in the list I have just given the order is alphabetical). There is no mystery about my own position. I am a very ordinary layman of the Church of England, not especially "high," nor especially "low," nor especially anything else. But in this book I am not trying to convert anyone to my own position. Ever since I became a Christian I have thought that the best, perhaps the only, service I could do for my unbelieving neighbours was to explain and defend the belief that has been common to nearly all Christians at all times. I had more than one reason for thinking this. In the first place, the questions which divide Christians from one another often involve points of high Theology or even of ecclesiastical history which ought never to be treated except by real experts. I should have been out of my depth in such waters: more in need of help myself than able to help others. And secondly, I think we must admit that the discussion of these disputed points has no tendency at all to bring an outsider into the Christian fold. So long as we write and talk about them we are much more likely to deter him from entering any Christian communion than to draw him into our own. Our divisions should never be discussed except in the presence of those who have already come to believe that there is one God and that Jesus Christ is His only Son. Finally, I got the impression that far more, and more talented, authors were already engaged in such controversial matters than in the defence of what Baxter calls "mere" Christianity. That part of the line where I thought I could serve best was also the part that seemed to be thinnest. And to it I naturally went.

So far as I know, these were my only motives, and I should be very glad if people would not draw fanciful inferences from my silence on certain disputed matters.

For example, such silence need not mean that I myself am sitting on the fence. Sometimes I am. There are questions at issue between Christians to which I do not think I have the answer. There are some to which I may never know the answer: if I asked them, even in a better world, I might (for all I know) be answered as a far greater questioner was answered: "What is that to thee?

Follow thou Me." But there are other questions as to which I am definitely on one side of the fence, and yet say nothing. For I was not writing to expound something I could call "my religion," but to expound "mere" Christianity, which is what it is and was what it was long before I was born and whether I like it or not.

Some people draw unwarranted conclusions from the fact that I never say more about the Blessed Virgin Mary than is involved in asserting the Virgin Birth of Christ. But surely my reason for not doing so is obvious? To say more would take me at once into highly controversial regions. And there is no controversy between Christians which needs to be so delicately touched as this. The Roman Catholic beliefs on that subject are held not only with the ordinary fervour that attaches to all sincere religious belief, but (very naturally) with the peculiar and, as it were, chivalrous sensibility that a man feels when the honour of his mother or his beloved is at stake. It is very difficult so to dissent from them that you will not appear to them a cad as well as a heretic. And contrariwise, the opposed Protestant beliefs on this subject call forth feelings which go down to the very roots of all Monotheism whatever. To radical Protestants it seems that the distinction between Creator and creature (however holy) is imperilled: that Polytheism is risen again. Hence it is hard so to dissent from them that you will not appear something worse than a heretic—an idolator, a Pagan. If any topic could be relied upon to wreck a book about "mere" Christianity—if any topic makes utterly unprofitable reading for those who do not yet believe that the Virgin's son is God—surely this is it.

Oddly enough, you cannot even conclude, from my silence on disputed points, either that I think them important or that I think them unimportant. For this is itself one of the disputed points. One of the things Christians are disagreed about is the importance of their disagreements. When two Christians of different denominations start arguing, it is usually not long before one asks whether such-and-such a point "really matters" and the other replies: "Matter? Why, it's absolutely essential."

All this is said simply in order to make clear what kind of book I was trying to write; not in the least to conceal or evade responsibility for my own beliefs. About those, as I said before, there is no secret. To quote Uncle Toby: "They are written in the Common-Prayer Book."

The danger clearly was that I should put forward as common Christianity anything that was peculiar to the Church of England or (worse still) to myself. I tried to guard against this by sending the original script of what is now Book II to four clergymen (Anglican, Methodist, Presbyterian, Roman Catholic) and asking for their criticism. The Methodist thought I had not said enough about Faith, and the Roman Catholic thought I had gone rather too far about the comparative unimportance of theories in explanation of the Atonement. Otherwise all five of us were agreed. I did not have the remaining books similarly "vetted" because in them, though differences might arise among Christians, these would be differences between individuals or schools of thought, not between denominations.

So far as I can judge from reviews and from the numerous letters written to me, the book, however faulty in other respects, did at least succeed in presenting an agreed, or common, or central, or "mere" Christianity. In that way it may possibly be of some help in silencing the view that, if we omit the disputed points, we shall have left only a vague and bloodless H.C.F. The H.C.F. turns out to be something not only positive but pungent; divided from all non-Christian beliefs by a chasm to which the worst divisions inside Christendom are not really comparable at all. If I have not directly helped the cause of reunion, I have perhaps made it clear why we ought to be reunited. Certainly I have met with little of the fabled *odium theologicum* from convinced members of communions different from my own. Hostility has come more from borderline people whether within the Church of England or without it: men not exactly obedient to any communion. This I find curiously consoling. It is at her centre, where her truest children dwell, that each communion is really closest to every other in spirit, if not in doctrine. And this suggests that at the centre of each there is something, or a Someone, who against all divergences of belief, all differences of temperament, all memories of mutual persecution, speaks with the same voice.

So much for my omissions on doctrine. In Book III, which deals with morals, I have also passed over some things in silence, but for a different reason. Ever since I served as an infantryman in the first world war I have had a great dislike of people who, themselves in ease and safety, issue exhortations to men in the front line. As a result I have a reluctance to say much about temptations to which I myself am not exposed. No man, I suppose, is tempted to every sin. It so happens that the impulse which makes men gamble has been left out of my make-up; and, no doubt, I pay for this by lacking some good impulse of which it is the excess or perversion. I therefore did not feel myself qualified to give advice about permissable and impermissable gambling: if there is any permissable, for I do not claim to know even that. I have also said nothing about birth-control. I am not a woman nor even a married man, nor am I a priest. I did not think it my place to take a firm line about pains, dangers and expenses from which I am protected; having no pastoral office which obliged me to do so.

Far deeper objections may be felt—and have been expressed—against my use of the word *Christian* to mean one who accepts the common doctrines of Christianity. People ask: "Who are you, to lay down who is, and who is not a Christian?" or "May not many a man who cannot believe these doctrines be far more truly a Christian, far closer to the spirit of Christ, than some who do?" Now this objection is in one sense very right, very charitable, very spiritual, very sensitive. It has every amiable quality except that of being useful. We simply cannot, without disaster, use language as these objectors want us to use it. I will try to make this clear by the history of another, and very much less important, word.

The word *gentleman* originally meant something recognisable; one who had a coat of arms and some landed property. When you called someone "a gentleman" you were not paying him a compliment, but merely stating a fact. If you said he was not "a gentleman" you were not insulting him, but giving information. There was no contradiction in saying that John was a liar and a gentleman; any more than there now is in saying that James is a fool and an M.A. But then there came people who said—so rightly, charitably, spiritually, sensitively, so anything but usefully—"Ah, but surely the important thing about a gentleman is not the coat of arms and the land, but the behaviour? Surely he is the true gentleman who behaves as a gentleman should? Surely in that sense Edward is far more truly a gentleman than John?" They meant well. To be honourable and courteous and brave is of course a far better thing than to have a coat of arms. But it is not the same thing. Worse still, it is not a thing everyone will agree about. To call a man "a gentleman" in this new, refined sense, becomes, in fact, not a way of giving information about him, but a way of praising him: to deny that he is "a gentleman" becomes simply a way of insulting him. When a word ceases to be a term of description and becomes merely a term of praise, it no longer tells you facts about the object: it only tells you about the speaker's attitude to that object. (A "nice" meal only means a meal the speaker likes.) A *gentleman,* once it has been spiritualised and refined out of its old coarse, objective sense, means hardly more than a man whom the speaker likes. As a result, *gentleman* is now a useless word. We had lots of terms of approval already, so it was not needed for that use; on the other hand if anyone (say, in a historical work) wants to use it in its old sense, he cannot do so without explanations. It has been spoiled for that purpose.

Now if once we allow people to start spiritualising and refining, or as they might say "deepening," the sense of the word *Christian,* it too will speedily become a useless word. In the first place, Christians themselves will never be able to apply it to anyone. It is not for us to say who, in the deepest sense, is or is not close to the spirit of Christ. We do not see into men's hearts. We cannot judge, and are indeed forbidden to judge. It would be wicked arrogance for us to say that any man is, or is not, a Christian in this refined sense. And obviously a word which we can never apply is not going to be a very useful word. As for the unbelievers, they will no doubt cheerfully use the word in the refined sense. It will become in their mouths simply a term of praise. In calling anyone a Christian they will mean that they think him a good man. But that way of using the word will be no enrichment of the language, for we already have the word *good.* Meanwhile, the word *Christian* will have been spoiled for any really useful purpose it might have served.

We must therefore stick to the original, obvious meaning. The name *Christians* was first given at Antioch (Acts xi. 26) to "the disciples," to those who accepted the teaching of the apostles. There is no question of its being restricted to those who profited by that teaching as much as they should have. There is no question of its being extended to those who in some refined, spiritual, inward fashion were "far closer to the spirit of Christ" than the less satisfactory of the disciples. The point is not a theological, or moral one. It is only a question of using words so that we can all understand what is being said. When a man who accepts the Christian doctrine lives unworthily of it, it is much clearer to say he is a bad Christian than to say he is not a Christian.

I hope no reader will suppose that "mere" Christianity is here put forward as an alternative to the creeds of the existing communions—as if a man could adopt it in preference to Congregationalism or Greek Orthodoxy or anything else. It is more like a hall out of which doors open into several rooms. If I can bring anyone into that hall I shall have done what I attempted. But it is in the rooms, not in the hall, that there are fires and chairs and meals. The hall is a place to wait in, a place from which to try the various doors, not a place to live in. For that purpose the worst of the rooms (whichever that may be) is, I think, preferable. It is true that some people may find they have to wait in the hall for a considerable time, while others feel certain almost at once which door they must knock at. I do not know why there is this difference, but I am sure God keeps no one waiting unless He sees that it is good for him to wait. When you do get into your room you will find that the long wait has done you some kind of good which you would not have had otherwise. But you must regard it as waiting, not as camping. You must keep on praying for light: and, of course, even in the hall, you must begin trying to obey the rules which are common to the whole house. And above all you must be asking which door is the true one; not which pleases you best by its paint and panelling. In plain language, the question should never be: "Do I like that kind of service?" but "Are these doctrines true: Is holiness here? Does my conscience move me towards this? Is my reluctance to knock at this door due to my pride, or my mere taste, or my personal dislike of this particular door-keeper?"

When you have reached your own room, be kind to those who have chosen different doors and to those who are still in the hall. If they are wrong they need your prayers all the more; and if they are your enemies, then you are under orders to pray for them. That is one of the rules common to the whole house.

CONTENTS

BOOK III—*continued*

BOOK IV. BEYOND PERSONALITY: OR FIRST STEPS
IN THE DOCTRINE OF THE TRINITY

BOOK I

RIGHT AND WRONG AS A CLUE TO THE MEANING OF THE UNIVERSE

I.

THE LAW OF HUMAN NATURE

Every one has heard people quarrelling. Sometimes it sounds funny and sometimes it sounds merely unpleasant; but however it sounds, I believe we can learn something very important from listening to the kind of things they say. They say things like this: "How'd you like it if anyone did the same to you?"—"That's my seat, I was there first"—"Leave him alone, he isn't doing you any harm"—"Why should you shove in first?"—"Give me a bit of your orange, I gave you a bit of mine"—"Come on, you promised." People say things like that every day, educated people as well as uneducated, and children as well as grown-ups.

Now what interests me about all these remarks is that the man who makes them is not merely saying that the other man's behaviour does not happen to please him. He is appealing to some kind of standard of behaviour which he expects the other man to know about. And the other man very seldom replies: "To hell with your standard." Nearly always he tries to make out that what he has been doing does not really go against the standard, or that if it does there is some special excuse. He pretends there is some special reason in this particular case why the person who took the seat first should not keep it, or that things were quite different when he was given the bit of orange, or that something has turned up which lets him off keeping his promise. It looks, in fact, very much as if both parties had in mind some kind of Law or Rule of fair play or decent behaviour or morality or whatever you like to call it, about which they really agreed. And they have. If they had not, they might, of course, fight like animals, but they could not *quarrel* in the human sense of the word. Quarrelling means trying to show that the other man is in the wrong. And there would

3

be no sense in trying to do that unless you and he had some sort of agreement as to what Right and Wrong are; just as there would be no sense in saying that a footballer had committed a foul unless there was some agreement about the rules of football.

Now this Law or Rule about Right and Wrong used to be called the Law of Nature. Nowadays, when we talk of the "laws of nature" we usually mean things like gravitation, or heredity, or the laws of chemistry. But when the older thinkers called the Law of Right and Wrong "the Law of Nature," they really meant the Law of *Human* Nature. The idea was that, just as all bodies are governed by the law of gravitation and organisms by biological laws, so the creature called man also had *his* law—with this great difference, that a body could not choose whether it obeyed the law of gravitation or not, but a man could choose either to obey the Law of Human Nature or to disobey it.

We may put this in another way. Each man is at every moment subjected to several different sets of law but there is only one of these which he is free to disobey. As a body, he is subjected to gravitation and cannot disobey it; if you leave him unsupported in mid-air, he has no more choice about falling than a stone has. As an organism, he is subjected to various biological laws which he cannot disobey any more than an animal can. That is, he cannot disobey those laws which he shares with other things; but the law which is peculiar to his human nature, the law he does not share with animals or vegetables or inorganic things, is the one he can disobey if he chooses.

This law was called the Law of Nature because people thought that every one knew it by nature and did not need to be taught it. They did not mean, of course, that you might not find an odd individual here and there who did not know it, just as you find a few people who are colour-blind or have no ear for a tune. But taking the race as a whole, they thought that the human idea of decent behaviour was obvious to every one. And I believe they were right. If they were not, then all the things we said about the war were nonsense. What was the sense in saying the enemy were in the wrong unless Right is a real thing which the Nazis at bottom knew as well as we did and ought to have practised? If they had had no notion of what we mean by right, then, though we might still have had to fight them, we could no more have blamed them for that than for the colour of their hair.

I know that some people say the idea of a Law of Nature or decent behaviour known to all men is unsound, because different civilisations and different ages have had quite different moralities.

But this is not true. There have been differences between their moralities, but these have never amounted to anything like a total difference. If anyone will take the trouble to compare the moral teaching of, say, the ancient Egyptians, Babylonians, Hindus, Chinese, Greeks and Romans, what will really strike him will be how very like they are to each other and to our own. Some of the evidence for this I have put together in the appendix of another book called *The Abolition of Man;* but for our present purpose I need only ask the reader to think what a totally different morality would mean. Think of a country where people were admired for running away in battle, or where a man felt proud of double-crossing all the people who had been kindest to him. You might just as well try to imagine a country where two and two made five. Men have differed as regards what people you ought to be un-selfish to—whether it was only your own family, or your fellow countrymen, or everyone. But they have always agreed that you ought not to put yourself first. Selfishness has never been admired. Men have differed as to whether you should have one wife or four. But they have always agreed that you must not simply have any woman you liked.

But the most remarkable thing is this. Whenever you find a man who says he does not believe in a real Right and Wrong, you will find the same man going back on this a moment later. He may break his promise to you, but if you try breaking one to him he will be complaining "It's not fair" before you can say Jack Robinson. A nation may say treaties do not matter; but then, next minute, they spoil their case by saying that the particular treaty they want to break was an unfair one. But if treaties do not matter, and if there is no such thing as Right and Wrong—in other words, if there is no Law of Nature—what is the difference between a fair treaty and an unfair one? Have they not let the cat out of the bag and shown that, whatever they say, they really know the Law of Nature just like anyone else?

It seems, then, we are forced to believe in a real Right and Wrong. People may be sometimes mistaken about them, just as people sometimes get their sums wrong; but they are not a matter of mere taste and opinion any more than the multiplication table. Now if we are agreed about that, I go on to my next point, which is this. None of us are really keeping the Law of Nature. If there are any exceptions among you, I apologise to them. They had much better read some other work, for nothing I am going to say concerns them. And now, turning to the ordinary human beings who are left:

I hope you will not misunderstand what I am going to say. I am not preaching, and Heaven knows I do not pretend to be better than anyone else. I am only trying to call attention to a fact; the fact that this year, or this month, or, more likely, this very day, we have failed to practise ourselves the kind of behaviour we expect from other people. There may be all sorts of excuses for us. That time you were so unfair to the children was when you were very tired. That slightly shady business about the money—the one you have almost forgotten—came when you were very hard up. And what you promised to do for old So-and-so and have never done—well, you never would have promised if you had known how frightfully busy you were going to be. And as for your behaviour to your wife (or husband) or sister (or brother) if I knew how irritating they could be, I would not wonder at it—and who the dickens am I, anyway? I am just the same. That is to say, I do not succeed in keeping the Law of Nature very well, and the moment anyone tells me I am not keeping it, there starts up in my mind a string of excuses as long as your arm. The question at the moment is not whether they are good excuses. The point is that they are one more proof of how deeply, whether we like it or not, we believe in the Law of Nature. If we do not believe in decent behaviour, why should we be so anxious to make excuses for not having behaved decently? The truth is, we believe in decency so much—we feel the Rule or Law pressing on us so— that we cannot bear to face the fact that we are breaking it, and consequently we try to shift the responsibility. For you notice that it is only for our bad behaviour that we find all these explanations. It is only our bad temper that we put down to being tired or worried or hungry; we put our good temper down to ourselves.

These, then, are the two points I wanted to make. First, that human beings, all over the earth, have this curious idea that they ought to behave in a certain way, and cannot really get rid of it. Secondly, that they do not in fact behave in that way. They know the Law of Nature; they break it. These two facts are the foundation of all clear thinking about ourselves and the universe we live in.

2.

SOME OBJECTIONS

If they are the foundation, I had better stop to make that foundation firm before I go on. Some of the letters I have had show that a
good many people find it difficult to understand just what this
Law of Human Nature, or Moral Law, or Rule of Decent Behaviour is.

For example, some people wrote to me saying, "Isn't what you
call the Moral Law simply our herd instinct and hasn't it been
developed just like all our other instincts?" Now I do not deny
that we may have a herd instinct: but that is not what I mean
by the Moral Law. We all know what it feels like to be prompted
by instinct—by mother love, or sexual instinct, or the instinct for
food. It means that you feel a strong want or desire to act in a certain way. And, of course, we sometimes do feel just that sort of
desire to help another person: and no doubt that desire is due
to the herd instinct. But feeling a desire to help is quite different
from feeling that you ought to help whether you want to or not.
Supposing you hear a cry for help from a man in danger. You will
probably feel two desires—one a desire to give help (due to your
herd instinct), the other a desire to keep out of danger (due to the
instinct for self-preservation). But you will find inside you, in addition to these two impulses, a third thing which tells you that
you ought to follow the impulse to help, and suppress the impulse
to run away. Now this thing that judges between two instincts,
that decides which should be encouraged, cannot itself be either
of them. You might as well say that the sheet of music which tells
you, at a given moment, to play one note on the piano and not
another, is itself one of the notes on the keyboard. The Moral Law
tells us the tune we have to play: our instincts are merely the keys.

Another way of seeing that the Moral Law is not simply one of our instincts is this. If two instincts are in conflict, and there is nothing in a creature's mind except those two instincts, obviously the stronger of the two must win. But at those moments when we are most conscious of the Moral Law, it usually seems to be telling us to side with the weaker of the two impulses. You probably *want* to be safe much more than you want to help the man who is drowning: but the Moral Law tells you to help him all the same. And surely it often tells us to try to make the right impulse stronger than it naturally is? I mean, we often feel it our duty to stimulate the herd instinct, by waking up our imaginations and arousing our pity and so on, so as to get up enough steam for doing the right thing. But clearly we are not acting *from* instinct when we set about making an instinct stronger than it is. The thing that says to you, "Your herd instinct is asleep. Wake it up," cannot itself *be* the herd instinct. The thing that tells you which note on the piano needs to be played louder cannot itself be that note.

Here is a third way of seeing it. If the Moral Law was one of our instincts, we ought to be able to point to some one impulse inside us which was always what we call "good," always in agreement with the rule of right behaviour. But you cannot. There is none of our impulses which the Moral Law may not sometimes tell us to suppress, and none which it may not sometimes tell us to encourage. It is a mistake to think that some of our impulses— say mother love or patriotism—are good, and others, like sex or the fighting instinct, are bad. All we mean is that the occasions on which the fighting instinct or the sexual desire need to be restrained are rather more frequent than those for restraining mother love or patriotism. But there are situations in which it is the duty of a married man to encourage his sexual impulse and of a soldier to encourage the fighting instinct. There are also occasions on which a mother's love for her own children or a man's love for his own country have to be suppressed or they will lead to unfairness towards other people's children or countries. Strictly speaking, there are no such things as good and bad impulses. Think once again of a piano. It has not got two kinds of notes on it, the "right" notes and the "wrong" ones. Every single note is right at one time and wrong at another. The Moral Law is not any one instinct or any set of instincts: it is something which makes a kind of tune (the tune we call goodness or right conduct) by directing the instincts.

By the way, this point is of great practical consequence. The most dangerous thing you can do is to take any one impulse of your own nature and set it up as the thing you ought to follow at all costs. There is not one of them which will not make us into devils if we set it up as an absolute guide. You might think love of humanity in general was safe, but it is not. If you leave out justice you will find yourself breaking agreements and faking evidence in trials "for the sake of humanity," and become in the end a cruel and treacherous man.

Other people wrote to me saying, "Isn't what you call the Moral Law just a social convention, something that is put into us by education?" I think there is a misunderstanding here. The people who ask that question are usually taking it for granted that if we have learned a thing from parents and teachers, then that thing must be merely a human invention. But, of course, that is not so. We all learned the multiplication table at school. A child who grew up alone on a desert island would not know it. But surely it does not follow that the multiplication table is simply a human convention, something human beings have made up for themselves and might have made different if they had liked? I fully agree that we learn the Rule of Decent Behaviour from parents and teachers, and friends and books, as we learn everything else. But some of the things we learn are mere conventions which might have been different—we learn to keep to the left of the road, but it might just as well have been the rule to keep to the right—and others of them, like mathematics, are real truths. The question is to which class the Law of Human Nature belongs.

There are two reasons for saying it belongs to the same class as mathematics. The first is, as I said in the first chapter, that though there are differences between the moral ideas of one time or country and those of another, the differences are not really very great—not nearly so great as most people imagine—and you can recognise the same law running through them all: whereas mere conventions, like the rule of the road or the kind of clothes people wear, may differ to any extent. The other reason is this. When you think about these differences between the morality of one people and another, do you think that the morality of one people is ever better or worse than that of another? Have any of the changes been improvements? If not, then of course there could never be any moral progress. Progress means not just changing, but changing for the better. If no set of moral ideas were truer or better than any other, there would be no sense in preferring civilised morality to savage morality, or Christian morality to Nazi morality. In fact, of course, we all do believe that some moralities are better than others. We do believe that some of the people who tried to change the moral ideas of their own age were what we would call Reformers or Pioneers—people who understood morality better than their neighbours did. Very well then. The moment you say that one set of moral ideas can be better than another, you are, in fact, measuring them both by a standard, saying that one of them conforms to that standard more nearly than the other. But the standard that measures two things is something different from either. You are, in fact, comparing them both with some Real Morality, admitting that there is such a thing as a real Right, independent of what people think, and that some people's ideas get nearer to that real Right than others. Or put it this way. If your moral ideas can be truer, and those of the Nazis less true, there must be something—some Real Morality—for them to be true about. The reason why your idea of New York can be truer or less true than mine is that New York is a real place, existing quite apart from what either of us thinks. If when each of us said "New York" each meant merely "The town I am imagining in my own head," how could one of us have truer ideas than the other? There would be no question of truth or falsehood at all. In the same way, if the Rule of Decent Behaviour meant simply "whatever each nation happens to approve," there would be no sense in saying that any one nation had ever been more correct in its approval than any other; no sense in saying that the world could ever grow morally better or morally worse.

I conclude then, that though the differences between people's ideas of Decent Behaviour often make you suspect that there is no real natural Law of Behaviour at all, yet the things we are bound to think about these differences really prove just the opposite. But one word before I end. I have met people who exaggerate the differences, because they have not distinguished between differences of morality and differences of belief about facts. For example, one man said to me, "Three hundred years ago people in England were putting witches to death. Was that what you call the Rule of Human Nature or Right Conduct?" But surely the reason we do not execute witches is that we do not believe there are such things. If we did—if we really thought that there were people going about who had sold themselves to the devil and received supernatural powers from him in return and were using these powers to kill their neighbours or drive them mad or bring bad weather, surely we would all agree that if anyone deserved the death penalty, then these filthy quislings did. There is no difference of moral principle here: the difference is simply about matter of fact. It may be a great advance in knowledge not to believe in witches: there is no moral advance in not executing them when you do not think they are there. You would not call a man humane for ceasing to set mousetraps if he did so because he believed there were no mice in the house.

3.

THE REALITY OF THE LAW

I now go back to what I said at the end of the first chapter, that there were two odd things about the human race. First, that they were haunted by the idea of a sort of behaviour they ought to practise, what you might call fair play, or decency, or morality, or the Law of Nature. Second, that they did not in fact do so. Now some of you may wonder why I called this odd. It may seem to you the most natural thing in the world. In particular, you may have thought I was rather hard on the human race. After all, you may say, what I call breaking the Law of Right and Wrong or of Nature, only means that people are not perfect. And why on earth should I expect them to be? That would be a good answer if what I was trying to do was to fix the exact amount of blame which is due to us for not behaving as we expect others to behave. But that is not my job at all. I am not concerned at present with blame; I am trying to find out truth. And from that point of view the very idea of something being imperfect, of its not being what it ought to be, has certain consequences.

If you take a thing like a stone or a tree, it is what it is and there seems no sense in saying it ought to have been otherwise. Of course you may say a stone is "the wrong shape" if you want to use it for a rockery, or that a tree is a bad tree because it does not give you as much shade as you expected. But all you mean is that the stone or tree does not happen to be convenient for some purpose of your own. You are not, except as a joke, blaming them for that. You really know, that, given the weather and the soil, the tree could not have been any different. What we, from our point of view, call a "bad" tree is obeying the laws of its nature just as much as a "good" one.

13

Now have you noticed what follows? It follows that what we usually call the laws of nature—the way weather works on a tree for example—may not really be *laws* in the strict sense, but only in a manner of speaking. When you say that falling stones always obey the law of gravitation, is not this much the same as saying that the law only means "what stones always do"? You do not really think that when a stone is let go, it suddenly remembers that it is under orders to fall to the ground. You only mean that, in fact, it does fall. In other words, you cannot be sure that there is anything over and above the facts themselves, any law about what ought to happen, as distinct from what does happen. The laws of nature, as applied to stones or trees, may only mean "what Nature, in fact, does." But if you turn to the Law of Human Nature, the Law of Decent Behaviour, it is a different matter. That law certainly does not mean "what human beings, in fact, do"; for as I said before, many of them do not obey this law at all, and none of them obey it completely. The law of gravity tells you what stones do if you drop them; but the Law of Human Nature tells you what human beings ought to do and do not. In other words, when you are dealing with humans, something else comes in above and beyond the actual facts. You have the facts (how men do behave) and you also have something else (how they ought to behave). In the rest of the universe there need not be anything but the facts. Electrons and molecules behave in a certain way, and certain results follow, and that may be the whole story.* But men behave in a certain way and that is not the whole story, for all the time you know that they ought to behave differently.

Now this is really so peculiar that one is tempted to try to explain it away. For instance, we might try to make out that when you say a man ought not to act as he does, you only mean the same as when you say that a stone is the wrong shape; namely, that what he is doing happens to be inconvenient to you. But that is simply untrue. A man occupying the corner seat in the train because he got there first, and a man who slipped into it while my back was turned and removed my bag, are both equally inconvenient. But I blame the second man and do not blame the first.

---

* I do not think it *is* the whole story, as you will see later. I mean that, as far as the argument has gone up to date, it *may* be.

I am not angry—except perhaps for a moment before I come to my senses—with a man who trips me up by accident; I am angry with a man who tries to trip me up even if he does not succeed. Yet the first has hurt me and the second has not. Sometimes the behaviour which I call bad is not inconvenient to me at all, but the very opposite. In war, each side may find a traitor on the other side very useful. But though they use him and pay him they regard him as human vermin. So you cannot say that what we call decent behaviour in others is simply the behaviour that happens to be useful to us. And as for decent behaviour in ourselves, I suppose it is pretty obvious that it does not mean the behaviour that pays. It means things like being content with thirty shillings when you might have got three pounds, doing school work honestly when it would be easy to cheat, leaving a girl alone when you would like to make love to her, staying in dangerous places when you could go somewhere safer, keeping promises you would rather not keep, and telling the truth even when it makes you look a fool.

Some people say that though decent conduct does not mean what pays each particular person at a particular moment, still, it means what pays the human race as a whole; and that consequently there is no mystery about it. Human beings, after all, have some sense; they see that you cannot have real safety or happiness except in a society where every one plays fair, and it is because they see this that they try to behave decently. Now, of course, it is perfectly true that safety and happiness can only come from individuals, classes, and nations being honest and fair and kind to each other. It is one of the most important truths in the world. But as an explanation of why we feel as we do about Right and Wrong it just misses the point. If we ask: "Why ought I to be unselfish?" and you reply "Because it is good for society," we may then ask, "Why should I care what's good for society except when it happens to pay *me* personally?" and then you will have to say, "Because you ought to be unselfish"—which simply brings us back to where we started. You are saying what is true, but you are not getting any further. If a man asked what was the point of playing football, it would not be much good saying "in order to score'goals," for trying to score goals is the game itself, not the reason for the game, and you would really only be saying that football was football—

which is true, but not worth saying. In the same way, if a man asks what is the point of behaving decently, it is no good replying, "in order to benefit society," for trying to benefit society, in other words being unselfish (for "society" after all only means "other people"), is one of the things decent behaviour consists in; all you are really saying is that decent behaviour is decent behaviour. You would have said just as much if you had stopped at the statement, "Men ought to be unselfish."

And that is where I do stop. Men ought to be unselfish, ought to be fair. Not that men are unselfish, nor that they like being unselfish, but that they ought to be. The Moral Law, or Law of Human Nature, is not simply a fact about human behaviour in the same way as the Law of Gravitation is, or may be, simply a fact about how heavy objects behave. On the other hand, it is not a mere fancy, for we cannot get rid of the idea, and most of the things we say and think about men would be reduced to nonsense if we did. And it is not simply a statement about how we should like men to behave for our own convenience; for the behaviour we call bad or unfair is not exactly the same as the behaviour we find inconvenient, and may even be the opposite. Consequently, this Rule of Right and Wrong, or Law of Human Nature, or whatever you call it, must somehow or other be a real thing—a thing that is really there, not made up by ourselves. And yet it is not a fact in the ordinary sense, in the same way as our actual behaviour is a fact. It begins to look as if we shall have to admit that there is more than one kind of reality; that, in this particular case, there is something above and beyond the ordinary facts of men's behaviour, and yet quite definitely real—a real law, which none of us made, but which we find pressing on us.

4.

WHAT LIES BEHIND THE LAW

Let us sum up what we have reached so far. In the case of stones and trees and things of that sort, what we call the Laws of Nature may not be anything except a way of speaking. When you say that nature is governed by certain laws, this may only mean that nature does, in fact, behave in a certain way. The so-called laws may not be anything real—anything above and beyond the actual facts which we observe. But in the case of Man, we saw that this will not do. The Law of Human Nature, or of Right and Wrong, must be something above and beyond the actual facts of human behaviour. In this case, besides the actual facts, you have something else—a real law which we did not invent and which we know we ought to obey.

I now want to consider what this tells us about the universe we live in. Ever since men were able to think, they have been wondering what this universe really is and how it came to be there. And, very roughly, two views have been held. First, there is what is called the materialist view. People who take that view think that matter and space just happen to exist, and always have existed, nobody knows why; and that the matter, behaving in certain fixed ways, has just happened, by a sort of fluke, to produce creatures like ourselves who are able to think. By one chance in a thousand something hit our sun and made it produce the planets; and by another thousandth chance the chemicals necessary for life, and the right temperature, occurred on one of these planets, and so some of the matter on this earth came alive; and then, by a very long series of chances, the living creatures developed into things like us. The other view is the religious view.* According to it, what is behind the universe is more like

* See Note at the end of this chapter.

17

a mind than it is like anything else we know. That is to say, it is conscious, and has purposes, and prefers one thing to another. And on this view it made the universe, partly for purposes we do not know, but partly, at any rate, in order to produce creatures like itself—I mean, like itself to the extent of having minds. Please do not think that one of these views was held a long time ago and that the other has gradually taken its place. Wherever there have been thinking men both views turn up. And note this too. You cannot find out which view is the right one by science in the ordinary sense. Science works by experiments. It watches how things behave. Every scientific statement in the long run, however complicated it looks, really means something like, "I pointed the telescope to such and such a part of the sky at 2:20 A.M. on January 15th and saw so-and-so," or, "I put some of this stuff in a pot and heated it to such-and-such a temperature and it did so-and-so." Do not think I am saying anything against science: I am only saying what its job is. And the more scientific a man is, the more (I believe) he would agree with me that this is the job of science— and a very useful and necessary job it is too. But why anything comes to be there at all, and whether there is anything behind the things science observes—something of a different kind—this is not a scientific question. If there is "Something Behind," then either it will have to remain altogether unknown to men or else make itself known in some different way. The statement that there is any such thing, and the statement that there is no such thing, are neither of them statements that science can make. And real scientists do not usually make them. It is usually the journalists and popular novelists who have picked up a few odds and ends of half-baked science from textbooks who go in for them. After all, it is really a matter of common sense. Supposing science ever became complete so that it knew every single thing in the whole universe. Is it not plain that the questions, "Why is there a universe?" "Why does it go on as it does?" "Has it any meaning?" would remain just as they were?

Now the position would be quite hopeless but for this. There is one thing, and only one, in the whole universe which we know more about than we could learn from external observation. That one thing is Man. We do not merely observe men, we *are* men.

In this case we have, so to speak, inside information; we are in the know. And because of that, we know that men find themselves under a moral law, which they did not make, and cannot quite forget even when they try, and which they know they ought to obey. Notice the following point. Anyone studying Man from the outside as we study electricity or cabbages, not knowing our language and consequently not able to get any inside knowledge from us, but merely observing what we did, would never get the slightest evidence that we had this moral law. How could he? for his observations would only show what we did, and the moral law is about what we ought to do. In the same way, if there were anything above or behind the observed facts in the case of stones or the weather, we, by studying them from outside, could never hope to discover it.

The position of the question, then, is like this. We want to know whether the universe simply happens to be what it is for no reason or whether there is a power behind it that makes it what it is. Since that power, if it exists, would be not one of the observed facts but a reality which makes them, no mere observation of the facts can find it. There is only one case in which we can know whether there is anything more, namely our own case. And in that one case we find there is. Or put it the other way round. If there was a controlling power outside the universe, it could not show itself to us as one of the facts inside the universe— no more than the architect of a house could actually be a wall or staircase or fireplace in that house. The only way in which we could expect it to show itself would be inside ourselves as an influence or a command trying to get us to behave in a certain way. And that is just what we do find inside ourselves. Surely this ought to arouse our suspicions? In the only case where you can expect to get an answer, the answer turns out to be Yes; and in the other cases, where you do not get an answer, you see why you do not. Suppose someone asked me, when I see a man in a blue uniform going down the street leaving little paper packets at each house, why I suppose that they contain letters? I should reply, "Because whenever he leaves a similar little packet for me I find it does contain a letter." And if he then objected, "But you've never seen all these letters which you think the other people are getting," I should say, "Of course not, and I shouldn't expect to, because they're not addressed to me. I'm explaining the packets I'm not allowed to open by the ones I am allowed to open." It is the same about this question. The only packet I am allowed to open is Man. When I do, especially when I open that particular man called Myself, I find that I do not exist on my own, that I am under a law; that somebody or something wants me to behave in a certain way. I do not, of course, think that if I could get inside a stone or a tree I should find exactly the same thing, just as I do not think all the other people in the street get the same letters as I do. I should expect, for instance, to find that the stone had to obey the law of gravity—that whereas the sender of the letters merely tells me to obey the law of my human nature, He compels the stone to obey the laws of its stony nature. But I should expect to find that there was, so to speak, a sender of letters in both cases, a Power behind the facts, a Director, a Guide.

Do not think I am going faster than I really am. I am not yet within a hundred miles of the God of Christian theology. All I have got to is a Something which is directing the universe, and which appears in me as a law urging me to do right and making me feel responsible and uncomfortable when I do wrong. I think we have to assume it is more like a mind than it is like anything else we know—because after all the only other thing we know is matter and you can hardly imagine a bit of matter giving instructions. But, of course, it need not be very like a mind, still less like a person. In the next chapter we shall see if we can find out anything more about it. But one word of warning. There has been a great deal of soft soap talked about God for the last hundred years. That is not what I am offering. You can cut all that out.

$$\cdot \quad \cdot \quad \cdot \quad \cdot \quad \cdot$$

NOTE.—In order to keep this section short enough when it was given on the air, I mentioned only the Materialist view and the Religious view. But to be complete I ought to mention the In-between view called Life-Force philosophy, or Creative Evolution, or Emergent Evolution. The wittiest expositions of it come in the works of Bernard Shaw, but the most profound ones in those of Bergson. People who hold this view say that the small variations by which life on this planet "evolved" from the lowest forms to Man were not due to chance but to the "striving" or "purposiveness" of a Life-Force. When people say this we must ask them whether by Life-Force they mean something with a mind or not. If they do, then "a mind bringing life into existence and leading it to perfection" is really a God, and their view is thus identical with the Religious. If they do not, then what is the sense in saying that something without a mind "strives" or has "purposes"? This seems to me fatal to their view. One reason why many people find Creative Evolution so attractive is that it gives one much of the emotional comfort of believing in God and none of the less pleasant consequences. When you are feeling fit and the sun is shining and you do not want to believe that the whole universe is a mere mechanical dance of atoms, it is nice to be able to think of this great mysterious Force rolling on through the centuries and carrying you on its crest. If, on the other hand, you want to do something rather shabby, the Life-Force, being only a blind force, with no morals and no mind, will never interfere with you like that troublesome God we learned about when we were children. The Life-Force is a sort of tame God. You can switch it on when you want, but it will not bother you. All the thrills of religion and none of the cost. Is the Life-Force the greatest achievement of wishful thinking the world has yet seen?

5.

WE HAVE CAUSE TO BE UNEASY

I ended my last chapter with the idea that in the Moral Law somebody or something from beyond the material universe was actually getting at us. And I expect when I reached that point some of you felt a certain annoyance. You may even have thought that I had played a trick on you—that I had been carefully wrapping up to look like philosophy what turns out to be one more "religious jaw." You may have felt you were ready to listen to me as long as you thought I had anything new to say; but if it turns out to be only religion, well, the world has tried that and you cannot put the clock back. If anyone is feeling that way I should like to say three things to him.

First, as to putting the clock back. Would you think I was joking if I said that you can put a clock back, and that if the clock is wrong it is often a very sensible thing to do? But I would rather get away from that whole idea of clocks. We all want progress. But progress means getting nearer to the place where you want to be. And if you have taken a wrong turning, then to go forward does not get you any nearer. If you are on the wrong road, progress means doing an about-turn and walking back to the right road; and in that case the man who turns back soonest is the most progressive man. We have all seen this when doing arithmetic. When I have started a sum the wrong way, the sooner I admit this and go back and start over again, the faster I shall get on. There is nothing progressive about being pigheaded and refusing to admit a mistake. And I think if you look at the present state of the world, it is pretty plain that humanity has been making some big mistake. We are on the wrong road. And if that is so, we must go back. Going back is the quickest way on.

Then, secondly, this has not yet turned exactly into a "religious jaw." We have not yet got as far as the God of any actual religion, still less the God of that particular religion called Christianity. We have only got as far as a Somebody or Something behind the Moral Law. We are not taking anything from the Bible or the Churches, we are trying to see what we can find out about this Somebody on our own steam. And I want to make it quite clear that what we find out on our own steam is something that gives us a shock. We have two bits of evidence about the Somebody. One is the universe He has made. If we used that as our only clue, then I think we should have to conclude that He was a great artist (for the universe is a very beautiful place), but also that He is quite merciless and no friend to man (for the universe is a very dangerous and terrifying place). The other bit of evidence is that Moral Law which He has put into our minds. And this is a better bit of evidence than the other, because it is inside information. You find out more about God from the Moral Law than from the universe in general just as you find out more about a man by listening to his conversation than by looking at a house he has built. Now, from this second bit of evidence we conclude that the Being behind the universe is intensely interested in right conduct —in fair play, unselfishness, courage, good faith, honesty and truthfulness. In that sense we should agree with the account given by Christianity and some other religions, that God is "good." But do not let us go too fast here. The Moral Law does not give us any grounds for thinking that God is "good" in the sense of being indulgent, or soft, or sympathetic. There is nothing indulgent about the Moral Law. It is as hard as nails. It tells you to do the straight thing and it does not seem to care how painful, or dangerous, or difficult it is to do. If God is like the Moral Law, then He is not soft. It is no use, at this stage, saying that what you mean by a "good" God is a God who can forgive. You are going too quickly. Only a Person can forgive. And we have not yet got as far as a personal God—only as far as a power, behind the Moral Law, and more like a mind than it is like anything else. But it may still be very unlike a Person. If it is pure impersonal mind, there may be no sense in asking it to make allowances for you or let you off, just as there is no sense in asking the multiplication table to let you off when you do your sums wrong. You are bound to get the wrong answer. And it is no use either saying that if there is a God of that sort—an impersonal absolute goodness—then you do not like Him and are not going to bother about Him. For the trouble is that one part of you is on His side and really agrees with His disapproval of human greed and trickery and exploitation. You may want Him to make an exception in your own case, to let you off this one time; but you know at bottom that unless the power behind the world really and unalterably detests that sort of behaviour, then He cannot be good. On the other hand, we know that if there does exist an absolute goodness it must hate most of what we do. That is the terrible fix we are in. If the universe is not governed by an absolute goodness, then all our efforts are in the long run hopeless. But if it is, then we are making ourselves enemies to that goodness every day, and are not in the least likely to do any better tomorrow, and so our case is hopeless again. We cannot do without it, and we cannot do with it. God is the only comfort, He is also the supreme terror: the thing we most need and the thing we most want to hide from. He is our only possible ally, and we have made ourselves His enemies. Some people talk as if meeting the gaze of absolute goodness would be fun. They need to think again. They are still only playing with religion. Goodness is either the great safety or the great danger—according to the way you react to it. And we have reacted the wrong way.

Now my third point. When I chose to get to my real subject in this roundabout way, I was not trying to play any kind of trick on you. I had a different reason. My reason was that Christianity simply does not make sense until you have faced the sort of facts I have been describing. Christianity tells people to repent and promises them forgiveness. It therefore has nothing (as far as I know) to say to people who do not know they have done anything to repent of and who do not feel that they need any forgiveness. It is after you have realised that there is a real Moral Law, and a Power behind the law, and that you have broken that law and put yourself wrong with that Power—it is after all this, and not a moment sooner, that Christianity begins to talk. When you know you are sick, you will listen to the doctor. When you have realised that our position is nearly desperate you will begin to understand what the Christians are talking about. They offer an explanation of how we got into our present state of both hating goodness and loving it. They offer an explanation of how God can be this impersonal mind at the back of the Moral Law and yet also a Person. They tell you how the demands of this law, which you and I cannot meet, have been met on our behalf, how God Himself becomes a man to save man from the disapproval of God. It is an old story and if you want to go into it you will no doubt consult people who have more authority to talk about it than I have. All I am doing is to ask people to face the facts—to understand the questions which Christianity claims to answer. And they are very terrifying facts. I wish it was possible to say something more agreeable. But I must say what I think true. Of course, I quite agree that the Christian religion is, in the long run, a thing of unspeakable comfort. But it does not begin in comfort; it begins in the dismay I have been describing, and it is no use at all trying to go on to that comfort without first going through that dismay. In religion, as in war and everything else, comfort is the one thing you cannot get by looking for it. If you look for truth, you may find comfort in the end: if you look for comfort you will not get either comfort or truth—only soft soap and wishful thinking to begin with and, in the end, despair. Most of us have got over the pre-war wishful thinking about international politics. It is time we did the same about religion.

BOOK II

WHAT CHRISTIANS BELIEVE

I.

THE RIVAL CONCEPTIONS OF GOD

I have been asked to tell you what Christians believe, and I am going to begin by telling you one thing that Christians do not need to believe. If you are a Christian you do not have to believe that all the other religions are simply wrong all through. If you are an atheist you do have to believe that the main point in all the religions of the whole world is simply one huge mistake. If you are a Christian, you are free to think that all these religions, even the queerest ones, contain at least some hint of the truth. When I was an atheist I had to try to persuade myself that most of the human race have always been wrong about the question that mattered to them most; when I became a Christian I was able to take a more liberal view. But, of course, being a Christian does mean thinking that where Christianity differs from other religions, Christianity is right and they are wrong. As in arithmetic—there is only one right answer to a sum, and all other answers are wrong: but some of the wrong answers are much nearer being right than others.

The first big division of humanity is into the majority, who believe in some kind of God or gods, and the minority who do not. On this point, Christianity lines up with the majority—lines up with ancient Greeks and Romans, modern savages, Stoics, Platonists, Hindus, Mohammedans, etc., against the modern Western European materialist.

Now I go on to the next big division. People who all believe in God can be divided according to the sort of God they believe in. There are two very different ideas on this subject. One of them is the idea that He is beyond good and evil. We humans call one thing good and another thing bad. But according to some people

that is merely our human point of view. These people would say
that the wiser you become the less you would want to call anything
good or bad, and the more clearly you would see that everything is
good in one way and bad in another, and that nothing could have
been different. Consequently, these people think that long before
you got anywhere near the divine point of view the distinction
would have disappeared altogether. We call a cancer bad, they
would say, because it kills a man; but you might just as well call
a successful surgeon bad because he kills a cancer. It all depends
on the point of view. The other and opposite idea is that God is
quite definitely "good" or "righteous," a God who takes sides, who
loves love and hates hatred, who wants us to behave in one way
and not in another. The first of these views—the one that thinks
God beyond good and evil—is called Pantheism. It was held by
the great Prussian philosopher Hegel and, as far as I can understand them, by the Hindus. The other view is held by Jews, Mohammedans and Christians.

And with this big difference between Pantheism and the Christian idea of God, there usually goes another. Pantheists usually
believe that God, so to speak, animates the universe as you animate
your body: that the universe almost *is* God, so that if it did not
exist He would not exist either, and anything you find in the
universe is a part of God. The Christian idea is quite different.
They think God invented and made the universe—like a man
making a picture or composing a tune. A painter is not a picture,
and he does not die if his picture is destroyed. You may say, "He's
put a lot of himself into it," but you only mean that all its beauty
and interest has come out of his head. His skill is not in the picture
in the same way that it is in his head, or even in his hands. I
expect you see how this difference between Pantheists and Christians hangs together with the other one. If you do not take the
distinction between good and bad very seriously, then it is easy to
say that anything you find in this world is a part of God. But, of
course, if you think some things really bad, and God really good,
then you cannot talk like that. You must believe that God is separate from the world and that some of the things we see in it are
contrary to His will. Confronted with a cancer or a slum the Pan-
theist can say, "If you could only see it from the divine point of
view, you would realise that this also is God." The Christian re-

plies, "Don't talk damned nonsense." * For Christianity is a fighting religion. It thinks God made the world—that space and time, heat and cold, and all the colours and tastes, and all the animals and vegetables, are things that God "made up out of His head" as a man makes up a story. But it also thinks that a great many things have gone wrong with the world that God made and that God insists, and insists very loudly, on our putting them right again.

And, of course, that raises a very big question. If a good God made the world why has it gone wrong? And for many years I simply refused to listen to the Christian answers to this question, because I kept on feeling "whatever you say, and however clever your arguments are, isn't it much simpler and easier to say that the world was not made by any intelligent power? Aren't all your arguments simply a complicated attempt to avoid the obvious?" But then that threw me back into another difficulty.

My argument against God was that the universe seemed so cruel and unjust. But how had I got this idea of *just* and *unjust*? A man does not call a line crooked unless he has some idea of a straight line. What was I comparing this universe with when I called it unjust? If the whole show was bad and senseless from A to Z, so to speak, why did I, who was supposed to be part of the show, find myself in such violent reaction against it? A man feels wet when he falls into water, because man is not a water animal: a fish would not feel wet. Of course I could have given up my idea of justice by saying it was nothing but a private idea of my own. But if I did that, then my argument against God collapsed too— for the argument depended on saying that the world was really unjust, not simply that it did not happen to please my private fancies. Thus in the very act of trying to prove that God did not exist—in other words, that the whole of reality was senseless—I found I was forced to assume that one part of reality—namely my idea of justice—was full of sense. Consequently atheism turns out to be too simple. If the whole universe has no meaning, we should never have found out that it has no meaning: just as, if there were no light in the universe and therefore no creatures with eyes, we should never know it was dark. *Dark* would be without meaning.

* One listener complained of the word *damned* as frivolous swearing. But I mean exactly what I say—nonsense that is *damned* is under God's curse, and will (apart from God's grace) lead those who believe it to eternal death.

2.

THE INVASION

Very well then, atheism is too simple. And I will tell you another view that is also too simple. It is the view I call Christianity-and-water, the view which simply says there is a good God in Heaven and everything is all right—leaving out all the difficult and terrible doctrines about sin and hell and the devil, and the redemption. Both these are boys' philosophies.

It is no good asking for a simple religion. After all, real things are not simple. They look simple, but they are not. The table I am sitting at looks simple: but ask a scientist to tell you what it is really made of—all about the atoms and how the light waves rebound from them and hit my eye and what they do to the optic nerve and what it does to my brain—and, of course, you find that what we call "seeing a table" lands you in mysteries and complications which you can hardly get to the end of. A child saying a child's prayer looks simple. And if you are content to stop there, well and good. But if you are not—and the modern world usually is not—if you want to go on and ask what is really happening—then you must be prepared for something difficult. If we ask for something more than simplicity, it is silly then to complain that the something more is not simple.

Very often, however, this silly procedure is adopted by people who are not silly, but who, consciously or unconsciously, want to destroy Christianity. Such people put up a version of Christianity suitable for a child of six and make that the object of their attack. When you try to explain the Christian doctrine as it is really held by an instructed adult, they then complain that you are making their heads turn round and that it is all too complicated and that if there really were a God they are sure He would have made "religion" simple, because simplicity is so beautiful, etc. You must be on your guard against these people for they will change their ground every minute and only waste your time. Notice, too, their idea of God "making religion simple": as if "religion" were something God invented, and not His statement to us of certain quite unalterable facts about His own nature.

Besides being complicated, reality, in my experience, is usually odd. It is not neat, not obvious, not what you expect. For instance, when you have grasped that the earth and the other planets all go round the sun, you would naturally expect that all the planets were made to match—all at equal distances from each other, say, or distances that regularly increased, or all the same size, or else getting bigger or smaller as you go farther from the sun. In fact, you find no rhyme or reason (that we can see) about either the sizes or the distances: and some of them have one moon, one has four, one has two, some have none, and one has a ring.

Reality, in fact, is usually something you could not have guessed. That is one of the reasons I believe Christianity. It is a religion you could not have guessed. If it offered us just the kind of universe we had always expected, I should feel we were making it up. But, in fact, it is not the sort of thing anyone would have made up. It has just that queer twist about it that real things have. So let us leave behind all these boys' philosophies—these over-simple answers. The problem is not simple and the answer is not going to be simpler either.

What is the problem? A universe that contains much that is obviously bad and apparently meaningless, but containing creatures like ourselves who know that it is bad and meaningless. There are only two views that face all the facts. One is the Christian view that this is a good world that has gone wrong, but still retains the memory of what it ought to have been. The other is the view called Dualism. Dualism means the belief that there are two equal and independent powers at the back of everything, one of them good and the other bad, and that this universe is the battlefield in which they fight out an endless war. I personally think that next to Christianity Dualism is the manliest and most sensible creed on the market. But it has a catch in it.

The two powers, or spirits, or gods—the good one and the bad one—are supposed to be quite independent. They both existed from all eternity. Neither of them made the other, neither of them has any more right than the other to call itself God. Each presumably thinks it is good and thinks the other bad. One of them likes hatred and cruelty, the other likes love and mercy, and each backs its own view. Now what do we mean when we call one of them the Good Power and the other the Bad Power? Either we are merely saying that we happen to prefer the one to the other—like preferring beer to cider—or else we are saying that, whatever the two powers think about it, and whichever we humans, at the moment, happen to like, one of them is actually wrong, actually mistaken, in regarding itself as good. Now if we mean merely that we happen to prefer the first, then we must give up talking about good and evil at all. For good means what you ought to prefer quite regardless of what you happen to like at any given moment. If "being good" meant simply joining the side you happened to fancy, for no real reason, then good would not deserve to be called good. So we must mean that one of the two powers is actually wrong and the other actually right.

But the moment you say that, you are putting into the universe a third thing in addition to the two Powers: some law or standard or rule of good which one of the powers conforms to and the other fails to conform to. But since the two powers are judged by this standard, then this standard, or the Being who made this standard, is farther back and higher up than either of them, and He will be the real God. In fact, what we meant by calling them good and bad turns out to be that one of them is in a right relation to the real ultimate God and the other in a wrong relation to Him.

The same point can be made in a different way. If Dualism is true, then the bad Power must be a being who likes badness for its own sake. But in reality we have no experience of anyone liking badness just because it is bad. The nearest we can get to it is in cruelty. But in real life people are cruel for one of two reasons—either because they are sadists, that is, because they have a sexual perversion which makes cruelty a cause of sensual pleasure to them, or else for the sake of something they are going to get out of it—money, or power, or safety. But pleasure, money, power, and safety are all, as far as they go, good things. The badness consists in pursuing them by the wrong method, or in the wrong way, or too much. I do not mean, of course, that the people who do this are not desperately wicked. I do mean that wickedness, when you examine it, turns out to be the pursuit of some good in the wrong way. You can be good for the mere sake of goodness: you cannot be bad for the mere sake of badness. You can do a kind action when you are not feeling kind and when it gives you no pleasure, simply because kindness is right; but no one ever did a cruel action simply because cruelty is wrong—only because cruelty was pleasant or useful to him. In other words badness cannot succeed even in being bad in the same way in which goodness is good. Goodness is, so to speak, itself: badness is only spoiled goodness. And there must be something good first before it can be spoiled. We called sadism a sexual perversion; but you must first have the idea of a normal sexuality before you can talk of its being perverted; and you can see which is the perversion, because you can explain the perverted from the normal, and cannot explain the normal from the perverted. It follows that this Bad Power, who is supposed to be on an equal footing with the Good Power, and to love badness in the same way as the Good Power loves goodness, is a mere bogy. In order to be bad he must have good things to want and then to pursue in the wrong way: he must have impulses which were originally good in order to be able to pervert them. But if he is bad he cannot supply himself either with good things to desire or with good impulses to pervert. He must be getting both from the Good Power. And if so, then he is not independent. He is part of the Good Power's world: he was made either by the Good Power or by some power above them both.

Put it more simply still. To be bad, he must exist and have intelligence and will. But existence, intelligence and will are in themselves good. Therefore he must be getting them from the Good Power: even to be bad he must borrow or steal from his opponent. And do you now begin to see why Christianity has always said that the devil is a fallen angel? That is not a mere story for the children. It is a real recognition of the fact that evil is a parasite, not an original thing. The powers which enable evil to carry on are powers given it by goodness. All the things which enable a bad man to be effectively bad are in themselves good things—resolution, cleverness, good looks, existence itself. That is why Dualism, in a strict sense, will not work.

But I freely admit that real Christianity (as distinct from Christianity-and-water) goes much nearer to Dualism than people think. One of the things that surprised me when I first read the New Testament seriously was that it talked so much about a Dark Power in the universe—a mighty evil spirit who was held to be the Power behind death and disease, and sin. The difference is that Christianity thinks this Dark Power was created by God, and was good when he was created, and went wrong. Christianity agrees with Dualism that this universe is at war. But it does not think this is a war between independent powers. It thinks it is a civil war, a rebellion, and that we are living in a part of the universe occupied by the rebel.

Enemy-occupied territory—that is what this world is. Christianity is the story of how the rightful king has landed, you might say landed in disguise, and is calling us all to take part in a great campaign of sabotage. When you go to church you are really listening-in to the secret wireless from our friends: that is why the enemy is so anxious to prevent us from going. He does it by playing on our conceit and laziness and intellectual snobbery. I know someone will ask me, "Do you really mean, at this time of day, to re-introduce our old friend the devil—hoofs and horns and all?" Well, what the time of day has to do with it I do not know. And I am not particular about the hoofs and horns. But in other respects my answer is "Yes, I do." I do not claim to know anything about his personal appearance. If anybody really wants to know him better I would say to that person, "Don't worry. If you really want to, you will. Whether you'll like it when you do is another question."

3.

THE SHOCKING ALTERNATIVE

Christians, then, believe that an evil power has made himself for the present the Prince of this World. And, of course, that raises problems. Is this state of affairs in accordance with God's will or not? If it is, He is a strange God, you will say: and if it is not, how can anything happen contrary to the will of a being with absolute power?

But anyone who has been in authority knows how a thing can be in accordance with your will in one way and not in another. It may be quite sensible for a mother to say to the children, "I'm not going to go and make you tidy the schoolroom every night. You've got to learn to keep it tidy on your own." Then she goes up one night and finds the Teddy bear and the ink and the French Grammar all lying in the grate. That is against her will. She would prefer the children to be tidy. But on the other hand, it is her will which has left the children free to be untidy. The same thing arises in any regiment, or trade union, or school. You make a thing voluntary and then half the people do not do it. That is not what you willed, but your will has made it possible.

It is probably the same in the universe. God created things which had free will. That means creatures which can go either wrong or right. Some people think they can imagine a creature which was free but had no possibility of going wrong; I cannot. If a thing is free to be good it is also free to be bad. And free will is what has made evil possible. Why, then, did God give them free will? Because free will, though it makes evil possible, is also the only thing that makes possible any love or goodness or joy worth having. A world of automata—of creatures that worked like machines—would hardly be worth creating. The happiness

37

which God designs for His higher creatures is the happiness of
being freely, voluntarily united to Him and to each other in an
ecstasy of love and delight compared with which the most rapturous love between a man and a woman on this earth is mere
milk and water. And for that they must be free.

Of course God knew what would happen if they used their freedom the wrong way: apparently He thought it worth the risk. Perhaps we feel inclined to disagree with Him. But there is a difficulty
about disagreeing with God. He is the source from which all your
reasoning power comes: you could not be right and He wrong
any more than a stream can rise higher than its own source. When
you are arguing against Him you are arguing against the very
power that makes you able to argue at all: it is like cutting off the
branch you are sitting on. If God thinks this state of war in the
universe a price worth paying for free will—that is, for making a
live world in which creatures can do real good or harm and something of real importance can happen, instead of a toy world which
only moves when He pulls the strings—then we may take it it is
worth paying.

When we have understood about free will, we shall see how
silly it is to ask, as somebody once asked me: "Why did God
make a creature of such rotten stuff that it went wrong?" The
better stuff a creature is made of—the cleverer and stronger and
freer it is—then the better it will be if it goes right, but also the
worse it will be if it goes wrong. A cow cannot be very good
or very bad; a dog can be both better and worse; a child better
and worse still; an ordinary man, still more so; a man of genius,
still more so; a superhuman spirit best—or worst—of all.

How did the Dark Power go wrong? Here, no doubt, we ask
a question to which human beings cannot give an answer with
any certainty. A reasonable (and traditional) guess, based on our
own experiences of going wrong, can, however, be offered. The
moment you have a self at all, there is a possibility of putting yourself first—wanting to be the centre—wanting to be God, in fact.
That was the sin of Satan: and that was the sin he taught the
human race. Some people think the fall of man had something
to do with sex, but that is a mistake. (The story in the Book of
Genesis rather suggests that some corruption in our sexual nature

followed the fall and was its result, not its cause.) What Satan put into the heads of our remote ancestors was the idea that they could "be like gods"—could set up on their own as if they had created themselves—be their own masters—invent some sort of happiness for themselves outside God, apart from God. And out of that hopeless attempt has come nearly all that we call human history—money, poverty, ambition, war, prostitution, classes, empires, slavery—the long terrible story of man trying to find something other than God which will make him happy.

The reason why it can never succeed is this. God made us: invented us as a man invents an engine. A car is made to run on gasoline, and it would not run properly on anything else. Now God designed the human machine to run on Himself. He Himself is the fuel our spirits were designed to burn, or the food our spirits were designed to feed on. There is no other. That is why it is just no good asking God to make us happy in our own way without bothering about religion. God cannot give us a happiness and peace apart from Himself, because it is not there. There is no such thing.

That is the key to history. Terrific energy is expended—civilisations are built up—excellent institutions devised; but each time something goes wrong. Some fatal flaw always brings the selfish and cruel people to the top and it all slides back into misery and ruin. In fact, the machine conks. It seems to start up all right and runs a few yards, and then it breaks down. They are trying to run it on the wrong juice. That is what Satan has done to us humans.

And what did God do? First of all He left us conscience, the sense of right and wrong: and all through history there have been people trying (some of them very hard) to obey it. None of them ever quite succeeded. Secondly, He sent the human race what I call good dreams: I mean those queer stories scattered all through the heathen religions about a god who dies and comes to life again and, by his death, has somehow given new life to men. Thirdly, He selected one particular people and spent several centuries hammering into their heads the sort of God He was —that there was only one of Him and that He cared about right conduct. Those people were the Jews, and the Old Testament gives an account of the hammering process.

Then comes the real shock. Among these Jews there suddenly turns up a man who goes about talking as if He was God. He claims to forgive sins. He says He has always existed. He says He is coming to judge the world at the end of time. Now let us get this clear. Among Pantheists, like the Indians, anyone might say that he was a part of God, or one with God: there would be nothing very odd about it. But this man, since He was a Jew, could not mean that kind of God. God, in their language, meant the Being outside the world Who had made it and was infinitely different from anything else. And when you have grasped that, you will see that what this man said was, quite simply, the most shocking thing that has ever been uttered by human lips.

One part of the claim tends to slip past us unnoticed because we have heard it so often that we no longer see what it amounts to. I mean the claim to forgive sins: any sins. Now unless the speaker is God, this is really so preposterous as to be comic. We can all understand how a man forgives offences against himself. You tread on my toe and I forgive you, you steal my money and I forgive you. But what should we make of a man, himself unrobbed and untrodden on, who announced that he forgave you for treading on other men's toes and stealing other men's money? Asinine fatuity is the kindest description we should give of his conduct. Yet this is what Jesus did. He told people that their sins were forgiven, and never waited to consult all the other people whom their sins had undoubtedly injured. He unhesitatingly behaved as if He was the party chiefly concerned, the person chiefly offended in all offences. This makes sense only if He really was the God whose laws are broken and whose love is wounded in every sin. In the mouth of any speaker who is not God, these words would imply what I can only regard as a silliness and conceit unrivalled by any other character in history.

Yet (and this is the strange, significant thing) even His enemies, when they read the Gospels, do not usually get the impression of silliness and conceit. Still less do unprejudiced readers. Christ says that He is "humble and meek" and we believe Him; not noticing that, if He were merely a man, humility and meekness are the very last characteristics we could attribute to some of His sayings.

I am trying here to prevent anyone saying the really foolish thing that people often say about Him: "I'm ready to accept Jesus as a great moral teacher, but I don't accept His claim to be God." That is the one thing we must not say. A man who was merely a man and said the sort of things Jesus said would not be a great moral teacher. He would either be a lunatic—on a level with the man who says he is a poached egg—or else he would be the Devil of Hell. You must make your choice. Either this man was, and is, the Son of God: or else a madman or something worse. You can shut Him up for a fool, you can spit at Him and kill Him as a demon; or you can fall at His feet and call Him Lord and God. But let us not come with any patronising nonsense about His being a great human teacher. He has not left that open to us. He did not intend to.

4.

THE PERFECT PENITENT

We are faced, then, with a frightening alternative. This man **we**
are talking about either was (and is) just what He said or else **a**
lunatic, or something worse. Now it seems to me obvious that
He was neither a lunatic nor a fiend: and consequently, however
strange or terrifying or unlikely it may seem, I have to accept the
view that He was and is God. God has landed on this enemy-
occupied world in human form.

And now, what was the purpose of it all? What did He come to
do? Well, to teach, of course; but as soon as you look into the New
Testament or any other Christian writing you will find they are
constantly talking about something different—about His death
and His coming to life again. It is obvious that Christians think
the chief point of the story lies here. They think the main thing
He came to earth to do was to suffer and be killed.

Now before I became a Christian I was under the impression
that the first thing Christians had to believe was one particular
theory as to what the point of this dying was. According to that
theory God wanted to punish men for having deserted and joined
the Great Rebel, but Christ volunteered to be punished instead,
and so God let us off. Now I admit that even this theory does not
seem to me quite so immoral and so silly as it used to; but that
is not the point I want to make. What I came to see later on was
that neither this theory nor any other is Christianity. The central
Christian belief is that Christ's death has somehow put us right
with God and given us a fresh start. Theories as to how it did this
are another matter. A good many different theories have been held
as to how it works; what all Christians are agreed on is that it **does**
work. I will tell you what I think it is like. All sensible people

know that if you are tired and hungry a meal will do you good. But the modern theory of nourishment—all about the vitamins and proteins—is a different thing. People ate their dinners and felt better long before the theory of vitamins was ever heard of: and if the theory of vitamins is some day abandoned they will go on eating their dinners just the same. Theories about Christ's death are not Christianity: they are explanations about how it works. Christians would not all agree as to how important these theories are. My own church—the Church of England—does not lay down any one of them as the right one. The Church of Rome goes a bit further. But I think they will all agree that the thing itself is infinitely more important than any explanations that theologians have produced. I think they would probably admit that no explanation will ever be quite adequate to the reality. But as I said in the preface to this book, I am only a layman, and at this point we are getting into deep water. I can only tell you, for what it is worth, how I, personally, look at the matter.

On my view the theories are not themselves the thing you are asked to accept. Many of you no doubt have read Jeans or Eddington. What they do when they want to explain the atom, or something of that sort, is to give you a description out of which you can make a mental picture. But then they warn you that this picture is not what the scientists actually believe. What the scientists believe is a mathematical formula. The pictures are there only to help you to understand the formula. They are not really true in the way the formula is; they do not give you the real thing but only something more or less like it. They are only meant to help, and if they do not help you can drop them. The thing itself cannot be pictured, it can only be expressed mathematically. We are in the same boat here. We believe that the death of Christ is just that point in history at which something absolutely unimaginable from outside shows through into our own world. And if we cannot picture even the atoms of which our own world is built, of course we are not going to be able to picture this. Indeed, if we found that we could fully understand it, that very fact would show it was not what it professes to be—the inconceivable, the uncreated, the thing from beyond nature, striking down into nature like lightning. You may ask what good will it be to us if we do not understand it. But that is easily answered. A man can eat his dinner without understanding exactly how food nourishes him. A man can accept what Christ has done without knowing how it works: indeed, he certainly would not know how it works until he has accepted it.

We are told that Christ was killed for us, that His death has washed out our sins, and that by dying He disabled death itself. That is the formula. That is Christianity. That is what has to be believed. Any theories we build up as to how Christ's death did all this are, in my view, quite secondary: mere plans or diagrams to be left alone if they do not help us, and, even if they do help us, not to be confused with the thing itself. All the same, some of these theories are worth looking at.

The one most people have heard is the one I mentioned before —the one about our being let off because Christ had volunteered to bear a punishment instead of us. Now on the face of it that is a very silly theory. If God was prepared to let us off, why on earth did He not do so? And what possible point could there be in punishing an innocent person instead? None at all that I can see, if you are thinking of punishment in the police-court sense. On the other hand, if you think of a debt, there is plenty of point in a person who has some assets paying it on behalf of someone who has not. Or if you take "paying the penalty," not in the sense of being punished, but in the more general sense of "standing the racket" or "footing the bill," then, of course, it is a matter of common experience that, when one person has got himself into a hole, the trouble of getting him out usually falls on a kind friend.

Now what was the sort of "hole" man had got himself into? He had tried to set up on his own, to behave as if he belonged to himself. In other words, fallen man is not simply an imperfect creature who needs improvement: he is a rebel who must lay down his arms. Laying down your arms, surrendering, saying you are sorry, realising that you have been on the wrong track and getting ready to start life over again from the ground floor—that is the only way out of a "hole." This process of surrender—this movement full speed astern—is what Christians call repentance. Now repentance is no fun at all. It is something much harder than merely eating humble pie. It means unlearning all the self-conceit and self-will that we have been training ourselves into for thousands of years. It means killing part of yourself, undergoing a kind of death. In fact, it needs a good man to repent. And here comes the catch. Only a bad person needs to repent: only a good person can repent perfectly. The worse you are the more you need it and the less you can do it. The only person who could do it perfectly would be a perfect person—and he would not need it.

Remember, this repentance, this willing submission to humiliation and a kind of death, is not something God demands of you before He will take you back and which He could let you off if He chose: it is simply a description of what going back to Him is like. If you ask God to take you back without it, you are really asking Him to let you go back without going back. It cannot happen. Very well, then, we must go through with it. But the same badness which makes us need it, makes us unable to do it. Can we do it if God helps us? Yes, but what do we mean when we talk of God helping us? We mean God putting into us a bit of Himself, so to speak. He lends us a little of His reasoning powers and that is how we think: He puts a little of His love into us and that is how we love one another. When you teach a child writing, you hold its hand while it forms the letters: that is, it forms the letters because you are forming them. We love and reason because God loves and reasons and holds our hand while we do it. Now if we had not fallen, that would be all plain sailing. But unfortunately we now need God's help in order to do something which God, in His own nature, never does at all—to surrender, to suffer, to submit, to die. Nothing in God's nature corresponds to this process at all. So that the one road for which we now need God's leadership most of all is a road God, in His own nature, has never walked. God can share only what He has: this thing, in His own nature, He has not.

But supposing God became a man—suppose our human nature which can suffer and die was amalgamated with God's nature in one person—then that person could help us. He could surrender His will, and suffer and die, because He was man; and He could do it perfectly because He was God. You and I can go through this process only if God does it in us; but God can do it only if He becomes man. Our attempts at this dying will succeed only if we men share in God's dying, just as our thinking can succeed only because it is a drop out of the ocean of His intelligence: but we cannot share God's dying unless God dies; and He cannot die except by being a man. That is the sense in which He pays our debt, and suffers for us what He Himself need not suffer at all.

I have heard some people complain that if Jesus was God as well as man, then His sufferings and death lose all value in their eyes, "because it must have been so easy for him." Others may (very rightly) rebuke the ingratitude and ungraciousness of this objection; what staggers me is the misunderstanding it betrays. In one sense, of course, those who make it are right. They have even understated their own case. The perfect submission, the perfect suffering, the perfect death were not only easier to Jesus because He was God, but were possible only because He was God. But surely that is a very odd reason for not accepting them? The teacher is able to form the letters for the child because the teacher is grown-up and knows how to write. That, of course, makes it easier for the teacher; and only because it is easier for him can he help the child. If it rejected him because "it's easy for grown-ups" and waited to learn writing from another child who could not write itself (and so had no "unfair" advantage), it would not get on very quickly. If I am drowning in a rapid river, a man who still has one foot on the bank may give me a hand which saves my life. Ought I to shout back (between my gasps) "No, it's not fair! You have an advantage! You're keeping one foot on the bank"? That advantage—call it "unfair" if you like—is the only reason why he can be of any use to me. To what will you look for help if you will not look to that which is stronger than yourself?

Such is my own way of looking at what Christians call the Atonement. But remember this is only one more picture. Do not mistake it for the thing itself: and if it does not help you, drop it.

5.

THE PRACTICAL CONCLUSION

The perfect surrender and humiliation were undergone by Christ: perfect because He was God, surrender and humiliation because He was man. Now the Christian belief is that if we somehow share the humility and suffering of Christ we shall also share in His conquest for death and find a new life after we have died and in it become perfect, and perfectly happy, creatures. This means something much more than our trying to follow His teaching. People often ask when the next step in evolution—the step to something beyond man—will happen. But on the Christian view, it has happened already. In Christ a new kind of man appeared: and the new kind of life which began in Him is to be put into us.

How is this to be done? Now, please remember how we acquired the old, ordinary kind of life. We derived it from others, from our father and mother and all our ancestors, without our consent—and by a very curious process, involving pleasure, pain, and danger. A process you would never have guessed. Most of us spend a good many years in childhood trying to guess it: and some children, when they are first told, do not believe it—and I am not sure that I blame them, for it is very odd. Now the God who arranged that process is the same God who arranges how the new kind of life—the Christ life—is to be spread. We must be prepared for it being odd too. He did not consult us when He invented sex: He has not consulted us either when He invented this.

There are three things that spread the Christ life to us: baptism, belief, and that mysterious action which different Christians call by different names—Holy Communion, the Mass, the Lord's Supper. At least, those are the three ordinary methods. I am not saying there may not be special cases where it is spread without one or

47

more of these. I have not time to go into special cases, and I do not know enough. If you are trying in a few minutes to tell a man how to get to Edinburgh you will tell him the trains: he can, it is true, get there by boat or by a plane, but you will hardly bring that in. And I am not saying anything about which of these three things is the most essential. My Methodist friend would like me to say more about belief and less (in proportion) about the other two. But I am not going into that. Anyone who professes to teach you Christian doctrine will, in fact, tell you to use all three, and that is enough for our present purpose.

I cannot myself see why these things should be the conductors of the new kind of life. But then, if one did not happen to know, I should never have seen any connection between a particular physical pleasure and the appearance of a new human being in the world. We have to take reality as it comes to us: there is no good jabbering about what it ought to be like or what we should have expected it to be like. But though I cannot see why it should be so, I can tell you why I believe it is so. I have explained why I have to believe that Jesus was (and is) God. And it seems plain as a matter of history that He taught His followers that the new life was communicated in this way. In other words, I believe it on His authority. Do not be scared by the word authority. Believing things on authority only means believing them because you have been told them by someone you think trustworthy. Ninety-nine per cent of the things you believe are believed on authority. I believe there is such a place as New York. I have not seen it myself. I could not prove by abstract reasoning that there must be such a place. I believe it because reliable people have told me so. The ordinary man believes in the Solar System, atoms, evolution, and the circulation of the blood on authority—because the scientists say so. Every historical statement in the world is believed on authority. None of us has seen the Norman Conquest or the defeat of the Armada. None of us could prove them by pure logic as you prove a thing in mathematics. We believe them simply because people who did see them have left writings that tell us about them: in fact, on authority. A man who jibbed at authority in other things as some people do in religion would have to be content to know nothing all his life.

Do not think I am setting up baptism and belief and the Holy Communion as things that will do instead of your own attempts to copy Christ. Your natural life is derived from your parents; that does not mean it will stay there if you do nothing about it. You can lose it by neglect, or you can drive it away by committing suicide. You have to feed it and look after it: but always remember you are not making it, you are only keeping up a life you got from someone else. In the same way a Christian can lose the Christ-life which has been put into him, and he has to make efforts to keep it. But even the best Christian that ever lived is not acting on his own steam—he is only nourishing or protecting a life he could never have acquired by his own efforts. And that has practical consequences. As long as the natural life is in your body, it will do a lot towards repairing that body. Cut it, and up to a point it will heal, as a dead body would not. A live body is not one that never gets hurt, but one that can to some extent repair itself. In the same way a Christian is not a man who never goes wrong, but a man who is enabled to repent and pick himself up and begin over again after each stumble—because the Christ-life is inside him, repairing him all the time, enabling him to repeat (in some degree) the kind of voluntary death which Christ Himself carried out.

That is why the Christian is in a different position from other people who are trying to be good. They hope, by being good, to please God if there is one; or—if they think there is not—at least they hope to deserve approval from good men. But the Christian thinks any good he does comes from the Christ-life inside him. He does not think God will love us because we are good, but that God will make us good because He loves us; just as the roof of a greenhouse does not attract the sun because it is bright, but becomes bright because the sun shines on it.

And let me make it quite clear that when Christians say the Christ-life is in them, they do not mean simply something mental or moral. When they speak of being "in Christ" or of Christ being "in them," this is not simply a way of saying that they are thinking about Christ or copying Him. They mean that Christ is actually operating through them; that the whole mass of Christians are the physical organism through which Christ acts—that we are

His fingers and muscles, the cells of His body. And perhaps that explains one or two things. It explains why this new life is spread not only by purely mental acts like belief, but by bodily acts like baptism and Holy Communion. It is not merely the spreading of an idea; it is more like evolution—a biological or super-biological fact. There is no good trying to be more spiritual than God. God never meant man to be a purely spiritual creature. That is why He uses material things like bread and wine to put the new life into us. We may think this rather crude and unspiritual. God does not: He invented eating. He likes matter. He invented it.

Here is another thing that used to puzzle me. Is it not frightfully unfair that this new life should be confined to people who have heard of Christ and been able to believe in Him? But the truth is God has not told us what His arrangements about the other people are. We do know that no man can be saved except through Christ; we do not know that only those who know Him can be saved through Him. But in the meantime, if you are worried about the people outside, the most unreasonable thing you can do is to remain outside yourself. Christians are Christ's body, the organism through which He works. Every addition to that body enables Him to do more. If you want to help those outside you must add your own little cell to the body of Christ who alone can help them. Cutting off a man's fingers would be an odd way of getting him to do more work.

Another possible objection is this. Why is God landing in this enemy-occupied world in disguise and starting a sort of secret society to undermine the devil? Why is He not landing in force, invading it? Is it that He is not strong enough? Well, Christians think He is going to land in force; we do not know when. But we can guess why He is delaying. He wants to give us the chance of joining His side freely. I do not suppose you and I would have thought much of a Frenchman who waited till the Allies were marching into Germany and then announced he was on our side. God will invade. But I wonder whether people who ask God to interfere openly and directly in our world quite realise what it will be like when He does. When that happens, it is the end of the world. When the author walks on to the stage the play is over. God is going to invade, all right: but what is the good of saying you are on His side then, when you see the whole natural universe melting away like a dream and something else—something it never entered your head to conceive—comes crashing in; something so beautiful to some of us and so terrible to others that none of us will have any choice left? For this time it will be God without disguise; something so overwhelming that it will strike either irresistible love or irresistible horror into every creature. It will be too late then to choose your side. There is no use saying you choose to lie down when it has become impossible to stand up. That will not be the time for choosing: it will be the time when we discover which side we really have chosen, whether we realised it before or not. Now, today, this moment, is our chance to choose the right side. God is holding back to give us that chance. It will not last for ever. We must take it or leave it.

BOOK III

CHRISTIAN BEHAVIOUR

I.

THE THREE PARTS OF MORALITY

There is a story about a schoolboy who was asked what he thought God was like. He replied that, as far as he could make out, God was "The sort of person who is always snooping round to see if anyone is enjoying himself and then trying to stop it." And I am afraid that is the sort of idea that the word Morality raises in a good many people's minds: something that interferes, something that stops you having a good time. In reality, moral rules are directions for running the human machine. Every moral rule is there to prevent a breakdown, or a strain, or a friction, in the running of that machine. That is why these rules at first seem to be constantly interfering with our natural inclinations. When you are being taught how to use any machine, the instructor keeps on saying, "No, don't do it like that," because, of course, there are all sorts of things that look all right and seem to you the natural way of treating the machine, but do not really work.

Some people prefer to talk about moral "ideals" rather than moral rules and about moral "idealism" rather than moral obedience. Now it is, of course, quite true that moral perfection is an "ideal" in the sense that we cannot achieve it. In that sense every kind of perfection is, for us humans, an ideal; we cannot succeed in being perfect car drivers or perfect tennis players or in drawing perfectly straight lines. But there is another sense in which it is very misleading to call moral perfection an ideal. When a man says that a certain woman, or house, or ship, or garden is "his ideal" he does not mean (unless he is rather a fool) that everyone else ought to have the same ideal. In such matters we are entitled to have different tastes and, therefore, different ideals. But it is dangerous to describe a man who tries very hard to keep the moral

55

law as a "man of high ideals," because this might lead you to think
that moral perfection was a private taste of his own and that the
rest of us were not called on to share it. This would be a disastrous
mistake. Perfect behaviour may be as unattainable as perfect gear-
changing when we drive; but it is a necessary ideal prescribed for
all men by the very nature of the human machine just as perfect
gear-changing is an ideal prescribed for all drivers by the very
nature of cars. And it would be even more dangerous to think of
oneself as a person "of high ideals" because one is trying to tell no
lies at all (instead of only a few lies) or never to commit adultery
(instead of committing it only seldom) or not to be a bully (instead
of being only a moderate bully). It might lead you to become a
prig and to think you were rather a special person who deserved
to be congratulated on his "idealism." In reality you might just as
well expect to be congratulated because, whenever you do a sum,
you try to get it quite right. To be sure, perfect arithmetic is "an
ideal"; you will certainly make some mistakes in some calcula-
tions. But there is nothing very fine about trying to be quite accurate at each step in each sum. It would be idiotic not to try;
for every mistake is going to cause you trouble later on. In the
same way every moral failure is going to cause trouble, probably
to others and certainly to yourself. By talking about rules and
obedience instead of "ideals" and "idealism" we help to remind
ourselves of these facts.

Now let us go a step further. There are two ways in which the
human machine goes wrong. One is when human individuals
drift apart from one another, or else collide with one another and
do one another damage, by cheating or bullying. The other is
when things go wrong inside the individual—when the different
parts of him (his different faculties and desires and so on) either
drift apart or interfere with one another. You can get the idea
plain if you think of us as a fleet of ships sailing in formation. The
voyage will be a success only, in the first place, if the ships do not
collide and get in one another's way; and, secondly, if each ship
is seaworthy and has her engines in good order. As a matter of
fact, you cannot have either of these two things without the other.
If the ships keep on having collisions they will not remain seaworthy very long. On the other hand, if their steering gears are

out of order they will not be able to avoid collisions. Or, if you like, think of humanity as a band playing a tune. To get a good result, you need two things. Each player's individual instrument must be in tune and also each must come in at the right moment so as to combine with all the others.

But there is one thing we have not yet taken into account. We have not asked where the fleet is trying to get to, or what piece of music the band is trying to play. The instruments might be all in tune and might all come in at the right moment, but even so the performance would not be a success if they had been engaged to provide dance music and actually played nothing but Dead Marches. And however well the fleet sailed, its voyage would be a failure if it were meant to reach New York and actually arrived at Calcutta.

Morality, then, seems to be concerned with three things. Firstly, with fair play and harmony between individuals. Secondly, with what might be called tidying up or harmonising the things inside each individual. Thirdly, with the general purpose of human life as a whole: what man was made for: what course the whole fleet ought to be on: what tune the conductor of the band wants it to play.

You may have noticed that modern people are nearly always thinking about the first thing and forgetting the other two. When people say in the newspapers that we are striving for Christian moral standards, they usually mean that we are striving for kindness and fair play between nations, and classes, and individuals; that is, they are thinking only of the first thing. When a man says about something he wants to do, "It can't be wrong because it doesn't do anyone else any harm," he is thinking only of the first thing. He is thinking it does not matter what his ship is like inside provided that he does not run into the next ship. And it is quite natural, when we start thinking about morality, to begin with the first thing, with social relations. For one thing, the results of bad morality in that sphere are so obvious and press on us every day: war and poverty and graft and lies and shoddy work. And also, as long as you stick to the first thing, there is very little disagreement about morality. Almost all people at all times have agreed (in theory) that human beings ought to be honest and kind and helpful to one another. But though it is natural to begin with all that, if our thinking about morality stops there, we might just as well not have thought at all. Unless we go on to the second thing—the tidying up inside each human being—we are only deceiving ourselves.

What is the good of telling the ships how to steer so as to avoid collisions if, in fact, they are such crazy old tubs that they cannot be steered at all? What is the good of drawing up, on paper, rules for social behaviour, if we know that, in fact, our greed, cowardice, ill temper, and self-conceit are going to prevent us from keeping them? I do not mean for a moment that we ought not to think, and think hard, about improvements in our social and economic system. What I do mean is that all that thinking will be mere moonshine unless we realise that nothing but the courage and unselfishness of individuals is ever going to make any system work properly. It is easy enough to remove the particular kinds of graft or bullying that go on under the present system: but as long as men are twisters or bullies they will find some new way of carrying on the old game under the new system. You cannot make men good by law: and without good men you cannot have a good society. That is why we must go on to think of the second thing: of morality inside the individual.

But I do not think we can stop there either. We are now getting to the point at which different beliefs about the universe lead to different behaviour. And it would seem, at first sight, very sensible to stop before we got there, and just carry on with those parts of morality that all sensible people agree about. But can we? Remember that religion involves a series of statements about facts, which must be either true or false. If they are true, one set of conclusions will follow about the right sailing of the human fleet: if they are false, quite a different set. For example, let us go back to the man who says that a thing cannot be wrong unless it hurts some other human being. He quite understands that he must not damage the other ships in the convoy, but he honestly thinks that what he does to his own ship is simply his own business. But does it not make a great difference whether his ship is his own property or not? Does it not make a great difference whether I am, so to speak, the landlord of my own mind and body, or only a tenant, responsible to the real landlord? If somebody else made me, for his own purposes, then I shall have a lot of duties which I should not have if I simply belonged to myself.

Again, Christianity asserts that every individual human being is going to live for ever, and this must be either true or false. Now there are a good many things which would not be worth bothering about if I were going to live only seventy years, but which I had better bother about very seriously if I am going to live for ever. Perhaps my bad temper or my jealousy are gradually getting worse —so gradually that the increase in seventy years will not be very noticeable. But it might be absolute hell in a million years: in fact, if Christianity is true, Hell is the precisely correct technical term for what it would be. And immortality makes this other difference, which, by the by, has a connection with the difference between totalitarianism and democracy. If individuals live only seventy years, then a state, or a nation, or a civilisation, which may last for a thousand years, is more important than an individual. But if Christianity is true, then the individual is not only more important but incomparably more important, for he is everlasting and the life of a state or a civilisation, compared with his, is only a moment.

It seems, then, that if we are to think about morality, we must think of all three departments: relations between man and man: things inside each man: and relations between man and the power that made him. We can all co-operate in the first one. Disagreements begin with the second and become serious with the third. It is in dealing with the third that the main differences between Christian and non-Christian morality come out. For the rest of this book I am going to assume the Christian point of view, and look at the whole picture as it will be if Christianity is true.

2.

THE "CARDINAL VIRTUES"

The previous section was originally composed to be given as a short talk on the air.

If you are allowed to talk for only ten minutes, pretty well everything else has to be sacrificed to brevity. One of my chief reasons for dividing morality up into three parts (with my picture of the ships sailing in convoy) was that this seemed the shortest way of covering the ground. Here I want to give some idea of another way in which the subject has been divided by old writers, which was too long to use in my talk, but which is a very good one.

According to this longer scheme there are seven "virtues." Four of them are called "Cardinal" virtues, and the remaining three are called "Theological" virtues. The "Cardinal" ones are those which all civilised people recognise: the "Theological" are those which, as a rule, only Christians know about. I shall deal with the Theological ones later on: at present I am talking about the four Cardinal virtues. (The word "cardinal" has nothing to do with "Cardinals" in the Roman Church. It comes from a Latin word meaning "the hinge of a door." These were called "cardinal" virtues because they are, as we should say, "pivotal.") They are PRUDENCE, TEMPERANCE, JUSTICE, and FORTITUDE.

Prudence means practical common sense, taking the trouble to think out what you are doing and what is likely to come of it. Nowadays most people hardly think of Prudence as one of the "virtues." In fact, because Christ said we could only get into His world by being like children, many Christians have the idea that, provided you are "good," it does not matter being a fool. But that is a misunderstanding. In the first place, most children show plenty of "prudence" about doing the things they are really inter-

60

ested in, and think them out quite sensibly. In the second place, as St. Paul points out, Christ never meant that we were to remain children in *intelligence:* on the contrary, He told us to be not only "as harmless as doves," but also "as wise as serpents." He wants a child's heart, but a grown-up's head. He wants us to be simple, single-minded, affectionate, and teachable, as good children are; but He also wants every bit of intelligence we have to be alert at its job, and in first-class fighting trim. The fact that you are giving money to a charity does not mean that you need not try to find out whether that charity is a fraud or not. The fact that what you are thinking about is God Himself (for example, when you are praying) does not mean that you can be content with the same babyish ideas which you had when you were a five-year-old. It is, of course, quite true that God will not love you any the less, or have less use for you, if you happen to have been born with a very second-rate brain. He has room for people with very little sense, but He wants every one to use what sense they have. The proper motto is not "Be good, sweet maid, and let who can be clever," but "Be good, sweet maid, and don't forget that this involves being as clever as you can." God is no fonder of intellectual slackers than of any other slackers. If you are thinking of becoming a Christian, I warn you you are embarking on something which is going to take the whole of you, brains and all. But, fortunately, it works the other way round. Anyone who is honestly trying to be a Christian will soon find his intelligence being sharpened: one of the reasons why it needs no special education to be a Christian is that Christianity is an education itself. That is why an uneducated believer like Bunyan was able to write a book that has astonished the whole world.

Temperance is, unfortunately, one of those words that has changed its meaning. It now usually means teetotalism. But in the days when the second Cardinal virtue was christened "Temperance," it meant nothing of the sort. Temperance referred not specially to drink, but to all pleasures; and it meant not abstaining, but going the right length and no further. It is a mistake to think that Christians ought all to be teetotallers; Mohammedanism, not Christianity, is the teetotal religion. Of course it may be the duty of a particular Christian. or of any Christian, at a particular time, to abstain from strong drink, either because he is the sort of man who cannot drink at all without drinking too much, or because he wants to give the money to the poor, or because he is with people who are inclined to drunkenness and must not encourage them by drinking himself. But the whole point is that he is abstaining, for a good reason, from something which he does not condemn and which he likes to see other people enjoying. One of the marks of a certain type of bad man is that he cannot give up a thing himself without wanting every one else to give it up. That is not the Christian way. An individual Christian may see fit to give up all sorts of things for special reasons—marriage, or meat, or beer, or the cinema; but the moment he starts saying the things are bad in themselves, or looking down his nose at other people who do use them, he has taken the wrong turning.

One great piece of mischief has been done by the modern restriction of the word Temperance to the question of drink. It helps people to forget that you can be just as intemperate about lots of other things. A man who makes his golf or his motor-bicycle the centre of his life, or a woman who devotes all her thoughts to clothes or bridge or her dog, is being just as "intemperate" as someone who gets drunk every evening. Of course, it does not show on the outside so easily: bridge-mania or golf-mania do not make you fall down in the middle of the road. But God is not deceived by externals.

Justice means much more than the sort of thing that goes on in law courts. It is the old name for everything we should now call "fairness"; it includes honesty, give and take, truthfulness, keeping promises, and all that side of life. And Fortitude includes both kinds of courage—the kind that faces danger as well as the kind that "sticks it" under pain. "Guts" is perhaps the nearest modern English. You will notice, of course, that you cannot practise any of the other virtues very long without bringing this one into play.

There is one further point about the virtues that ought to be noticed. There is a difference between doing some particular just or temperate action and being a just or temperate man. Someone who is not a good tennis player may now and then make a good shot. What you mean by a good player is the man whose eye and muscles and nerves have been so trained by making innumerable good shots that they can now be relied on. They have a certain tone or quality which is there even when he is not playing, just as a mathematician's mind has a certain habit and outlook which is there even when he is not doing mathematics. In the same way a man who perseveres in doing just actions gets in the end a certain quality of character. Now it is that quality rather than the particular actions which we mean when we talk of "virtue."

This distinction is important for the following reason. If we thought only of the particular actions we might encourage three wrong ideas.

(1) We might think that, provided you did the right thing, it did not matter how or why you did it—whether you did it willingly or unwillingly, sulkily or cheerfully, through fear of public opinion or for its own sake. But the truth is that right actions done for the wrong reason do not help to build the internal quality or character called a "virtue," and it is this quality or character that really matters. (If the bad tennis player hits very hard, not because he sees that a very hard stroke is required, but because he has lost his temper, his stroke might possibly, by luck, help him to win that particular game; but it will not be helping him to become a reliable player.)

(2) We might think that God wanted simply obedience to a set of rules: whereas He really wants people of a particular sort.

(3) We might think that the "virtues" were necessary only for this present life—that in the other world we could stop being just because there is nothing to quarrel about and stop being brave because there is no danger. Now it is quite true that there will probably be no occasion for just or courageous acts in the next world, but there will be every occasion for being the sort of people that we can become only as the result of doing such acts here. The point is not that God will refuse you admission to His eternal world if you have not got certain qualities of character: the point is that if people have not got at least the beginnings of those qualities inside them, then no possible external conditions could make a "Heaven" for them—that is, could make them happy with the deep, strong, unshakable kind of happiness God intends for us.

3.

SOCIAL MORALITY

The first thing to get clear about Christian morality between man and man is that in this department Christ did not come to preach any brand new morality. The Golden Rule of the New Testament (Do as you would be done by) is a summing up of what everyone, at bottom, had always known to be right. Really great moral teachers never do introduce new moralities: it is quacks and cranks who do that. As Dr. Johnson said, "People need to be reminded more often than they need to be instructed." The real job of every moral teacher is to keep on bringing us back, time after time, to the old simple principles which we are all so anxious not to see; like bringing a horse back and back to the fence it has refused to jump or bringing a child back and back to the bit in its lesson that it wants to shirk.

The second thing to get clear is that Christianity has not, and does not profess to have, a detailed political programme for applying "Do as you would be done by" to a particular society at a particular moment. It could not have. It is meant for all men at all times and the particular programme which suited one place or time would not suit another. And, anyhow, that is not how Christianity works. When it tells you to feed the hungry it does not give you lessons in cookery. When it tells you to read the Scriptures it does not give you lessons in Hebrew and Greek, or even in English grammar. It was never intended to replace or supersede the ordinary human arts and sciences: it is rather a director which will set them all to the right jobs, and a source of energy which will give them all new life, if only they will put themselves at its disposal.

People say, "The Church ought to give us a lead." That is true if they mean it in the right way, but false if they mean it in the wrong way. By the Church they ought to mean the whole body of practising Christians. And when they say that the Church should give us a lead, they ought to mean that some Christians— those who happen to have the right talents—should be economists and statesmen, and that all economists and statesmen should be Christians, and that their whole efforts in politics and economics should be directed to putting "Do as you would be done by" into action. If that happened, and if we others were really ready to take it, then we should find the Christian solution for our own social problems pretty quickly. But, of course, when they ask for a lead from the Church most people mean they want the clergy to put out a political programme. That is silly. The clergy are those particular people within the whole Church who have been specially trained and set aside to look after what concerns us as creatures who are going to live for ever: and we are asking them to do a quite different job for which they have not been trained. The job is really on us, on the laymen. The application of Christian principles, say, to trade unionism or education, must come from Christian trade unionists and Christian schoolmasters: just as Christian literature comes from Christian novelists and dramatists —not from the bench of bishops getting together and trying to write plays and novels in their spare time.

All the same, the New Testament, without going into details, gives us a pretty clear hint of what a fully Christian society would be like. Perhaps it gives us more than we can take. It tells us that there are to be no passengers or parasites: if man does not work, he ought not to eat. Every one is to work with his own hands, and what is more, every one's work is to produce something good: there will be no manufacture of silly luxuries and then of sillier advertisements to persuade us to buy them. And there is to be no "swank" or "side," no putting on airs. To that extent a Christian society would be what we now call Leftist. On the other hand, it is always insisting on obedience—obedience (and outward marks of respect) from all of us to properly appointed magistrates, from children to parents, and (I am afraid this is going to be very un- popular) from wives to husbands. Thirdly, it is to be a cheerful society: full of singing and rejoicing, and regarding worry or anxiety as wrong. Courtesy is one of the Christian virtues; and the New Testament hates what it calls "busybodies."

If there were such a society in existence and you or I visited it, I think we should come away with a curious impression. We should feel that its economic life was very socialistic and, in that sense, "advanced," but that its family life and its code of manners were rather old-fashioned—perhaps even ceremonious and aristocratic. Each of us would like some bits of it, but I am afraid very few of us would like the whole thing. That is just what one would expect if Christianity is the total plan for the human machine. We have all departed from that total plan in different ways, and each of us wants to make out that his own modification of the original plan is the plan itself. You will find this again and again about anything that is really Christian: every one is attracted by bits of it and wants to pick out those bits and leave the rest. That is why we do not get much further: and that is why people who are fighting for quite opposite things can both say they are fighting for Christianity.

Now another point. There is one bit of advice given to us by the ancient heathen Greeks, and by the Jews in the Old Testament, and by the great Christian teachers of the Middle Ages, which the modern economic system has completely disobeyed. All these people told us not to lend money at interest: and lending money at interest—what we call investment—is the basis of our whole system. Now it may not absolutely follow that we are wrong. Some people say that when Moses and Aristotle and the Christians agreed in forbidding interest (or "usury" as they called it), they could not foresee the joint stock company, and were only thinking of the private moneylender, and that, therefore, we need not bother about what they said. That is a question I cannot decide on. I am not an economist and I simply do not know whether the investment system is responsible for the state we are in or not. This is where we want the Christian economist. But I should not have been honest if I had not told you that three great civilisations had agreed (or so it seems at first sight) in condemning the very thing on which we have based our whole life.

One more point and I am done. In the passage where the New Testament says that every one must work, it gives as a reason "in

order that he may have something to give to those in need."
Charity—giving to the poor—is an essential part of Christian
morality: in the frightening parable of the sheep and the goats it
seems to be the point on which everything turns. Some people
nowadays say that charity ought to be unnecessary and that instead of giving to the poor we ought to be producing a society in
which there were no poor to give to. They may be quite right in
saying that we ought to produce that kind of society. But if anyone thinks that, as a consequence, you can stop giving in the meantime, then he has parted company with all Christian morality. I
do not believe one can settle how much we ought to give. I am
afraid the only safe rule is to give more than we can spare. In
other words, if our expenditure on comforts, luxuries, amusements, etc., is up to the standard common among those with the
same income as our own, we are probably giving away too little.
If our charities do not at all pinch or hamper us, I should say
they are too small. There ought to be things we should like to do
and cannot do because our charitable expenditure excludes them.
I am speaking now of "charities" in the common way. Particular
cases of distress among your own relatives, friends, neighbours or
employees, which God, as it were, forces upon your notice, may
demand much more: even to the crippling and endangering of
your own position. For many of us the great obstacle to charity
lies not in our luxurious living or desire for more money, but in
our fear—fear of insecurity. This must often be recognised as a
temptation. Sometimes our pride also hinders our charity; we are
tempted to spend more than we ought on the showy forms of
generosity (tipping, hospitality) and less than we ought on those
who really need our help.

And now, before I end, I am going to venture on a guess as to
how this section has affected any who have read it. My guess is
that there are some Leftist people among them who are very
angry that it has not gone further in that direction, and some
people of an opposite sort who are angry because they think it has
gone much too far. If so, that brings us right up against the real
snag in all this drawing up of blueprints for a Christian society.
Most of us are not really approaching the subject in order to find
out what Christianity says: we are approaching it in the hope

of finding support from Christianity for the views of our own party. We are looking for an ally where we are offered either a Master or—a Judge. I am just the same. There are bits in this section that I wanted to leave out. And that is why nothing whatever is going to come of such talks unless we go a much longer way round. A Christian society is not going to arrive until most of us really want it: and we are not going to want it until we become fully Christian. I may repeat "Do as you would be done by" till I am black in the face, but I cannot really carry it out till I love my neighbour as myself: and I cannot learn to love my neighbour as myself till I learn to love God: and I cannot learn to love God except by learning to obey Him. And so, as I warned you, we are driven on to something more inward —driven on from social matters to religious matters. For the longest way round is the shortest way home.

4.

MORALITY AND PSYCHOANALYSIS

I have said that we should never get a Christian society unless most of us became Christian individuals. That does not mean, of course, that we can put off doing anything about society until some imaginary date in the far future. It means that we must begin both jobs at once—(1) the job of seeing how "Do as you would be done by" can be applied in detail to modern society, and (2) the job of becoming the sort of people who really would apply it if we saw how. I now want to begin considering what the Christian idea of a good man is—the Christian specification for the human machine.

Before I come down to details there are two more general points I should like to make. First of all, since Christian morality claims to be a technique for putting the human machine right, I think you would like to know how it is related to another technique which seems to make a similar claim—namely, psychoanalysis.

Now you want to distinguish very clearly between two things: between the actual medical theories and technique of the psychoanalysts, and the general philosophical view of the world which Freud and some others have gone on to add to this. The second thing—the philosophy of Freud—is in direct contradiction to Christianity: and also in direct contradiction to the other great psychologist, Jung. And furthermore, when Freud is talking about how to cure neurotics he is speaking as a specialist on his own subject, but when he goes on to talk general philosophy he is speaking as an amateur. It is therefore quite sensible to attend to him with respect in the one case and not in the other—and that is what I do. I am all the readier to do it because I have found that when he is talking off his own subject and on a subject I do know something about (namely, languages) he is very ignorant. But psychoanalysis itself, apart from all the philosophical additions that Freud and others have made to it, is not in the least contradictory to Christianity. Its technique overlaps with Christian morality at some points and it would not be a bad thing if every parson knew something about it: but it does not run the same course all the way, for the two techniques are doing rather different things.

When a man makes a moral choice two things are involved. One is the act of choosing. The other is the various feelings, impulses and so on which his psychological outfit presents him with, and which are the raw material of his choice. Now this raw material may be of two kinds. Either it may be what we would call normal: it may consist of the sort of feelings that are common to all men. Or else it may consist of quite unnatural feelings due to things that have gone wrong in his subconscious. Thus fear of things that are really dangerous would be an example of the first kind: an irrational fear of cats or spiders would be an example of the second kind. The desire of a man for a woman would be of the first kind: the perverted desire of a man for a man would be of the second. Now what psychoanalysis undertakes to do is to remove the abnormal feelings, that is, to give the man better raw material for his acts of choice: morality is concerned with the acts of choice themselves.

Put it this way. Imagine three men who go to war. One has the ordinary natural fear of danger that any man has and he subdues it by moral effort and becomes a brave man. Let us suppose that the other two have, as a result of things in their subconsciousness, exaggerated, irrational fears, which no amount of moral effort can do anything about. Now suppose that a psychoanalyst comes along and cures these two: that is, he puts them both back in the position of the first man. Well it is just then that the psychoanalytical problem is over and the moral problem begins. Because, now that they are cured, these two men might take quite different lines. The first might say, "Thank goodness I've got rid of all those doo-dahs. Now at last I can do what I always wanted to do—my duty to the cause of freedom." But the other might say, "Well, I'm very glad that I now feel moderately cool under fire, but, of course, that doesn't alter the fact that I'm still jolly well determined to look after Number One and let the other chap do the dangerous job whenever I can. Indeed one of the good things about feeling less frightened is that I can now look after myself much more efficiently and can be much cleverer at hiding the fact from the others." Now this difference is a purely moral one and psychoanalysis cannot do anything about it. However much you improve the man's raw material, you have still got something else: the real, free choice of the man, on the material presented to him, either to put his own advantage first or to put it last. And this free choice is the only thing that morality is concerned with.

The bad psychological material is not a sin but a disease. It does not need to be repented of, but to be cured. And by the way, that is very important. Human beings judge one another by their external actions. God judges them by their moral choices. When a neurotic who has a pathological horror of cats forces himself to pick up a cat for some good reason, it is quite possible that in God's eyes he has shown more courage than a healthy man may have shown in winning the V.C. When a man who has been perverted from his youth and taught that cruelty is the right thing, does some tiny little kindness, or refrains from some cruelty he might have committed, and thereby, perhaps, risks being sneered at by his companions, he may, in God's eyes, be doing more than you and I would do if we gave up life itself for a friend.

It is as well to put this the other way round. Some of us who seem quite nice people may, in fact, have made so little use of a good heredity and a good upbringing that we are really worse than those whom we regard as fiends. Can we be quite certain how we should have behaved if we had been saddled with the psychological outfit, and then with the bad upbringing, and then with the power, say, of Himmler? That is why Christians are told not to judge. We see only the results which a man's choices make out of his raw material. But God does not judge him on the raw material at all, but on what he has done with it. Most of the man's psychological make-up is probably due to his body: when his body dies all that will fall off him, and the real central man, the thing that chose, that made the best or the worst out of this material, will stand naked. All sorts of nice things which we thought our own, but which were really due to a good digestion, will fall off some of us: all sorts of nasty things which were due to complexes or bad health will fall off others. We shall then, for the first time, see every one as he really was. There will be surprises.

And that leads on to my second point. People often think of Christian morality as a kind of bargain in which God says, "If you keep a lot of rules I'll reward you, and if you don't I'll do the other thing." I do not think that is the best way of looking at it. I would much rather say that every time you make a choice you are turning the central part of you, the part of you that chooses, into something a little different from what it was before. And taking your life as a whole, with all your innumerable choices, all your life long you are slowly turning this central thing either into a heavenly creature or into a hellish creature: either into a creature that is in harmony with God, and with other creatures, and with itself, or else into one that is in a state of war and hatred with God, and with its fellow-creatures, and with itself. To be the one kind of creature is heaven: that is, it is joy and peace and knowledge and power. To be the other means madness, horror, idiocy, rage, impotence, and eternal loneliness. Each of us at each moment is progressing to the one state or the other.

That explains what always used to puzzle me about Christian writers; they seem to be so very strict at one moment and so very free and easy at another. They talk about mere sins of thought as if they were immensely important: and then they talk about the most frightful murders and treacheries as if you had only got to repent and all would be forgiven. But I have come to see that they are right. What they are always thinking of is the mark which the action leaves on that tiny central self which no one sees in this life but which each of us will have to endure—or enjoy—for ever. One man may be so placed that his anger sheds the blood of thousands, and another so placed that however angry he gets he will only be laughed at. But the little mark on the soul may be much the same in both. Each has done something to himself which, unless he repents, will make it harder for him to keep out of the rage next time he is tempted, and will make the rage worse when he does fall into it. Each of them, if he seriously turns to God, can have that twist in the central man straightened out again: each is, in the long run, doomed if he will not. The bigness or smallness of the thing, seen from the outside, is not what really matters.

One last point. Remember that, as I said, the right direction leads not only to peace but to knowledge. When a man is getting better he understands more and more clearly the evil that is still left in him. When a man is getting worse, he understands his own badness less and less. A moderately bad man knows he is not very good: a thoroughly bad man thinks he is all right. This is common sense, really. You understand sleep when you are awake, not while you are sleeping. You can see mistakes in arithmetic when your mind is working properly: while you are making them you cannot see them. You can understand the nature of drunkenness when you are sober, not when you are drunk. Good people know about both good and evil: bad people do not know about either.

5·

SEXUAL MORALITY

We must now consider Christian morality as regards sex, what Christians call the virtue of chastity. The Christian rule of chastity must not be confused with the social rule of "modesty" (in one sense of that word); i.e. propriety, or decency. The social rule of propriety lays down how much of the human body should be displayed and what subjects can be referred to, and in what words, according to the customs of a given social circle. Thus, while the rule of chastity is the same for all Christians at all times, the rule of propriety changes. A girl in the Pacific islands wearing hardly any clothes and a Victorian lady completely covered in clothes might both be equally "modest," proper, or decent, according to the standards of their own societies: and both, for all we could tell by their dress, might be equally chaste (or equally unchaste). Some of the language which chaste women used in Shakespeare's time would have been used in the nineteenth century only by a woman completely abandoned. When people break the rule of propriety current in their own time and place, if they do so in order to excite lust in themselves or others, then they are offending against chastity. But if they break it through ignorance or carelessness they are guilty only of bad manners. When, as often happens, they break it defiantly in order to shock or embarrass others, they are not necessarily being unchaste, but they are being uncharitable: for it is uncharitable to take pleasure in making other people uncomfortable. I do not think that a very strict or fussy standard of propriety is any proof of chastity or any help to it, and I therefore regard the great relaxation and simplifying of the rule which has taken place in my own lifetime as a good thing. At its present stage, however, it has this inconvenience, that

74

people of different ages and different types do not all acknowledge the same standard, and we hardly know where we are. While this confusion lasts I think that old, or old-fashioned, people should be very careful not to assume that young or "emancipated" people are corrupt whenever they are (by the old standard) improper; and, in return, that young people should not call their elders prudes or puritans because they do not easily adopt the new standard. A real desire to believe all the good you can of others and to make others as comfortable as you can will solve most of the problems.

Chastity is the most unpopular of the Christian virtues. There is no getting away from it: the old Christian rule is, "Either marriage, with complete faithfulness to your partner, or else total abstinence." Now this is so difficult and so contrary to our instincts, that obviously either Christianity is wrong or our sexual instinct, as it now is, has gone wrong. One or the other. Of course, being a Christian, I think it is the instinct which has gone wrong.

But I have other reasons for thinking so. The biological purpose of sex is children, just as the biological purpose of eating is to repair the body. Now if we eat whenever we feel inclined and just as much as we want, it is quite true that most of us will eat too much: but not terrifically too much. One man may eat enough for two, but he does not eat enough for ten. The appetite goes a little beyond its biological purpose, but not enormously. But if a healthy young man indulged his sexual appetite whenever he felt inclined, and if each act produced a baby, then in ten years he might easily populate a small village. This appetite is in ludicrous and preposterous excess of its function.

Or take it another way. You can get a large audience together for a strip-tease act—that is, to watch a girl undress on the stage. Now suppose you came to a country where you could fill a theatre by simply bringing a covered plate on to the stage and then slowly lifting the cover so as to let every one see, just before the lights went out, that it contained a mutton chop or a bit of bacon, would you not think that in that country something had gone wrong with the appetite for food? And would not anyone who had grown up in a different world think there was something equally queer about the state of the sex instinct among us?

One critic said that if he found a country in which such strip-tease acts with food were popular, he would conclude that the people of that country were starving. He meant, of course, to imply that such things as the strip-tease act resulted not from sexual corruption but from sexual starvation. I agree with him that if, in some strange land, we found that similar acts with mutton chops were popular, one of the possible explanations which would occur to me would be famine. But the next step would be to test our hypothesis by finding out whether, in fact, much or little food was being consumed in that country. If the evidence showed that a good deal was being eaten, then of course we should have to abandon the hypothesis of starvation and try to think of another one. In the same way, before accepting sexual starvation as the cause of the strip-tease, we should have to look for evidence that there is in fact more sexual abstinence in our age than in those ages when things like the strip-tease were unknown. But surely there is no such evidence. Contraceptives have made sexual indulgence far less costly within marriage and far safer outside it than ever before, and public opinion is less hostile to illicit unions and even to perversion than it has been since Pagan times. Nor is the hypothesis of "starvation" the only one we can imagine. Everyone knows that the sexual appetite, like our other appetites, grows by indulgence. Starving men may think much about food, but so do gluttons; the gorged, as well as the famished, like titillations.

Here is a third point. You find very few people who want to eat things that really are not food or to do other things with food instead of eating it. In other words, perversions of the food appetite are rare. But perversions of the sex instinct are numerous, hard to cure, and frightful. I am sorry to have to go into all these details, but I must. The reason why I must is that you and I, for the last twenty years, have been fed all day long on good solid lies about sex. We have been told, till one is sick of hearing it, that sexual desire is in the same state as any of our other natural desires and that if only we abandon the silly old Victorian idea of hushing it up, everything in the garden will be lovely. It is not true. The moment you look at the facts, and away from the propaganda, you see that it is not.

They tell you sex has become a mess because it was hushed up.

But for the last twenty years it has not been hushed up. It has been chattered about all day long. Yet it is still in a mess. If hushing up had been the cause of the trouble, ventilation would have set it right. But it has not. I think it is the other way round. I think the human race originally hushed it up because it had become such a mess. Modern people are always saying, "Sex is nothing to be ashamed of." They may mean two things. They may mean "There is nothing to be ashamed of in the fact that the human race reproduces itself in a certain way, nor in the fact that it gives pleasure." If they mean that, they are right. Christianity says the same. It is not the thing, nor the pleasure, that is the trouble. The old Christian teachers said that if man had never fallen, sexual pleasure, instead of being less than it is now, would actually have been greater. I know some muddle-headed Christians have talked as if Christianity thought that sex, or the body, or pleasure, were bad in themselves. But they were wrong. Christianity is almost the only one of the great religions which thoroughly approves of the body—which believes that matter is good, that God Himself once took on a human body, that some kind of body is going to be given to us even in Heaven and is going to be an essential part of our happiness, our beauty, and our energy. Christianity has glorified marriage more than any other religion: and nearly all the greatest love poetry in the world has been produced by Christians. If anyone says that sex, in itself, is bad, Christianity contradicts him at once. But, of course, when people say, "Sex is nothing to be ashamed of," they may mean "the state into which the sexual instinct has now got is nothing to be ashamed of."

If they mean that, I think they are wrong. I think it is everything to be ashamed of. There is nothing to be ashamed of in enjoying your food: there would be everything to be ashamed of if half the world made food the main interest of their lives and spent their time looking at pictures of food and dribbling and smacking their lips. I do not say you and I are individually responsible for the present situation. Our ancestors have handed over to us organisms which are warped in this respect: and we grow up surrounded by propaganda in favour of unchastity. There are people who want to keep our sex instinct inflamed in order to make money out of us. Because, of course, a man with an obsession is a man who has very little sales-resistance. God knows our situation; He will not judge us as if we had no difficulties to overcome. What matters is the sincerity and perseverance of our will to overcome them.

Before we can be cured we must want to be cured. Those who really wish for help will get it; but for many modern people even the wish is difficult. It is easy to think that we want something when we do not really want it. A famous Christian long ago told us that when he was a young man he prayed constantly for chastity; but years later he realised that while his lips had been saying, "Oh Lord, make me chaste," his heart had been secretly adding, "But please don't do it just yet." This may happen in prayers for other virtues too; but there are three reasons why it is now specially difficult for us to desire—let alone to achieve—complete chastity.

In the first place our warped natures, the devils who tempt us, and all the contemporary propaganda for lust, combine to make us feel that the desires we are resisting are so "natural," so "healthy," and so reasonable, that it is almost perverse and abnormal to resist them. Poster after poster, film after film, novel after novel, associate the idea of sexual indulgence with the ideas of health, normality, youth, frankness, and good humour. Now this association is a lie. Like all powerful lies, it is based on a truth—the truth, acknowledged above, that sex in itself (apart from the excesses and obsessions that have grown round it) is "normal" and "healthy," and all the rest of it. The lie consists in the suggestion that any sexual act to which you are tempted at the moment is also healthy and normal. Now this, on any conceivable view, and quite apart from Christianity, must be nonsense. Surrender to all our desires obviously leads to impotence, disease, jealousies, lies, concealment, and everything that is the reverse of health, good humour, and frankness. For any happiness, even in this world, quite a lot of restraint is going to be necessary; so the claim made by every desire, when it is strong, to be healthy and reasonable, counts for nothing. Every sane and civilised man must have some set of principles by which he chooses to reject some of his desires and to permit others. One man does this on Christian principles, another on hygienic principles, another on sociological principles. The real conflict is not between Christianity and "nature," but between Christian principle and other principles in the control of "nature." For "nature" (in the sense of natural desire) will have to be controlled anyway, unless you are going to ruin your whole life. The Christian principles are, admittedly, stricter than the others; but then we think you will get help towards obeying them which you will not get towards obeying the others.

In the second place, many people are deterred from seriously attempting Christian chastity because they think (before trying) that it is impossible. But when a thing has to be attempted, one must never think about possibility or impossibility. Faced with an optional question in an examination paper, one considers whether one can do it or not: faced with a compulsory question, one must do the best one can. You may get some marks for a very imperfect answer: you will certainly get none for leaving the question alone. Not only in examinations but in war, in mountain climbing, in learning to skate, or swim, or ride a bicycle, even in fastening a stiff collar with cold fingers, people quite often do what seemed impossible before they did it. It is wonderful what you can do when you have to.

We may, indeed, be sure that perfect chastity—like perfect charity—will not be attained by any merely human efforts. You must ask for God's help. Even when you have done so, it may seem to you for a long time that no help, or less help than you need, is being given. Never mind. After each failure, ask forgiveness, pick yourself up, and try again. Very often what God first helps us towards is not the virtue itself but just this power of always trying again. For however important chastity (or courage, or truthfulness, or any other virtue) may be, this process trains us in habits of the soul which are more important still. It cures our illusions about ourselves and teaches us to depend on God. We learn, on the one hand, that we cannot trust ourselves even in our best moments, and, on the other, that we need not despair even in our worst, for our failures are forgiven. The only fatal thing is to sit down content with anything less than perfection.

Thirdly, people often misunderstand what psychology teaches

about "repressions." It teaches us that "repressed" sex is dangerous. But "repressed" is here a technical term: it does not mean "suppressed" in the sense of "denied" or "resisted." A repressed desire or thought is one which has been thrust into the subconscious (usually at a very early age) and can now come before the mind only in a disguised and unrecognisable form. Repressed sexuality does not appear to the patient to be sexuality at all. When an adolescent or an adult is engaged in resisting a conscious desire, he is not dealing with a repression nor is he in the least danger of creating a repression. On the contrary, those who are seriously attempting chastity are more conscious, and soon know a great deal more about their own sexuality than anyone else. They come to know their desires as Wellington knew Napoleon, or as Sherlock Holmes knew Moriarty; as a rat-catcher knows rats or a plumber knows about leaky pipes. Virtue—even attempted virtue—brings light; indulgence brings fog.

Finally, though I have had to speak at some length about sex, I want to make it as clear as I possibly can that the centre of Christian morality is not here. If anyone thinks that Christians regard unchastity as the supreme vice, he is quite wrong. The sins of the flesh are bad, but they are the least bad of all sins. All the worst pleasures are purely spiritual: the pleasure of putting other people in the wrong, of bossing and patronising and spoiling sport, and back-biting; the pleasures of power, of hatred. For there are two things inside me, competing with the human self which I must try to become. They are the Animal self, and the Diabolical self. The Diabolical self is the worse of the two. That is why a cold, self-righteous prig who goes regularly to church may be far nearer to hell than a prostitute. But, of course, it is better to be neither.

6.

CHRISTIAN MARRIAGE

The last chapter was mainly negative. I discussed what was wrong with the sexual impulse in man, but said very little about its right working—in other words, about Christian marriage. There are two reasons why I do not particularly want to deal with marriage. The first is that the Christian doctrines on this subject are extremely unpopular. The second is that I have never been married myself, and, therefore, can speak only at second hand. But in spite of that, I feel I can hardly leave the subject out in an account of Christian morals.

The Christian idea of marriage is based on Christ's words that a man and wife are to be regarded as a single organism—for that is what the words "one flesh" would be in modern English. And the Christians believe that when He said this He was not expressing a sentiment but stating a fact—just as one is stating a fact when one says that a lock and its key are one mechanism, or that a violin and a bow are one musical instrument. The inventor of the human machine was telling us that its two halves, the male and the female, were made to be combined together in pairs, not simply on the sexual level, but totally combined. The monstrosity of sexual intercourse outside marriage is that those who indulge in it are trying to isolate one kind of union (the sexual) from all the other kinds of union which were intended to go along with it and make up the total union. The Christian attitude does not mean that there is anything wrong about sexual pleasure, any more than about the pleasure of eating. It means that you must not isolate that pleasure and try to get it by itself, any more than you ought to try to get the pleasures of taste without swallowing and digesting, by chewing things and spitting them out again.

As a consequence, Christianity teaches that marriage is for life. There is, of course, a difference here between different Churches: some do not admit divorce at all; some allow it reluctantly in very special cases. It is a great pity that Christians should disagree about such a question; but for an ordinary layman the thing to notice is that Churches all agree with one another about marriage a great deal more than any of them agrees with the outside world. I mean, they all regard divorce as something like cutting up a living body, as a kind of surgical operation. Some of them think the operation so violent that it cannot be done at all; others admit it as a desperate remedy in extreme cases. They are all agreed that it is more like having both your legs cut off than it is like dissolving a business partnership or even deserting a regiment. What they all disagree with is the modern view that it is a simple readjustment of partners, to be made whenever people feel they are no longer in love with one another, or when either of them falls in love with someone else.

Before we consider this modern view in its relation to chastity, we must not forget to consider it in relation to another virtue, namely justice. Justice, as I said before, includes the keeping of promises. Now everyone who has been married in a church has made a public, solemn promise to stick to his (or her) partner till death. The duty of keeping that promise has no special connection with sexual morality: it is in the same position as any other promise. If, as modern people are always telling us, the sexual impulse is just like all our other impulses, then it ought to be treated like all our other impulses; and as their indulgence is controlled by our promises, so should its be. If, as I think, it is not like all our other impulses, but is morbidly inflamed, then we should be especially careful not to let it lead us into dishonesty.

To this someone may reply that he regarded the promise made in church as a mere formality and never intended to keep it. Whom, then, was he trying to deceive when he made it? God? That was really very unwise. Himself? That was not very much wiser. The bride, or bridegroom, or the "in-laws"? That was treacherous. Most often, I think, the couple (or one of them) hoped to deceive the public. They wanted the respectability that is attached to marriage without intending to pay the price: that is, they were imposters, they cheated. If they are still contented cheats, I have nothing to say to them: who would urge the high and hard duty of chastity on people who have not yet wished to be merely honest? If they have now come to their senses and want to be honest, their promise, already made, constrains them. And this, you will see, comes under the heading of justice, not that of chastity. If people do not believe in permanent marriage, it is perhaps better that they should live together unmarried than that they should make vows they do not mean to keep. It is true that by living together without marriage they will be guilty (in Christian eyes) of fornication. But one fault is not mended by adding another: unchastity is not improved by adding perjury.

The idea that "being in love" is the only reason for remaining married really leaves no room for marriage as a contract or promise at all. If love is the whole thing, then the promise can add nothing; and if it adds nothing, then it should not be made. The curious thing is that lovers themselves, while they remain really in love, know this better than those who talk about love. As Chesterton pointed out, those who are in love have a natural inclination to bind themselves by promises. Love songs all over the world are full of vows of eternal constancy. The Christian law is not forcing upon the passion of love something which is foreign to that passion's own nature: it is demanding that lovers should take seriously something which their passion of itself impels them to do.

And, of course, the promise, made when I am in love and because I am in love, to be true to the beloved as long as I live, commits one to being true even if I cease to be in love. A promise must be about things that I can do, about actions: no one can promise to go on feeling in a certain way. He might as well promise never to have a headache or always to feel hungry. But what, it may be asked, is the use of keeping two people together if they are no longer in love? There are several sound, social reasons; to provide a home for their children, to protect the woman (who has probably sacrificed or damaged her own career by getting married) from being dropped whenever the man is tired of her. But there is also another reason of which I am very sure, though I find it a little hard to explain.

It is hard because so many people cannot be brought to realise that when B is better than C, A may be even better than B. They like thinking in terms of good and bad, not of good, better, and best, or bad, worse and worst. They want to know whether you think patriotism a good thing: if you reply that it is, of course, far better than individual selfishness, but that it is inferior to universal charity and should always give way to universal charity when the two conflict, they think you are being evasive. They ask what you think of duelling. If you reply that it is far better to forgive a man than to fight a duel with him, but that even a duel might be better than a lifelong enmity which expresses itself in secret efforts to "do the man down," they go away complaining that you would not give them a straight answer. I hope no one will make this mistake about what I am now going to say.

What we call "being in love" is a glorious state, and, in several ways, good for us. It helps to make us generous and courageous, it opens our eyes not only to the beauty of the beloved but to all beauty, and it subordinates (especially at first) our merely animal sexuality; in that sense, love is the great conqueror of lust. No one in his senses would deny that being in love is far better than either common sensuality or cold self-centredness. But, as I said before, "the most dangerous thing you can do is to take any one impulse of our own nature and set it up as the thing you ought to follow at all costs." Being in love is a good thing, but it is not the best thing. There are many things below it, but there are also things above it. You cannot make it the basis of a whole life. It is a noble feeling, but it is still a feeling. Now no feeling can be relied on to last in its full intensity, or even to last at all. Knowledge can last, principles can last, habits can last; but feelings come and go. And in fact, whatever people say, the state called "being in love" usually does not last. If the old fairy-tale ending "They lived happily ever after" is taken to mean "They felt for the next fifty years exactly as they felt the day before they were married," then it says what probably never was nor ever could be true, and would be highly undesirable if it were. Who could bear to live in that excitement for even five years? What would become of your work, your appetite, your sleep, your friendships? But, of course, ceasing to be "in love" need not mean ceasing to love. Love in this second sense—love as distinct from "being in love" is not merely a feeling. It is a deep unity, maintained by the will and deliberately strengthened by habit; reinforced by (in Christian marriages) the grace which both parents ask, and receive, from God. They can have this love for each other even at those moments when they do not like each other; as you love yourself even when you do not like yourself. They can retain this love even when each would easily, if they allowed themselves, be "in love" with someone else. "Being in love" first moved them to promise fidelity: this quieter love enables them to keep the promise. It is on this love that the engine of marriage is run: being in love was the explosion that started it.

If you disagree with me, of course, you will say, "He knows nothing about it, he is not married." You may quite possibly be right. But before you say that, make quite sure that you are judging me by what you really know from your own experience and from watching the lives of your friends, and not by ideas you have derived from novels and films. This is not so easy to do as people think. Our experience is coloured through and through by books and plays and the cinema, and it takes patience and skill to disentangle the things we have really learned from life for ourselves.

People get from books the idea that if you have married the right person you may expect to go on "being in love" for ever. As a result, when they find they are not, they think this proves they have made a mistake and are entitled to a change—not realising that, when they have changed, the glamour will presently go out of the new love just as it went out of the old one. In this department of life, as in every other, thrills come at the beginning and do not last. The sort of thrill a boy has at the first idea of flying will not go on when he has joined the R.A.F. and is really learning to fly. The thrill you feel on first seeing some delightful place dies away when you really go to live there. Does this mean it would be better not to learn to fly and not to live in the beautiful place? By no means. In both cases, if you go through with it, the dying away of the first thrill will be compensated for by a quieter and more lasting kind of interest. What is more (and I can hardly find words to tell you how important I think this), it is just the people who are ready to submit to the loss of the thrill and settle down to the sober interest, who are then most likely to meet new thrills in some quite different direction. The man who has learned to fly and becomes a good pilot will suddenly discover music; the man who has settled down to live in the beauty spot will discover gardening.

This is, I think, one little part of what Christ meant by saying that a thing will not really live unless it first dies. It is simply no good trying to keep any thrill: that is the very worst thing you can do. Let the thrill go—let it die away—go on through that period of death into the quieter interest and happiness that follow —and you will find you are living in a world of new thrills all the time. But if you decide to make thrills your regular diet and try to prolong them artificially, they will all get weaker and weaker, and fewer and fewer, and you will be a bored, disillusioned old man for the rest of your life. It is because so few people understand this that you find many middle-aged men and women maundering about their lost youth, at the very age when new horizons ought to be appearing and new doors opening all round them. It is much better fun to learn to swim than to go on endlessly (and hopelessly) trying to get back the feeling you had when you first went paddling as a small boy.

Another notion we get from novels and plays is that "falling in love" is something quite irresistible; something that just happens to one, like measles. And because they believe this, some married people throw up the sponge and give in when they find themselves attracted by a new acquaintance. But I am inclined to think that these irresistible passions are much rarer in real life than in books, at any rate when one is grown up. When we meet someone beautiful and clever and sympathetic, of course we ought, in one sense, to admire and love these good qualities. But is it not very largely in our own choice whether this love shall, or shall not, turn into what we call "being in love"? No doubt, if our minds are full of novels and plays and sentimental songs, and our bodies full of alcohol, we shall turn any love we feel into that kind of love: just as if you have a rut in your path all the rainwater will run into that rut, and if you wear blue spectacles everything you see will turn blue. But that will be our own fault.

Before leaving the question of divorce, I should like to distinguish two things which are very often confused. The Christian conception of marriage is one: the other is the quite different question—how far Christians, if they are voters or Members of Parliament, ought to try to force their views of marriage on the rest of the community by embodying them in the divorce laws. A great many people seem to think that if you are a Christian yourself you should try to make divorce difficult for every one. I do not think that. At least I know I should be very angry if the Mohammedans tried to prevent the rest of us from drinking wine. My own view is that the Churches should frankly recognise that the majority of the British people are not Christians and, therefore, cannot be expected to live Christian lives. There ought to be two distinct kinds of marriage: one governed by the State with rules enforced on all citizens, the other governed by the Church with rules enforced by her on her own members. The distinction ought to be quite sharp, so that a man knows which couples are married in a Christian sense and which are not.

So much for the Christian doctrine about the permanence of marriage. Something else, even more unpopular, remains to be dealt with. Christian wives promise to obey their husbands. In Christian marriage the man is said to be the "head." Two questions obviously arise here. (1) Why should there be a head at all —why not equality? (2) Why should it be the man?

(1) The need for some head follows from the idea that marriage is permanent. Of course, as long as the husband and wife are agreed, no question of a head need arise; and we may hope that this will be the normal state of affairs in a Christian marriage. But when there is a real disagreement, what is to happen? Talk it over, of course; but I am assuming they have done that and still failed to reach agreement. What do they do next? They cannot decide by a majority vote, for in a council of two there can be no majority. Surely, only one or other of two things can happen: either they must separate and go their own ways or else one or other of them must have a casting vote. If marriage is permanent, one or other party must, in the last resort, have the power of deciding the family policy. You cannot have a permanent association without a constitution.

(2) If there must be a head, why the man? Well, firstly, is there

any very serious wish that it should be the woman? As I have said, I am not married myself, but as far as I can see, even a woman who wants to be the head of her own house does not usually admire the same state of things when she finds it going on next door. She is much more likely to say "Poor Mr. X! Why he allows that appalling woman to boss him about the way she does is more than I can imagine." I do not think she is even very flattered if anyone mentions the fact of her own "headship." There must be something unnatural about the rule of wives over husbands, because the wives themselves are half ashamed of it and despise the husbands whom they rule. But there is also another reason; and here I speak quite frankly as a bachelor, because it is a reason you can see from outside even better than from inside. The relations of the family to the outer world—what might be called its foreign policy—must depend, in the last resort, upon the man, because he always ought to be, and usually is, much more just to the outsiders. A woman is primarily fighting for her own children and husband against the rest of the world. Naturally, almost, in a sense, rightly, their claims override, for her, all other claims. She is the special trustee of their interests. The function of the husband is to see that this natural preference of hers is not given its head. He has the last word in order to protect other people from the intense family patriotism of the wife. If anyone doubts this, let me ask a simple question. If your dog has bitten the child next door, or if your child has hurt the dog next door, which would you sooner have to deal with, the master of that house or the mistress? Or, if you are a married woman, let me ask you this question. Much as you admire your husband, would you not say that his chief failing is his tendency not to stick up for his rights and yours against the neighbours as vigorously as you would like? A bit of an Appeaser?

7·

FORGIVENESS

I said in a previous chapter that chastity was the most unpopular of the Christian virtues. But I am not sure I was right. I believe the one I have to talk of today is even more unpopular: the Christian rule, "Thou shalt love thy neighbour as thyself." Because in Christian morals "thy neighbour" includes "thy enemy," and so we come up against this terrible duty of forgiving our enemies.

Every one says forgiveness is a lovely idea, until they have something to forgive, as we had during the war. And then, to mention the subject at all is to be greeted with howls of anger. It is not that people think this too high and difficult a virtue: it is that they think it hateful and contemptible. "That sort of talk makes them sick," they say. And half of you already want to ask me, "I wonder how you'd feel about forgiving the Gestapo if you were a Pole or a Jew?"

So do I. I wonder very much. Just as when Christianity tells me that I must not deny my religion even to save myself from death by torture, I wonder very much what I should do when it came to the point. I am not trying to tell you in this book what I could do—I can do precious little—I am telling you what Christianity is. I did not invent it. And there, right in the middle of it, I find "Forgive us our sins as we forgive those that sin against us." There is no slightest suggestion that we are offered forgiveness on any other terms. It is made perfectly clear that if we do not forgive we shall not be forgiven. There are no two ways about it. What are we to do?

It is going to be hard enough, anyway, but I think there are two things we can do to make it easier. When you start mathematics you do not begin with the calculus; you begin with simple addition. In the same way, if we really want (but all depends on really wanting) to learn how to forgive, perhaps we had better start with something easier than the Gestapo. One might start with forgiving one's husband or wife, or parents or children, or the nearest N.C.O., for something they have done or said in the last week. That will probably keep us busy for the moment. And secondly, we might try to understand exactly what loving your neighbour as yourself means. I have to love him as I love myself. Well, how exactly do I love myself?

Now that I come to think of it, I have not exactly got a feeling of fondness or affection for myself, and I do not even always enjoy my own society. So apparently "Love your neighbour" does not mean "feel fond of him" or "find him attractive." I ought to have seen that before, because, of course, you cannot feel fond of a person by trying. Do I think well of myself, think myself a nice chap? Well, I am afraid I sometimes do (and those are, no doubt, my worst moments) but that is not why I love myself. In fact it is the other way round: my self-love makes me think myself nice, but thinking myself nice is not why I love myself. So loving my enemies does not apparently mean thinking them nice either. That is an enormous relief. For a good many people imagine that forgiving your enemies means making out that they are really not such bad fellows after all, when it is quite plain that they are. Go a step further. In my most clear-sighted moments not only do I not think myself a nice man, but I know that I am a very nasty one. I can look at some of the things I have done with horror and loathing. So apparently I am allowed to loathe and hate some of the things my enemies do. Now that I come to think of it, I remember Christian teachers telling me long ago that I must hate a bad man's actions, but not hate the bad man: or, as they would say, hate the sin but not the sinner.

For a long time I used to think this a silly, straw-splitting distinction: how could you hate what a man did and not hate the man? But years later it occurred to me that there was one man to whom I had been doing this all my life—namely myself. However much I might dislike my own cowardice or conceit or greed, I went on loving myself. There had never been the slightest difficulty about it. In fact the very reason why I hated the things was that I loved the man. Just because I loved myself, I was sorry to find that I was the sort of man who did those things. Consequently, Christianity does not want us to reduce by one atom the hatred we feel for cruelty and treachery. We ought to hate them. Not one word of what we have said about them needs to be unsaid. But it does want us to hate them in the same way in which we hate things in ourselves: being sorry that the man should have done such things, and hoping, if it is anyway possible, that somehow, some-time, somewhere, he can be cured and made human again.

The real test is this. Suppose one reads a story of filthy atrocities in the paper. Then suppose that something turns up suggesting that the story might not be quite true, or not quite so bad as it was made out. Is one's first feeling, "Thank God, even they aren't quite so bad as that," or is it a feeling of disappointment, and even a determination to cling to the first story for the sheer pleasure of thinking your enemies as bad as possible? If it is the second then it is, I am afraid, the first step in a process which, if followed to the end, will make us into devils. You see, one is beginning to wish that black was a little blacker. If we give that wish its head, later on we shall wish to see grey as black, and then to see white itself as black. Finally, we shall insist on seeing everything—God and our friends and ourselves included—as bad, and not be able to stop doing it: we shall be fixed for ever in a universe of pure hatred.

Now a step further. Does loving your enemy mean not punish-ing him? No, for loving myself does not mean that I ought not to subject myself to punishment—even to death. If one had com-mitted a murder, the right Christian thing to do would be to give yourself up to the police and be hanged. It is, therefore, in my opinion, perfectly right for a Christian judge to sentence a man to death or a Christian soldier to kill an enemy. I always have thought so, ever since I became a Christian, and long before the war, and I still think so now that we are at peace. It is no good quoting "Thou shalt not kill." There are two Greek words: the ordinary word to *kill* and the word to *murder*. And when Christ quotes that commandment He uses the *murder* one in all three accounts, Matthew, Mark, and Luke. And I am told there is the same distinction in Hebrew. All killing is not murder any more than all sexual intercourse is adultery. When soldiers came to St. John the Baptist asking what to do, he never remotely suggested that they ought to leave the army: nor did Christ when He met a Roman sergeant-major—what they called a centurion. The idea of the knight—the Christian in arms for the defence of a good cause—is one of the great Christian ideas. War is a dreadful thing, and I can respect an honest pacifist, though I think he is entirely mistaken. What I cannot understand is this sort of semipacifism you get nowadays which gives people the idea that though you have to fight, you ought to do it with a long face and as if you were ashamed of it. It is that feeling that robs lots of magnificent young Christians in the Services of something they have a right to, something which is the natural accompaniment of courage— a kind of gaity and wholeheartedness.

I have often thought to myself how it would have been if, when I served in the first world war, I and some young German had killed each other simultaneously and found ourselves together a moment after death. I cannot imagine that either of us would have felt any resentment or even any embarrassment. I think we might have laughed over it.

I imagine somebody will say, "Well, if one is allowed to condemn the enemy's acts, and punish him, and kill him, what difference is left between Christian morality and the ordinary view?" All the difference in the world. Remember, we Christians think man lives for ever. Therefore, what really matters is those little marks or twists on the central, inside part of the soul which are going to turn it, in the long run, into a heavenly or a hellish creature. We may kill if necessary, but we must not hate and enjoy hating. We may punish if necessary, but we must not enjoy it. In other words, something inside us, the feeling of resentment, the feeling that wants to get one's own back, must be simply killed. I do not mean that anyone can decide this moment that he will never feel it any more. That is not how things happen. I mean that every time it bobs its head up, day after day, year after year, all our lives long, we must hit it on the head. It is hard work, but the attempt is not impossible. Even while we kill and punish we must try to feel about the enemy as we feel about ourselves— to wish that he were not bad, to hope that he may, in this world or another, be cured: in fact, to wish his good. That is what is meant in the Bible by loving him: wishing his good, not feeling fond of him nor saying he is nice when he is not.

I admit that this means loving people who have nothing lovable about them. But then, has oneself anything lovable about it? You love it simply because it is yourself. God intends us to love all selves in the same way and for the same reason: but He has given us the sum ready worked out on our own case to show us how it works. We have then to go on and apply the rule to all the other selves. Perhaps it makes it easier if we remember that that is how He loves us. Not for any nice, attractive qualities we think we have, but just because we are the things called selves. For really there is nothing else in us to love: creatures like us who actually find hatred such a pleasure that to give it up is like giving up beer or tobacco. . . .

8.

THE GREAT SIN

Today I come to that part of Christian morals where they differ most sharply from all other morals. There is one vice of which no man in the world is free; which every one in the world loathes when he sees it in someone else; and of which hardly any people, except Chistians, ever imagine that they are guilty themselves. I have heard people admit that they are bad-tempered, or that they cannot keep their heads about girls or drink, or even that they are cowards. I do not think I have ever heard anyone who was not a Christian accuse himself of this vice. And at the same time I have very seldom met anyone, who was not a Christian, who showed the slightest mercy to it in others. There is no fault which makes a man more unpopular, and no fault which we are more unconscious of in ourselves. And the more we have it ourselves, the more we dislike it in others.

The vice I am talking of is Pride or Self-Conceit: and the virtue opposite to it, in Christian morals, is called Humility. You may remember, when I was talking about sexual morality, I warned you that the centre of Christian morals did not lie there. Well, now, we have come to the centre. According to Christian teachers, the essential vice, the utmost evil, is Pride. Unchastity, anger, greed, drunkenness, and all that, are mere fleabites in comparison: it was through Pride that the devil became the devil: Pride leads to every other vice: it is the complete anti-God state of mind.

Does this seem to you exaggerated? If so, think it over. I pointed out a moment ago that the more pride one had, the more one disliked pride in others. In fact, if you want to find out how proud you are the easiest way is to ask yourself, "How much do I dislike it when other people snub me, or refuse to take any notice of me,

or shove their oar in, or patronise me, or show off?" The point is
that each person's pride is in competition with every one else's
pride. It is because I wanted to be the big noise at the party that
I am so annoyed at someone else being the big noise. Two of a
trade never agree. Now what you want to get clear is that Pride
is *essentially* competitive—is competitive by its very nature—while
the other vices are competitive only, so to speak, by accident. Pride
gets no pleasure out of having something, only out of having more
of it than the next man. We say that people are proud of being
rich, or clever, or good-looking, but they are not. They are proud
of being richer, or cleverer, or better-looking than others. If every
one else became equally rich, or clever, or good-looking there
would be nothing to be proud about. It is the comparison that
makes you proud: the pleasure of being above the rest. Once the
element of competition has gone, pride has gone. That is why I
say that Pride is essentially competitive in a way the other vices
are not. The sexual impulse may drive two men into competition
if they both want the same girl. But that is only by accident; they
might just as likely have wanted two different girls. But a proud
man will take your girl from you, not because he wants her, but
just to prove to himself that he is a better man than you. Greed
may drive men into competition if there is not enough to go round:
but the proud man, even when he has got more than he can possibly want, will try to get still more just to assert his power. Nearly
all those evils in the world which people put down to greed or
selfishness are really far more the result of Pride.

Take it with money. Greed will certainly make a man want
money, for the sake of a better house, better holidays, better things
to eat and drink. But only up to a point. What is it that makes a
man with £10,000 a year anxious to get £20,000 a year? It is not
the greed for more pleasure. £10,000 will give all the luxuries that
any man can really enjoy. It is Pride—the wish to be richer than
some other rich man, and (still more) the wish for power. For, of
course, power is what Pride really enjoys: there is nothing makes
a man feel so superior to others as being able to move them about
like toy soldiers. What makes a pretty girl spread misery wherever
she goes by collecting admirers? Certainly not her sexual instinct:
that kind of girl is quite often sexually frigid. It is Pride. What is

it that makes a political leader or a whole nation go on and on, demanding more and more? Pride again. Pride is competitive by its very nature: that is why it goes on and on. If I am a proud man, then, as long as there is one man in the whole world more powerful, or richer, or cleverer than I, he is my rival and my enemy.

The Christians are right: it is Pride which has been the chief cause of misery in every nation and every family since the world began. Other vices may sometimes bring people together: you may find good fellowship and jokes and friendliness among drunken people or unchaste people. But Pride always means enmity—it *is* enmity. And not only enmity between man and man, but enmity to God.

In God you come up against something which is in every respect immeasurably superior to yourself. Unless you know God as that—and, therefore, know yourself as nothing in comparison—you do not know God at all. As long as you are proud you cannot know God. A proud man is always looking down on things and people: and, of course, as long as you are looking down, you cannot see something that is above you.

That raises a terrible question. How is it that people who are quite obviously eaten up with Pride can say they believe in God and appear to themselves very religious? I am afraid it means they are worshipping an imaginary God. They theoretically admit themselves to be nothing in the presence of this phantom God, but are really all the time imagining how He approves of them and thinks them far better than ordinary people: that is, they pay a pennyworth of imaginary humility to Him and get out of it a pound's worth of Pride towards their fellow-men. I suppose it was of those people Christ was thinking when He said that some would preach about Him and cast out devils in His name, only to be told at the end of the world that He had never known them. And any of us may at any moment be in this death-trap. Luckily, we have a test. Whenever we find that our religious life is making us feel that we are good—above all, that we are better than someone else—I think we may be sure that we are being acted on, not by God, but by the devil. The real test of being in the presence of God is that you either forget about yourself altogether or see yourself as a small, dirty object. It is better to forget about yourself altogether.

It is a terrible thing that the worst of all the vices can smuggle itself into the very centre of our religious life. But you can see why. The other, and less bad, vices come from the devil working on us through our animal nature. But this does not come through our animal nature at all. It comes direct from Hell. It is purely spiritual: consequently it is far more subtle and deadly. For the same reason, Pride can often be used to beat down the simpler vices. Teachers, in fact, often appeal to a boy's Pride, or, as they call it, his self-respect, to make him behave decently: many a man has overcome cowardice, or lust, or ill-temper by learning to think that they are beneath his dignity—that is, by Pride. The devil laughs. He is perfectly content to see you becoming chaste and brave and self-controlled provided, all the time, he is setting up in you the Dictatorship of Pride—just as he would be quite content to see your chilblains cured if he was allowed, in return, to give you cancer. For Pride is spiritual cancer: it eats up the very possibility of love, or contentment, or even common sense.

Before leaving this subject I must guard against some possible misunderstandings:

(1) Pleasure in being praised is not Pride. The child who is patted on the back for doing a lesson well, the woman whose beauty is praised by her lover, the saved soul to whom Christ says "Well done," are pleased and ought to be. For here the pleasure lies not in what you are but in the fact that you have pleased someone you wanted (and rightly wanted) to please. The trouble begins when you pass from thinking, "I have pleased him; all is well," to thinking, "What a fine person I must be to have done it." The more you delight in yourself and the less you delight in the praise, the worse you are becoming. When you delight wholly in yourself and do not care about the praise at all, you have reached the bottom. That is why vanity, though it is the sort of Pride which shows most on the surface, is really the least bad and most pardonable sort. The vain person wants praise, applause, admiration, too much and is always angling for it. It is a fault, but a childlike and even (in an odd way) a humble fault. It shows that

you are not yet completely contented with your own admiration. You value other people enough to want them to look at you. You are, in fact, still human. The real black, diabolical Pride comes when you look down on others so much that you do not care what they think of you. Of course, it is very right, and often our duty, not to care what people think of us, if we do so for the right reason; namely, because we care so incomparably more what God thinks. But the Proud man has a different reason for not caring. He says "Why should I care for the applause of that rabble as if their opinion were worth anything? And even if their opinions were of value, am I the sort of man to blush with pleasure at a compliment like some chit of a girl at her first dance? No, I am an integrated, adult personality. All I have done has been done to satisfy my own ideals—or my artistic conscience—or the traditions of my family— or, in a word, because I'm That Kind of Chap. If the mob like it, let them. They're nothing to me." In this way real thoroughgoing Pride may act as a check on vanity; for, as I said a moment ago, the devil loves "curing" a small fault by giving you a great one. We must try not to be vain, but we must never call in our Pride to cure our vanity; better the frying-pan than the fire.

(2) We say in English that a man is "proud" of his son, or his father, or his school, or regiment, and it may be asked whether "pride" in this sense is a sin. I think it depends on what, exactly, we mean by "proud of." Very often, in such sentences, the phrase "is proud of" means "has a warm-hearted admiration for." Such an admiration is, of course, very far from being a sin. But it might, perhaps, mean that the person in question gives himself airs on the ground of his distinguished father, or because he belongs to a famous regiment. This would, clearly, be a fault; but even then, it would be better than being proud simply of himself. To love and admire anything outside yourself is to take one step away from utter spiritual ruin; though we shall not be well so long as we love and admire anything more than we love and admire God.

(3) We must not think Pride is something God forbids because He is offended at it, or that Humility is something He demands as due to His own dignity—as if God Himself was proud. He is not in the least worried about His dignity. The point is, He wants

you to know Him: wants to give you Himself. And He and you are two things of such a kind that if you really get into any kind of touch with Him you will, in fact, be humble—delightedly humble, feeling the infinite relief of having for once got rid of all the silly nonsense about your own dignity which has made you restless and unhappy all your life. He is trying to make you humble in order to make this moment possible: trying to take off a lot of silly, ugly, fancy-dress in which we have all got ourselves up and are strutting about like the little idiots we are. I wish I had got a bit further with humility myself: if I had, I could probably tell you more about the relief, the comfort, of taking the fancy-dress off—getting rid of the false self, with all its "Look at me" and "Aren't I a good boy?" and all its posing and posturing. To get even near it, even for a moment, is like a drink of cold water to a man in a desert.

(4) Do not imagine that if you meet a really humble man he will be what most people call "humble" nowadays: he will not be a sort of greasy, smarmy person, who is always telling you that, of course, he is nobody. Probably all you will think about him is that he seemed a cheerful, intelligent chap who took a real interest in what *you* said to *him*. If you do dislike him it will be because you feel a little envious of anyone who seems to enjoy life so easily. He will not be thinking about humility: he will not be thinking about himself at all.

If anyone would like to acquire humility, I can, I think, tell him the first step. The first step is to realise that one is proud. And a biggish step, too. At least, nothing whatever can be done before it. If you think you are not conceited, it means you are very conceited indeed.

9.

CHARITY

I said in an earlier chapter that there were four "Cardinal" virtues and three "Theological" virtues. The three Theological ones are Faith, Hope, and Charity. Faith is going to be dealt with in the last two chapters. Charity was partly dealt with in Chapter 7, but there I concentrated on that part of Charity which is called Forgiveness. I now want to add a little more.

First, as to the meaning of the word. "Charity" now means simply what used to be called "alms"—that is, giving to the poor. Originally it had a much wider meaning. (You can see how it got the modern sense. If a man has "charity," giving to the poor is one of the most obvious things he does, and so people came to talk as if that were the whole of charity. In the same way, "rhyme" is the most obvious thing about poetry, and so people come to mean by "poetry" simply rhyme and nothing more.) Charity means "Love, in the Christian sense." But love, in the Christian sense, does not mean an emotion. It is a state not of the feelings but of the will; that state of the will which we have naturally about ourselves, and must learn to have about other people.

I pointed out in the chapter on Forgiveness that our love for ourselves does not mean that we *like* ourselves. It means that we wish our own good. In the same way Christian Love (or Charity) for our neighbours is quite a different thing from liking or affection. We "like" or are "fond of" some people, and not of others. It is important to understand that this natural "liking" is neither a sin nor a virtue, any more than your likes and dislikes in food are a sin or a virtue. It is just a fact. But, of course, what we do about it is either sinful or virtuous.

Natural liking or affection for people makes it easier to be "charitable" towards them. It is, therefore, normally a duty to encourage our affections—to "like" people as much as we can (just as it is often our duty to encourage our liking for exercise or wholesome food)—not because this liking is itself the virtue of charity, but because it is a help to it. On the other hand, it is also necessary to keep a very sharp look-out for fear our liking for some one person makes us uncharitable, or even unfair, to some-one else. There are even cases where our liking conflicts with our charity towards the person we like. For example, a doting mother may be tempted by natural affection to "spoil" her child; that is, to gratify her own affectionate impulses at the expense of the child's real happiness later on.

But though natural likings should normally be encouraged, it would be quite wrong to think that the way to become chari-table is to sit trying to manufacture affectionate feelings. Some people are "cold" by temperament; that may be a misfortune for them, but it is no more a sin than having a bad digestion is a sin; and it does not cut them out from the chance, or excuse them from the duty, of learning charity. The rule for all of us is per-fectly simple. Do not waste time bothering whether you "love" your neighbour; act as if you did. As soon as we do this we find one of the great secrets. When you are behaving as if you loved someone, you will presently come to love him. If you injure some-one you dislike, you will find yourself disliking him more. If you do him a good turn, you will find yourself disliking him less. There is, indeed, one exception. If you do him a good turn, not to please God and obey the law of charity, but to show him what a fine forgiving chap you are, and to put him in your debt, and then sit down to wait for his "gratitude," you will probably be dis-appointed. (People are not fools: they have a very quick eye for anything like showing off, or patronage.) But whenever we do good to another self, just because it is a self, made (like us) by God, and desiring its own happiness as we desire ours, we shall have learned to love it a little more or, at least, to dislike it less.

Consequently, though Christian charity sounds a very cold thing to people whose heads are full of sentimentality, and though it is quite distinct from affection, yet it leads to affection. The differ-ence between a Christian and a worldly man is not that the worldly

man has only affections or "likings" and the Christian has only
"charity." The worldly man treats certain people kindly because
he "likes" them: the Christian, trying to treat every one kindly,
finds himself liking more and more people as he goes on—including people he could not even have imagined himself liking at the
beginning.

This same spiritual law works terribly in the opposite direction.
The Germans, perhaps, at first ill-treated the Jews because they
hated them: afterwards they hated them much more because they
had ill-treated them. The more cruel you are, the more you will
hate; and the more you hate, the more cruel you will become—and
so on in a vicious circle for ever.

Good and evil both increase at compound interest. That is
why the little decisions you and I make every day are of such
infinite importance. The smallest good act today is the capture
of a strategic point from which, a few months later, you may be
able to go on to victories you never dreamed of. An apparently
trivial indulgence in lust or anger today is the loss of a ridge or
railway line or bridgehead from which the enemy may launch an
attack otherwise impossible.

Some writers use the word charity to describe not only Christian
love between human beings, but also God's love for man and man's
love for God. About the second of these two, people are often
worried. They are told they ought to love God. They cannot find
any such feeling in themselves. What are they to do? The answer
is the same as before. Act as if you did. Do not sit trying to manufacture feelings. Ask yourself, "If I were sure that I loved God,
what would I do?" When you have found the answer, go and do it.

On the whole, God's love for us is a much safer subject to think
about than our love for Him. Nobody can always have devout feelings: and even if we could, feelings are not what God principally
cares about. Christian Love, either towards God or towards man,
is an affair of the will. If we are trying to do His will we are obeying the commandment, "Thou shalt love the Lord thy God." He
will give us feelings of love if He pleases. We cannot create them
for ourselves, and we must not demand them as a right. But the
great thing to remember is that, though our feelings come and go,

His love for us does not. It is not wearied by our sins, or our indifference; and, therefore, it is quite relentless in its determination that we shall be cured of those sins, at whatever cost to us, at whatever cost to Him.

IO.

HOPE

Hope is one of the Theological virtues. This means that a continual looking forward to the eternal world is not (as some modern people think) a form of escapism or wishful thinking, but one of the things a Christian is meant to do. It does not mean that we are to leave the present world as it is. If you read history you will find that the Christians who did most for the present world were just those who thought most of the next. The Apostles themselves, who set on foot the conversion of the Roman Empire, the great men who built up the Middle Ages, the English Evangelicals who abolished the Slave Trade, all left their mark on Earth, precisely because their minds were occupied with Heaven. It is since Christians have largely ceased to think of the other world that they have become so ineffective in this. Aim at Heaven and you will get earth "thrown in": aim at earth and you will get neither. It seems a strange rule, but something like it can be seen at work in other matters. Health is a great blessing, but the moment you make health one of your main, direct objects you start becoming a crank and imagining there is something wrong with you. You are only likely to get health provided you want other things more —food, games, work, fun, open air. In the same way, we shall never save civilisation as long as civilisation is our main object. We must learn to want something else even more.

Most of us find it very difficult to want "Heaven" at all—except in so far as "Heaven" means meeting again our friends who have died. One reason for this difficulty is that we have not been trained: our whole education tends to fix our minds on this world. Another reason is that when the real want for Heaven is present in us, we do not recognise it. Most people, if they had really learned to look into their own hearts, would know that they do want, and want acutely, something that cannot be had in this world. There are all sorts of things in this world that offer to give it to you, but they never quite keep their promise. The longings which arise in us when we first fall in love, or first think of some foreign country, or first take up some subject that excites us, are longings which no marriage, no travel, no learning, can really satisfy. I am not now speaking of what would be ordinarily called unsuccessful marriages, or holidays, or learned careers. I am speaking of the best possible ones. There was something we grasped at, in that first moment of longing, which just fades away in the reality. I think everyone knows what I mean. The wife may be a good wife, and the hotels and scenery may have been excellent, and chemistry may be a very interesting job: but something has evaded us. Now there are two wrong ways of dealing with this fact, and one right one.

(1) The Fool's Way.—He puts the blame on the things themselves. He goes on all his life thinking that if only he tried another woman, or went for a more expensive holiday, or whatever it is, then, this time, he really would catch the mysterious something we are all after. Most of the bored, discontented, rich people in the world are of this type. They spend their whole lives trotting from woman to woman (through the divorce courts), from continent to continent, from hobby to hobby, always thinking that the latest is "the Real Thing" at last, and always disappointed.

(2) The Way of the Disillusioned "Sensible Man."—He soon decides that the whole thing was moonshine. "Of course," he says, "one feels like that when one's young. But by the time you get to my age you've given up chasing the rainbow's end." And so he settles down and learns not to expect too much and represses the part of himself which used, as he would say, "to cry for the moon." This is, of course, a much better way than the first, and makes a man much happier, and less of a nuisance to society. It tends to make him a prig (he is apt to be rather superior towards what he calls "adolescents"), but, on the whole, he rubs along fairly comfortably. It would be the best line we could take if man did not live for ever. But supposing infinite happiness really is there, waiting for us? Supposing one really can reach the rainbow's end? In that case it would be a pity to find out too late (a moment after

death) that by our supposed "common sense" we had stifled in ourselves the faculty of enjoying it.

(3) The Christian Way.—The Christian says, "Creatures are not born with desires unless satisfaction for those desires exists. A baby feels hunger: well, there is such a thing as food. A duckling wants to swim: well, there is such a thing as water. Men feel sexual desire: well, there is such a thing as sex. If I find in myself a desire which no experience in this world can satisfy, the most probable explanation is that I was made for another world. If none of my earthly pleasures satisfy it, that does not prove that the universe is a fraud. Probably earthly pleasures were never meant to satisfy it, but only to arouse it, to suggest the real thing. If that is so, I must take care, on the one hand, never to despise, or be unthankful for, these earthly blessings, and on the other, never to mistake them for the something else of which they are only a kind of copy, or echo, or mirage. I must keep alive in myself the desire for my true country, which I shall not find till after death; I must never let it get snowed under or turned aside; I must make it the main object of life to press on to that other country and to help others to do the same."

There is no need to be worried by facetious people who try to make the Christian hope of "Heaven" ridiculous by saying they do not want "to spend eternity playing harps." The answer to such people is that if they cannot understand books written for grown-ups, they should not talk about them. All the scriptural imagery (harps, crowns, gold, etc.) is, of course, a merely symbolical attempt to express the inexpressible. Musical instruments are mentioned because for many people (not all) music is the thing known in the present life which most strongly suggests ecstasy and infinity. Crowns are mentioned to suggest the fact that those who are united with God in eternity share His splendour and power and joy. Gold is mentioned to suggest the timelessness of Heaven (gold does not rust) and the preciousness of it. People who take these symbols literally might as well think that when Christ told us to be like doves, He meant that we were to lay eggs.

I I.

FAITH

I must talk in this chapter about what the Christians call Faith. Roughly speaking, the word Faith seems to be used by Christians in two senses or on two levels, and I will take them in turn. In the first sense it means simply Belief—accepting or regarding as true the doctrines of Christianity. That is fairly simple. But what does puzzle people—at least it used to puzzle me—is the fact that Christians regard faith in this sense as a virtue. I used to ask how on earth it can be a virtue—what is there moral or immoral about believing or not believing a set of statements? Obviously, I used to say, a sane man accepts or rejects any statement, not because he wants or does not want to, but because the evidence seems to him good or bad. If he were mistaken about the goodness or badness of the evidence that would not mean he was a bad man, but only that he was not very clever. And if he thought the evidence bad but tried to force himself to believe in spite of it, that would be merely stupid.

Well, I think I still take that view. But what I did not see then—and a good many people do not see still—was this. I was assuming that if the human mind once accepts a thing as true it will automatically go on regarding it as true, until some real reason for reconsidering it turns up. In fact, I was assuming that the human mind is completely ruled by reason. But that is not so. For example, my reason is perfectly convinced by good evidence that anæsthetics do not smother me and that properly trained surgeons do not start operating until I am unconscious. But that does not alter the fact that when they have me down on the table and clap their horrible mask over my face, a mere childish panic begins inside me. I start thinking I am going to choke, and I am afraid they will start cut-

107

ting me up before I am properly under. In other words, I lose my faith in anæsthetics. It is not reason that is taking away my faith: on the contrary, my faith is based on reason. It is my imagination and emotions. The battle is between faith and reason on one side and emotion and imagination on the other.

When you think of it you will see lots of instances of this. A man knows, on perfectly good evidence, that a pretty girl of his acquaintance is a liar and cannot keep a secret and ought not to be trusted; but when he finds himself with her his mind loses its faith in that bit of knowledge and he starts thinking, "Perhaps she'll be different this time," and once more makes a fool of himself and tells her something he ought not to have told her. His senses and emotions have destroyed his faith in what he really knows to be true. Or take a boy learning to swim. His reason knows perfectly well that an unsupported human body will not necessarily sink in water: he has seen dozens of people float and swim. But the whole question is whether he will be able to go on believing this when the instructor takes away his hand and leaves him unsupported in the water—or whether he will suddenly cease to believe it and get in a fright and go down.

Now just the same thing happens about Christianity. I am not asking anyone to accept Christianity if his best reasoning tells him that the weight of the evidence is against it. That is not the point at which Faith comes in. But supposing a man's reason once decides that the weight of the evidence is for it. I can tell that man what is going to happen to him in the next few weeks. There will come a moment when there is bad news, or he is in trouble, or is living among a lot of other people who do not believe it, and all at once his emotions will rise up and carry out a sort of blitz on his belief. Or else there will come a moment when he wants a woman, or wants to tell a lie, or feels very pleased with himself, or sees a chance of making a little money in some way that is not per- fectly fair: some moment, in fact, at which it would be very con- venient if Christianity were not true. And once again his wishes and desires will carry out a blitz. I am not talking of moments at which any real new reasons against Christianity turn up. Those have to be faced and that is a different matter. I am talking about moments where a mere mood rises up against it.

Now Faith, in the sense in which I am here using the word, is the art of holding on to things your reason has once accepted, in spite of your changing moods. For moods will change, whatever view your reason takes. I know that by experience. Now that I am a Christian I do have moods in which the whole thing looks very improbable: but when I was an atheist I had moods in which Christianity looked terribly probable. This rebellion of your moods against your real self is going to come anyway. That is why Faith is such a necessary virtue: unless you teach your moods "where they get off," you can never be either a sound Christian or even a sound atheist, but just a creature dithering to and fro, with its beliefs really dependent on the weather and the state of its digestion. Consequently one must train the habit of Faith.

The first step is to recognise the fact that your moods change. The next is to make sure that, if you have once accepted Christianity, then some of its main doctrines shall be deliberately held before your mind for some time every day. That is why daily prayer and religious reading and churchgoing are necessary parts of the Christian life. We have to be continually reminded of what we believe. Neither this belief nor any other will automatically remain alive in the mind. It must be fed. And as a matter of fact, if you examined a hundred people who had lost their faith in Christianity, I wonder how many of them would turn out to have been reasoned out of it by honest argument? Do not most people simply drift away?

Now I must turn to Faith in the second or higher sense: and this is the most difficult thing I have tackled yet. I want to approach it by going back to the subject of Humility. You may remember I said that the first step towards humility was to realise that one is proud. I want to add now that the next step is to make some serious attempt to practise the Christian virtues. A week is not enough. Things often go swimmingly for the first week. Try six weeks. By that time, having, as far as one can see, fallen back completely or even fallen lower than the point one began from, one will have discovered some truths about oneself. No man knows how bad he is till he has tried very hard to be good. A silly idea is current that good people do not know what temptation means. This is an obvious lie. Only those who try to resist temptation

know how strong it is. After all, you find out the strength of the
German army by fighting against it, not by giving in. You find out
the strength of a wind by trying to walk against it, not by lying
down. A man who gives in to temptation after five minutes simply
does not know what it would have been like an hour later. That is
why bad people, in one sense, know very little about badness.
They have lived a sheltered life by always giving in. We never find
out the strength of the evil impulse inside us until we try to fight
it: and Christ, because He was the only man who never yielded
to temptation, is also the only man who knows to the full what
temptation means—the only complete realist. Very well, then. The
main thing we learn from a serious attempt to practise the Christian virtues is that we fail. If there was any idea that God had set us
a sort of exam. and that we might get good marks by deserving
them, that has to be wiped out. If there was any idea of a sort of
bargain—any idea that we could perform our side of the contract
and thus put God in our debts so that it was up to Him, in mere
justice, to perform His side—that has to be wiped out.

I think every one who has some vague belief in God, until he
becomes a Christian, has the idea of an exam. or of a bargain in
his mind. The first result of real Christianity is to blow that idea
into bits. When they find it blown into bits, some people think
this means that Christianity is a failure and give up. They seem to
imagine that God is very simple-minded! In fact, of course, He
knows all about this. One of the very things Christianity was designed to do was to blow this idea to bits. God has been waiting for
the moment at which you discover that there is no question of
earning a pass mark in this exam. or putting Him in your debt.

Then comes another discovery. Every faculty you have, your
power of thinking or of moving your limbs from moment to moment, is given you by God. If you devoted every moment of your
whole life exclusively to His service you could not give Him anything that was not in a sense His own already. So that when we talk
of a man doing anything for God or giving anything to God, I will
tell you what it is really like. It is like a small child going to its
father and saying, "Daddy, give me sixpence to buy you a birthday
present." Of course, the father does, and he is pleased with the
child's present. It is all very nice and proper, but only an idiot

would think that the father is sixpence to the good on the transaction. When a man has made these two discoveries God can really get to work. It is after this that real life begins. The man is awake now. We can now go on to talk of Faith in the second sense.

I 2.

FAITH

I want to start by saying something that I would like everyone to notice carefully. It is this. If this chapter means nothing to you, if it seems to be trying to answer questions you never asked, drop it at once. Do not bother about it at all. There are certain things in Christianity that can be understood from the outside, before you have become a Christian. But there are a great many things that cannot be understood until after you have gone a certain distance along the Christian road. These things are purely practical, though they do not look as if they were. They are directions for dealing with particular cross-roads and obstacles on the journey and they do not make sense until a man has reached those places. Whenever you find any statement in Christian writings which you can make nothing of, do not worry. Leave it alone. There will come a day, perhaps years later, when you suddenly see what it meant. If one could understand it now, it would only do one harm.

Of course all this tells against me as much as anyone else. The thing I am going to try to explain in this chapter may be ahead of me. I may be thinking I have got there when I have not. I can only ask instructed Christians to watch very carefully, and tell me when I go wrong; and others to take what I say with a grain of salt— as something offered, because it may be a help, not because I am certain that I am right.

I am trying to talk about Faith in the second sense, the higher sense. I said last week that the question of Faith in this sense arises after a man has tried his level best to practise the Christian virtues, and found that he fails, and seen that even if he could he would only be giving back to God what was already God's own.

In other words, he discovers his bankruptcy. Now, once again, what God cares about is not exactly our actions. What he cares about is that we should be creatures of a certain kind or quality— the kind of creatures He intended us to be—creatures related to Himself in a certain way. I do not add "and related to one another in a certain way," because that is included: if you are right with Him you will inevitably be right with all your fellow-creatures, just as if all the spokes of a wheel are fitted rightly into the hub and the rim they are bound to be in the right positions to one another. And as long as a man is thinking of God as an examiner who has set him a sort of paper to do, or as the opposite party in a sort of bargain—as long as he is thinking of claims and counter-claims between himself and God—he is not yet in the right relation to Him. He is misunderstanding what he is and what God is. And he cannot get into the right relation until he has discovered the fact of our bankruptcy.

When I say "discovered," I mean really discovered: not simply said it parrot-fashion. Of course, any child, if given a certain kind of religious education, will soon learn to *say* that we have nothing to offer to God that is not already His own and that we find ourselves failing to offer even that without keeping something back. But I am talking of really discovering this: really finding out by experience that it is true.

Now we cannot, in that sense, discover our failure to keep God's law except by trying our very hardest (and then failing). Unless we really try, whatever we say there will always be at the back of our minds the idea that if we try harder next time we shall succeed in being completely good. Thus, in one sense, the road back to God is a road of moral effort, of trying harder and harder. But in another sense it is not trying that is ever going to bring us home. All this trying leads up to the vital moment at which you turn to God and say, "You must do this. I can't." Do not, I implore you, start asking yourselves, "Have I reached that moment?" Do not sit down and start watching your own mind to see if it is coming along. That puts a man quite on the wrong track. When the most important things in our life happen we quite often do not know, at the moment, what is going on. A man does not always say to himself, "Hullo! I'm growing up." It is often only when he looks back that he realises what has happened and recognises it as what people call "growing up." You can see it even in simple matters. A man who starts anxiously watching to see whether he is going to sleep is very likely to remain wide awake. As well, the thing I am talking of now may not happen to every one in a sudden flash—as it did to St. Paul or Bunyan: it may be so gradual that no one could ever point to a particular hour or even a particular year. And what matters is the nature of the change in itself, not how we feel while it is happening. It is the change from being confident about our own efforts to the state in which we despair of doing anything for ourselves and leave it to God.

I know the words "leave it to God" can be misunderstood, but they must stay for the moment. The sense in which a Christian leaves it to God is that he puts all his trust in Christ: trusts that Christ will somehow share with him the perfect human obedience which He carried out from His birth to His crucifixion: that Christ will make the man more like Himself and, in a sense, make good his deficiencies. In Christian language, He will share His "sonship" with us, will make us, like Himself, "Sons of God": in Book IV I shall attempt to analyse the meaning of those words a little further. If you like to put it that way, Christ offers something for nothing: He even offers everything for nothing. In a sense, the whole Christian life consists in accepting that very remarkable offer. But the difficulty is to reach the point of recognising that all we have done and can do is nothing. What we should have liked would be for God to count our good points and ignore our bad ones. Again, in a sense, you may say that no temptation is ever overcome until we stop trying to overcome it— throw up the sponge. But then you could not "stop trying" in the right way and for the right reason until you had tried your very hardest. And, in yet another sense, handing everything over to Christ does not, of course, mean that you stop trying. To trust Him means, of course, trying to do all that He says. There would be no sense in saying you trusted a person if you would not take his advice. Thus if you have really handed yourself over to Him, it must follow that you are trying to obey Him. But trying in a new way, a less worried way. Not doing these things in order to be saved, but because He has begun to save you already. Not hoping to get to Heaven as a reward for your actions, but inevitably wanting to act in a certain way because a first faint gleam of Heaven is already inside you.

Christians have often disputed as to whether what leads the Christian home is good actions, or Faith in Christ. I have no right really to speak on such a difficult question, but it does seem to me like asking which blade in a pair of scissors is most necessary. A serious moral effort is the only thing that will bring you to the point where you throw up the sponge. Faith in Christ is the only thing to save you from despair at that point: and out of that Faith in Him good actions must inevitably come. There are two parodies of the truth which different sets of Christians have, in the past, been accused by other Christians of believing: perhaps they may make the truth clearer. One set were accused of saying, "Good actions are all that matters. The best good action is charity. The best kind of charity is giving money. The best thing to give money to is the Church. So hand us over £10,000 and we will see you through." The answer to that nonsense, of course, would be that good actions done for that motive, done with the idea that Heaven can be bought, would not be good actions at all, but only commercial speculations. The other set were accused of saying, "Faith is all that matters. Consequently, if you have faith, it doesn't matter what you do. Sin away, my lad, and have a good time and Christ will see that it makes no difference in the end." The answer to that nonsense is that, if what you call your "faith" in Christ does not involve taking the slightest notice of what He says, then it is not Faith at all—not faith or trust in Him, but only intellectual acceptance of some theory about Him.

The Bible really seems to clinch the matter when it puts the two things together into one amazing sentence. The first half is, "Work out your own salvation with fear and trembling"—which looks as if everything depended on us and our good actions: but the second half goes on, "For it is God who worketh in you"—which looks as if God did everything and we nothing. I am afraid that is the sort of thing we come up against in Christianity. I am puzzled, but I am not surprised. You see, we are now trying to understand, and to separate into water-tight compartments, what exactly God does and what man does when God and man are working together. And, of course, we begin by thinking it is like two men working together, so that you could say, "He did this bit and I did that." But this way of thinking breaks down. God is not like that. He is inside you as well as outside: even if we could understand who did what, I do not think human language could properly express it. In the attempt to express it different Churches say different things. But you will find that even those who insist most strongly on the importance of good actions tell you you need Faith; and even those who insist most strongly on Faith tell you to do good actions. At any rate that is as far as I go.

I think all Christians would agree with me if I said that though Christianity seems at first to be all about morality, all about duties and rules and guilt and virtue, yet it leads you on, out of all that, into something beyond. One has a glimpse of a country where they do not talk of those things, except perhaps as a joke. Every one there is filled full with what we should call goodness as a mirror is filled with light. But they do not call it goodness. They do not call it anything. They are not thinking of it. They are too busy looking at the source from which it comes. But this is near the stage where the road passes over the rim of our world. No one's eyes can see very far beyond that: lots of people's eyes can see further than mine.

BOOK IV

**BEYOND PERSONALITY: or FIRST STEPS
IN THE DOCTRINE OF THE TRINITY**

I.

MAKING AND BEGETTING

Everyone has warned me not to tell you what I am going to tell you in this last book. They all say "the ordinary reader does not want Theology; give him plain practical religion." I have rejected their advice. I do not think the ordinary reader is such a fool. Theology means "the science of God," and I think any man who wants to think about God at all would like to have the clearest and most accurate ideas about Him which are available. You are not children: why should you be treated like children?

In a way I quite understand why some people are put off by Theology. I remember once when I had been giving a talk to the R.A.F., an old, hard-bitten officer got up and said, "I've no use for all that stuff. But, mind you, I'm a religious man too. I *know* there's a God. I've *felt* Him: out alone in the desert at night: the tremendous mystery. And that's just why I don't believe all your neat little dogmas and formulas about Him. To anyone who's met the real thing they all seem so petty and pedantic and unreal!"

Now in a sense I quite agreed with that man. I think he had probably had a real experience of God in the desert. And when he turned from that experience to the Christian creeds, I think he really was turning from something real to something less real. In the same way, if a man has once looked at the Atlantic from the beach, and then goes and looks at a map of the Atlantic, he also will be turning from something real to something less real: turning from real waves to a bit of coloured paper. But here comes the point. The map is admittedly only coloured paper, but there are two things you have to remember about it. In the first place, it is based on what hundreds and thousands of people have found out by sailing the real Atlantic. In that way it has behind it masses of experience just as real as the one you could have from the beach; only, while yours would be a single isolated glimpse, the map fits all those different experiences together. In the second place, if you want to go anywhere, the map is absolutely necessary. As long as you are content with walks on the beach, your own glimpses are far more fun than looking at a map. But the map is going to be more use than walks on the beach if you want to get to America.

Now, Theology is like the map. Merely learning and thinking about the Christian doctrines, if you stop there, is less real and less exciting than the sort of thing my friend got in the desert. Doctrines are not God: they are only a kind of map. But that map is based on the experience of hundreds of people who really were in touch with God—experiences compared with which any thrills or pious feelings you and I are likely to get on our own are very elementary and very confused. And secondly, if you want to get any further, you must use the map. You see, what happened to that man in the desert may have been real, and was certainly exciting, but nothing comes of it. It leads nowhere. There is nothing to do about it. In fact, that is just why a vague religion—all about feeling God in nature, and so on—is so attractive. It is all thrills and no work; like watching the waves from the beach. But you will not get to Newfoundland by studying the Atlantic that way, and you will not get eternal life by simply feeling the presence of God in flowers or music. Neither will you get anywhere by looking at maps without going to sea. Nor will you be very safe if you go to sea without a map.

In other words, Theology is practical: especially now. In the old days, when there was less education and discussion, perhaps it was possible to get on with a very few simple ideas about God. But it is not so now. Everyone reads, everyone hears things discussed. Consequently, if you do not listen to Theology, that will not mean that you have no ideas about God. It will mean that you have a lot of wrong ones—bad, muddled, out-of-date ideas. For a great many of the ideas about God which are trotted out as novelties today, are simply the ones which real Theologians tried centuries ago and rejected. To believe in the popular religion of modern England is retrogression—like believing the earth is flat.

For when you get down to it, is not the popular idea of Christianity simply this: that Jesus Christ was a great moral teacher and that if only we took his advice we might be able to establish a better social order and avoid another war? Now, mind you, that is quite true. But it tells you much less than the whole truth about Christianity and it has no practical importance at all.

It is quite true that if we took Christ's advice we should soon be living in a happier world. You need not even go as far as Christ. If we did all that Plato or Aristotle or Confucius told us, we should get on a great deal better than we do. And so what? We never have followed the advice of the great teachers. Why are we likely to begin now? Why are we more likely to follow Christ than any of the others? Because he is the best moral teacher? But that makes it even less likely that we shall follow him. If we cannot take the elementary lessons, is it likely we are going to take the most advanced one? If Christianity only means one more bit of good advice, then Christianity is of no importance. There has been no lack of good advice for the last four thousand years. A bit more makes no difference.

But as soon as you look at any real Christian writings, you find that they are talking about something quite different from this popular religion. They say that Christ is the Son of God (whatever that means). They say that those who give Him their confidence can also become Sons of God (whatever that means). They say that His death saved us from our sins (whatever that means).

There is no good complaining that these statements are difficult. Christianity claims to be telling us about another world, about something behind the world we can touch and hear and see. You may think the claim false; but if it were true, what it tells us would be bound to be difficult—at least as difficult as modern Physics, and for the same reason.

Now the point in Christianity which gives us the greatest shock is the statement that by attaching ourselves to Christ, we can "become Sons of God." One asks "Aren't we Sons of God already? Surely the fatherhood of God is one of the main Christian ideas?" Well, in a certain sense, no doubt we are sons of God already. I mean, God has brought us into existence and loves us and looks after us, and in that way is like a father. But when the Bible talks of our "becoming" Sons of God, obviously it must mean something different. And that brings us up against the very centre of Theology.

One of the creeds says that Christ is the Son of God "begotten, not created"; and it adds "begotten by his Father before all worlds." Will you please get it quite clear that this has nothing to do with the fact that when Christ was born on earth as a man, that man was the son of a virgin? We are not now thinking about the Virgin Birth. We are thinking about something that happened before Nature was created at all, before time began. "Before all worlds" Christ is begotten, not created. What does it mean?

We don't use the words *begetting* or *begotten* much in modern English, but everyone still knows what they mean. To beget is to become the father of: to create is to make. And the difference is this. When you beget, you beget something of the same kind as yourself. A man begets human babies, a beaver begets little beavers and a bird begets eggs which turn into little birds. But when you make, you make something of a different kind from yourself. A bird makes a nest, a beaver builds a dam, a man makes a wireless set—or he may make something more like himself than a wireless set: say, a statue. If he is a clever enough carver he may make a statue which is very like a man indeed. But, of course, it is not a real man; it only looks like one. It cannot breathe or think. It is not alive.

Now that is the first thing to get clear. What God begets is God; just as what man begets is man. What God creates is not God; just as what man makes is not man. That is why men are not Sons of God in the sense that Christ is. They may be like God in certain ways, but they are not things of the same kind. They are more like statues or pictures of God.

A statue has the shape of a man but it is not alive. In the same way, man has (in a sense I am going to explain) the "shape" or likeness of God, but he has not got the kind of life God has. Let us take the first point (man's resemblance to God) first. Everything God has made has some likeness to Himself. Space is like Him in its hugeness: not that the greatness of space is the same kind of greatness as God's, but it is a sort of symbol of it, or a translation of it into non-spiritual terms. Matter is like God in having energy: though, again, of course, physical energy is a different kind of thing from the power of God. The vegetable world is like Him because it is alive, and He is the "living God." But life, in this biological sense, is not the same as the life there is in God: it is only a kind of symbol or shadow of it. When we come on to the animals, we find other kinds of resemblance in addition to biological life. The intense activity and fertility of the insects, for example, is a first dim resemblance to the unceasing activity and the creativeness of God. In the higher mammals we get the beginnings of instinctive affection. That is not the same thing as the love that exists in God: but it is like it—rather in the way that a picture drawn on a flat piece of paper can nevertheless be "like" a landscape. When we come to man, the highest of the animals, we get the completest resemblance to God which we know of. (There may be creatures in other worlds who are more like God than man is, but we do not know about them.) Man not only lives, but loves and reasons: biological life reaches its highest known level in him.

But what man, in his natural condition, has not got, is Spiritual life—the higher and different sort of life that exists in God. We use the same word *life* for both: but if you thought that both must therefore be the same sort of thing, that would be like thinking that the "greatness" of space and the "greatness" of God were the same sort of greatness. In reality, the difference between Biological life and spiritual life is so important that I am going to give them two distinct names. The Biological sort which comes to us through Nature, and which (like everything else in Nature) is always tending to run down and decay so that it can only be kept up by incessant subsidies from Nature in the form of air, water, food, etc., is *Bios*. The Spiritual life which is in God from all eternity, and which made the whole natural universe, is *Zoe*. *Bios* has, to be sure, a certain shadowy or symbolic resemblance to *Zoe*: but only the sort of resemblance there is between a photo and a place, or a statue and a man. A man who changed from having *Bios* to having *Zoe* would have gone through as big a change as a statue which changed from being a carved stone to being a real man.

And that is precisely what Christianity is about. This world is a great sculptor's shop. We are the statues and there is a rumour going round the shop that some of us are some day going to come to life.

2.

THE THREE-PERSONAL GOD

The last chapter was about the difference between begetting and making. A man begets a child, but he only makes a statue. God begets Christ but He only makes men. But by saying that, I have illustrated only one point about God, namely, that what God the Father begets is God, something of the same kind as Himself. In that way it is like a human father begetting a human son. But not quite like it. So I must try to explain a little more.

A good many people nowadays say, "I believe in a God, but not in a personal God." They feel that the mysterious something which is behind all other things must be more than a person. Now the Christians quite agree. But the Christians are the only people who offer any idea of what a being that is beyond personality could be like. All the other people, though they say that God is beyond personality, really think of Him as something impersonal: that is, as something less than personal. If you are looking for something super-personal, something more than a person, then it is not a question of choosing between the Christian idea and the other ideas. The Christian idea is the only one on the market.

Again, some people think that after this life, or perhaps after several lives, human souls will be "absorbed" into God. But when they try to explain what they mean, they seem to be thinking of our being absorbed into God as one material thing is absorbed into another. They say it is like a drop of water slipping into the sea. But of course that is the end of the drop. If that is what happens to us, then being absorbed is the same as ceasing to exist. It is only the Christians who have any idea of how human souls can be taken into the life of God and yet remain themselves—in fact, be very much more themselves than they were before.

I warned you that Theology is practical. The whole purpose for which we exist is to be thus taken into the life of God. Wrong ideas about what that life is, will make it harder. And now, for a few minutes, I must ask you to follow rather carefully.

You know that in space you can move in three ways—to left or right, backwards or forwards, up or down. Every direction is either one of these three or a compromise between them. They are called the three Dimensions. Now notice this. If you are using only one dimension, you could draw only a straight line. If you are using two, you could draw a figure: say, a square. And a square is made up of four straight lines. Now a step further. If you have three dimensions, you can then build what we call a solid body. say, a cube—-a thing like a dice or a lump of sugar. And a cube is made up of six squares.

Do you see the point? A world of one dimension would be a straight line. In a two-dimensional world, you still get straight lines, but many lines make one figure. In a three-dimensional world, you still get figures but many figures make one solid body. In other words, as you advance to more real and more complicated levels, you do not leave behind you the things you found on the simpler levels: you still have them, but combined in new ways—in ways you could not imagine if you knew only the simpler levels.

Now the Christian account of God involves just the same principle. The human level is a simple and rather empty level. On the human level one person is one being, and any two persons are two separate beings—just as, in two dimensions (say on a flat sheet of paper) one square is one figure, and any two squares are two separate figures. On the Divine level you still find personalities; but up there you find them combined in new ways which we, who do not live on that level, cannot imagine. In God's dimension, so to speak, you find a being who is three Persons while remaining one Being, just as a cube is six squares while remaining one cube. Of course we cannot fully conceive a Being like that: just as, if we were so made that we perceived only two dimensions in space we could never properly imagine a cube. But we can get a sort of faint notion of it. And when we do, we are then, for the first time in our lives, getting some positive idea, however faint, of something super-personal—something more than a person. It is something we could never have guessed, and yet, once we have been told, one almost feels one ought to have been able to guess it because it fits in so well with all the things we know already.

You may ask, "If we cannot imagine a three-personal Being, what is the good of talking about Him?" Well, there isn't any good talking about Him. The thing that matters is being actually drawn into that three-personal life, and that may begin any time —tonight, if you like.

What I mean is this. An ordinary simple Christian kneels down to say his prayers. He is trying to get into touch with God. But if he is a Christian he knows that what is prompting him to pray is also God: God, so to speak, inside him. But he also knows that all his real knowledge of God comes through Christ, the Man who was God—that Christ is standing beside him, helping him to pray, praying for him. You see what is happening. God is the thing to which he is praying—the goal he is trying to reach. God is also the thing inside him which is pushing him on—the motive power. God is also the road or bridge along which he is being pushed to that goal. So that the whole threefold life of the three-personal Being is actually going on in that ordinary little bedroom where an ordinary man is saying his prayers. The man is being caught up into the higher kind of life—what I called *Zoe* or spiritual life: he is being pulled into God, by God, while still remaining himself.

And that is how Theology started. People already knew about God in a vague way. Then came a man who claimed to be God; and yet he was not the sort of man you could dismiss as a lunatic. He made them believe Him. They met Him again after they had seen Him killed. And then, after they had been formed into a little society or community, they found God somehow inside them as well: directing them, making them able to do things they could not do before. And when they worked it all out they found they had arrived at the Christian definition of the three-personal God.

This definition is not something we have made up; Theology is, in a sense, experimental knowledge. It is the simple religions that are the made-up ones. When I say it is an experimental science "in a sense," I mean that it is like the other experimental sciences in some ways, but not in all. If you are a geologist studying rocks, you have to go and find the rocks. They will not come to you, and if you go to them they cannot run away. The initiative lies all on your side. They cannot either help or hinder. But suppose you are a zoologist and want to take photos of wild animals in their native haunts. That is a bit different from studying rocks. The wild animals will not come to you: but they can run away from you. Unless you keep very quiet, they will. There is beginning to be a tiny little trace of initiative on their side.

Now a stage higher; suppose you want to get to know a human person. If he is determined not to let you, you will not get to know him. You have to win his confidence. In this case the initiative is equally divided—it takes two to make a friendship.

When you come to knowing God, the initiative lies on His side. If He does not show Himself, nothing you can do will enable you to find Him. And, in fact, He shows much more of Himself to some people than to others—not because He has favourites, but because it is impossible for Him to show Himself to a man whose whole mind and character are in the wrong condition. Just as sunlight, though it has no favourites, cannot be reflected in a dusty mirror as clearly as a clean one.

You can put this another way by saying that while in other sciences the instruments you use are things external to yourself (things like microscopes and telescopes), the instrument through which you see God is your whole self. And if a man's self is not kept clean and bright, his glimpse of God will be blurred—like the Moon seen through a dirty telescope. That is why horrible nations have horrible religions: they have been looking at God through a dirty lens.

God can show Himself as He really is only to real men. And that means not simply to men who are individually good, but to men who are united together in a body, loving one another, helping one another, showing Him to one another. For that is what God meant humanity to be like; like players in one band, or organs in one body.

Consequently, the one really adequate instrument for learning about God, is the whole Christian community, waiting for Him together. Christian brotherhood is, so to speak, the technical equipment for this science—the laboratory outfit. That is why all these people who turn up every few years with some patent simplified religion of their own as a substitute for the Christian tradition are really wasting time. Like a man who has no instrument but an old pair of field glasses setting out to put all the real astronomers right. He may be a clever chap—he may be cleverer than some of the real astronomers, but he is not giving himself a chance. And two years later everyone has forgotten all about him, but the real science is still going on.

If Christianity was something we were making up, of course we could make it easier. But it is not. We cannot compete, in simplicity, with people who are inventing religions. How could we? We are dealing with Fact. Of course anyone can be simple if he has no facts to bother about.

3.

TIME AND BEYOND TIME

It is a very silly idea that in reading a book you must never "skip." All sensible people skip freely when they come to a chapter which they find is going to be no use to them. In this chapter I am going to talk about something which may be helpful to some readers, but which may seem to others merely an unnecessary complication. If you are one of the second sort of readers, then I advise you not to bother about this chapter at all but to turn on to the next.

In the last chapter I had to touch on the subject of prayer, and while that is still fresh in your mind and my own, I should like to deal with a difficulty that some people find about the whole idea of prayer. A man put it to me by saying "I can believe in God all right, but what I cannot swallow is the idea of Him attending to several hundred million human beings who are all addressing Him at the same moment." And I have found that quite a lot of people feel this.

Now, the first thing to notice is that the whole sting of it comes in the words *at the same moment*. Most of us can imagine God attending to any number of applicants if only they came one by one and He had an endless time to do it in. So what is really at the back of this difficulty is the idea of God having to fit too many things into one moment of time.

Well that is of course what happens to us. Our life comes to us moment by moment. One moment disappears before the next comes along: and there is room for very little in each. That is what Time is like. And of course you and I tend to take it for granted that this Time series—this arrangement of past, present and future—is not simply the way life comes to us but the way all things really exist. We tend to assume that the whole universe and God Himself are always moving on from past to future just as we do. But many learned men do not agree with that. It was the Theologians who first started the idea that some things are not in Time at all: later the Philosophers took it over: and now some of the scientists are doing the same.

Almost certainly God is not in Time. His life does not consist of moments following one another. If a million people are praying to Him at ten-thirty tonight, He need not listen to them all in that one little snippet which we call ten-thirty. Ten-thirty—and every other moment from the beginning of the world—is always the Present for Him. If you like to put it that way, He has all eternity in which to listen to the split second of prayer put up by a pilot as his plane crashes in flames.

That is difficult, I know. Let me try to give something, not the same, but a bit like it. Suppose I am writing a novel. I write "Mary laid down her work; next moment came a knock at the door!" For Mary who has to live in the imaginary time of my story there is no interval between putting down the work and hearing the knock. But I, who am Mary's maker, do not live in that imaginary time at all. Between writing the first half of that sentence and the second, I might sit down for three hours and think steadily about Mary. I could think about Mary as if she were the only character in the book and for as long as I pleased, and the hours I spent in doing so would not appear in Mary's time (the time inside the story) at all.

This is not a perfect illustration, of course. But it may give just a glimpse of what I believe to be the truth. God is not hurried along in the Time-stream of this universe any more than an author is hurried along in the imaginary time of his own novel. He has infinite attention to spare for each one of us. He does not have to deal with us in the mass. You are as much alone with Him as if you were the only being He had ever created. When Christ died, He died for you individually just as much as if you had been the only man in the world.

The way in which my illustration breaks down is this. In it the author gets out of one Time-series (that of the novel) only by going into another Time-series (the real one). But God, I believe, does not live in a Time-series at all. His life is not dribbled out moment by moment like ours: with Him it is, so to speak, still 1920 and already 1960. For His life is Himself.

If you picture Time as a straight line along which we have to travel, then you must picture God as the whole page on which the line is drawn. We come to the parts of the line one by one: we have to leave A behind before we get to B, and cannot reach C until we leave B behind. God, from above or outside or all round, contains the whole line, and sees it all.

The idea is worth trying to grasp because it removes some apparent difficulties in Christianity. Before I became a Christian one of my objections was as follows. The Christians said that the eternal God who is everywhere and keeps the whole universe going, once became a human being. Well then, said I, how did the whole universe keep going while He was a baby, or while He was asleep? How could He at the same time be God who knows everything and also a man asking his disciples "Who touched me?" You will notice that the sting lay in the *time* words: *"While* He was a baby"—"How could He *at the same time?"* In other words I was assuming that Christ's life as God was in time, and that His life as the man Jesus in Palestine was a shorter period taken out of that time—just as my service in the army was a shorter period taken out of my total life. And that is how most of us perhaps tend to think about it. We picture God living through a period when His human life was still in the future: then coming to a period when it was present: then going on to a period when He could look back on it as something in the past. But probably these ideas correspond to nothing in the actual facts. You cannot fit Christ's earthly life in Palestine into any time-relations with His life as God beyond all space and time. It is really, I suggest, a timeless truth about God that human nature, and the human experience of weakness and sleep and ignorance, are somehow included in His whole divine life. This human life in God is from our point of view a particular period in the history of our world (from the year A.D. one till the Crucifixion). We therefore imagine it is also a period in the history of God's own existence. But God has no history. He is too completely and utterly real to have one. For, of course, to have a history means losing part of your reality (because it had already slipped away into the past) and not yet having another part (because it is still in the future): in fact having nothing but the tiny little present, which has gone before you can speak about it. God forbid we should think God was like that. Even we may hope not to be always rationed in that way.

Another difficulty we get if we believe God to be in time is this. Everyone who believes in God at all believes that He knows what you and I are going to do tomorrow. But if He knows I am going to do so-and-so, how can I be free to do otherwise? Well, here once again, the difficulty comes from thinking that God is progressing along the Time-line like us: the only difference being that He can see ahead and we cannot. Well, if that were true, if God *foresaw* our acts, it would be very hard to understand how we could be free not to do them. But suppose God is outside and above the Time-line. In that case, what we call "tomorrow" is visible to Him in just the same way as what we call "today." All the days are "Now" for Him. He does not remember you doing things yesterday; He simply sees you doing them, because, though you have lost yesterday, He has not. He does not "foresee" you doing things tomorrow; He simply sees you doing them: because, though tomorrow is not yet there for you, it is for Him. You never supposed that your actions at this moment were any less free because God knows what you are doing. Well, He knows your tomorrow's actions in just the same way—because He is already in tomorrow and can simply watch you. In a sense, He does not know your action till you have done it: but then the moment at which you have done it is already "Now" for Him.

This idea has helped me a good deal. If it does not help you, leave it alone. It is a "Christian idea" in the sense that great and wise Christians have held it and there is nothing in it contrary to Christianity. But it is not in the Bible or any of the creeds. You can be a perfectly good Christian without accepting it, or indeed without thinking of the matter at all.

4.

GOOD INFECTION

I begin this chapter by asking you to get a certain picture clear in your minds. Imagine two books lying on a table one on top of the other. Obviously the bottom book is keeping the other one up—supporting it. It is because of the underneath book that the top one is resting, say, two inches from the surface of the table instead of touching the table. Let us call the underneath book A and the top one B. The position of A is causing the position of B. That is clear? Now let us imagine—it could not really happen, of course, but it will do for an illustration—let us imagine that both books have been in that position for ever and ever. In that case B's position would always have been resulting from A's position. But all the same, A's position would not have existed before B's position. In other words the result does not come *after* the cause. Of course, results usually do: you eat the cucumber first and have the indigestion afterwards. But it is not so with all causes, and results. You will see in a moment why I think this important.

I said a few pages back that God is a Being which contains three Persons while remaining one Being, just as a cube contains six squares while remaining one body. But as soon as I begin trying to explain how these Persons are connected I have to use words which make it sound as if one of them was there before the others. The First Person is called the Father and the Second the Son. We say that the First begets or produces the second; we call it *begetting,* not *making,* because what He produces is of the same kind as Himself. In that way the word Father is the only word to use. But unfortunately it suggests that He is there first—just as a human father exists before his son. But that is not so. There is no before and after about it. And that is why I have spent some time trying to make clear how one thing can be the source, or cause, or origin, of another without being there before it. The Son exists because the Father exists: but there never was a time before the Father produced the Son.

Perhaps the best way to think of it is this. I asked you just now to imagine those two books, and probably most of you did. That is, you made an act of imagination and as a result you had a mental picture. Quite obviously your act of imagining was the cause and the mental picture the result. But that does not mean that you first did the imagining and then got the picture. The moment you did it, the picture was there. Your will was keeping the picture before you all the time. Yet that act of will and the picture began at exactly the same moment and ended at the same moment. If there were a Being who had always existed and had always been imagining one thing, his act would always have been producing a mental picture; but the picture would be just as eternal as the act.

In the same way we must think of the Son always, so to speak, streaming forth from the Father, like light from a lamp, or heat from a fire, or thoughts from a mind. He is the self-expression of the Father—what the Father has to say. And there never was a time when He was not saying it. But have you noticed what is happening? All these pictures of light or heat are making it sound as if the Father and Son were two things instead of two Persons. So that after all, the New Testament picture of a Father and a Son turns out to be much more accurate than anything we try to substitute for it. That is what always happens when you go away from the words of the Bible. It is quite right to go away from them for a moment in order to make some special point clear. But you must always go back. Naturally God knows how to describe Himself much better than we know how to describe Him. He knows that Father and Son is more like the relation between the First and Second Persons than anything else we can think of. Much the most important thing to know is that it is a relation of love. The Father delights in His Son; the Son looks up to His Father.

Before going on, notice the practical importance of this. All sorts of people are fond of repeating the Christian statement that "God is love." But they seem not to notice that the words "God is love" have no real meaning unless God contains at least two

Persons. Love is something that one person has for another person. If God was a single person, then before the world was made, He was not love. Of course, what these people mean when they say that God is love is often something quite different: they really mean "Love is God." They really mean that our feelings of love, however and wherever they arise, and whatever results they produce, are to be treated with great respect. Perhaps they are: but that is something quite different from what Christians mean by the statement "God is love." They believe that the living, dynamic activity of love has been going on in God for ever and has created everything else.

And that, by the way, is perhaps the most important difference between Christianity and all other religions: that in Christianity God is not a static thing—not even a person—but a dynamic, pulsating activity, a life, almost a kind of drama. Almost, if you will not think me irreverent, a kind of dance. The union between the Father and Son is such a live concrete thing that this union itself is also a Person. I know this is almost inconceivable, but look at it thus. You know that among human beings, when they get together in a family, or a club, or a trade union, people talk about the "spirit" of that family, or club, or trade union. They talk about its "spirit" because the individual members, when they are together, do really develop particular ways of talking and behaving which they would not have if they were apart.* It is as if a sort of communal personality came into existence. Of course, it is not a real person: it is only rather like a person. But that is just one of the differences between God and us. What grows out of the joint life of the Father and Son is a real Person, is in fact the Third of the three Persons who are God.

This third Person is called, in technical language, the Holy Ghost or the "spirit" of God. Do not be worried or surprised if you find it (or Him) rather vaguer or more shadowy in your mind than the other two. I think there is a reason why that must be so. In the Christian life you are not usually looking *at* Him: He is always acting through you. If you think of the Father as something

---

* This corporate behaviour may, of course, be either better or worse than their individual behaviour.

"out there," in front of you, and of the Son as someone standing at your side, helping you to pray, trying to turn you into another son, then you have to think of the third Person as something inside you, or behind you. Perhaps some people might find it easier to begin with the third Person and work backwards. God is love, and that love works through men—especially through the whole community of Christians. But this spirit of love is, from all eternity, a love going on between the Father and Son.

And now, what does it all matter? It matters more than anything else in the world. The whole dance, or drama, or pattern of this three-Personal life is to be played out in each one of us: or (putting it the other way round) each one of us has got to enter that pattern, take his place in that dance. There is no other way to the happiness for which we were made. Good things as well as bad, you know, are caught by a kind of infection. If you want to get warm you must stand near the fire: if you want to be wet you must get into the water. If you want joy, power, peace, eternal life, you must get close to, or even into, the thing that has them. They are not a sort of prizes which God could, if He chose, just hand out to anyone. They are a great fountain of energy and beauty spurting up at the very centre of reality. If you are close to it, the spray will wet you: if you are not, you will remain dry. Once a man is united to God, how could he not live forever? Once a man is separated from God, what can he do but wither and die?

But how is he to be united to God? How is it possible for us to be taken into the three-Personal life?

You remember what I said in Chapter II about *begetting* and *making*. We are not begotten by God, we are only made by Him: in our natural state we are not sons of God, only (so to speak) statues. We have not got *Zoe* or spiritual life: only *Bios* or biological life which is presently going to run down and die. Now the whole offer which Christianity makes is this: that we can, if we let God have His way, come to share in the life of Christ. If we do, we shall then be sharing a life which was begotten, not made, which always has existed and always will exist. Christ is the Son of God. If we share in this kind of life we also shall be sons of

God. We shall love the Father as He does and the Holy Ghost will arise in us. He came to this world and became a man in order to spread to other men the kind of life He has—by what I call "good infection." Every Christian is to become a little Christ. The whole purpose of becoming a Christian is simply nothing else.

5.

THE OBSTINATE TOY SOLDIERS

The Son of God became a man to enable men to become sons of God. We do not know—anyway, *I* do not know—how things would have worked if the human race had never rebelled against God and joined the enemy. Perhaps every man would have been "in Christ," would have shared the life of the Son of God, from the moment he was born. Perhaps the *Bios* or natural life would have been drawn up into the *Zoe*, the uncreated life, at once and as a matter of course. But that is guesswork. You and I are concerned with the way things work now.

And the present state of things is this. The two kinds of life are now not only different (they would always have been that) but actually opposed. The natural life in each of us is something self-centred, something that wants to be petted and admired, to take advantage of other lives, to exploit the whole universe. And especially it wants to be left to itself: to keep well away from anything better or stronger or higher than it, anything that might make it feel small. It is afraid of the light and air of the spiritual world, just as people who have been brought up to be dirty are afraid of a bath. And in a sense it is quite right. It knows that if the spiritual life gets hold of it, all its self-centredness and self-will are going to be killed and it is ready to fight tooth and nail to avoid that.

Did you ever think, when you were a child, what fun it would be if your toys could come to life? Well suppose you could really have brought them to life. Imagine turning a tin soldier into a real little man. It would involve turning the tin into flesh. And suppose the tin soldier did not like it. He is not interested in flesh; all he sees is that the tin is being spoilt. He thinks you are killing him. He will do everything he can to prevent you. He will not be made into a man if he can help it.

What you would have done about that tin soldier I do not know. But what God did about us was this. The Second Person in God, the Son, became human Himself: was born into the world as an actual man—a real man of a particular height, with hair of a particular colour, speaking a particular language, weighing so many stone. The Eternal Being, who knows everything and who created the whole universe, became not only a man but (before that) a baby, and before that a *fœtus* inside a Woman's body. If you want to get the hang of it, think how you would like to become a slug or a crab.

The result of this was that you now had one man who really was what all men were intended to be: one man in whom the created life, derived from his Mother, allowed itself to be completely and perfectly turned into the begotten life. The natural human creature in Him was taken up fully into the divine Son. Thus in one instance humanity had, so to speak, arrived: had passed into the life of Christ. And because the whole difficulty for us is that the natural life has to be, in a sense, "killed," He chose an earthly career which involved the killing of His human desires at every turn—poverty, misunderstanding from His own family, betrayal by one of His intimate friends, being jeered at and manhandled by the Police, and execution by torture. And then, after being thus killed—killed every day in a sense—the human creature in Him, because it was united to the divine Son, came to life again. The Man in Christ rose again: not only the God. That is the whole point. For the first time we saw a real man. One tin soldier—real tin, just like the rest—had come fully and splendidly alive.

And here, of course, we come to the point where my illustration about the tin soldier breaks down. In the case of real toy soldiers or statues, if one came to life, it would obviously make no difference to the rest. They are all separate. But human beings are not. They look separate because you see them walking about separately. But then, we are so made that we can see only the present moment. If we could see the past, then of course it would look different. For there was a time when every man was part of his mother, and (earlier still) part of his father as well: and when they were part of his grandparents. If you could see humanity spread out in time, as God sees it, it would not look like a lot of separate things dotted about. It would look like one single growing thing— rather like a very complicated tree. Every individual would appear connected with every other. And not only that. Individuals are not really separate from God any more than from one another. Every man, woman, and child all over the world is feeling and breathing at this moment only because God, so to speak, is "keeping him going."

Consequently, when Christ becomes man it is not really as if you could become one particular tin soldier. It is as if something which is always affecting the whole human mass begins, at one point, to affect that whole human mass in a new way. From that point the effect spreads through all mankind. It makes a difference to people who lived before Christ as well as to people who lived after Him. It makes a difference to people who have never heard of Him. It is like dropping into a glass of water one drop of something which gives a new taste or a new colour to the whole lot. But, of course, none of these illustrations really works perfectly. In the long run God is no one but Himself and what He does is like nothing else. You could hardly expect it to be.

What, then, is the difference which He has made to the whole human mass? It is just this; that the business of becoming a son of God, of being turned from a created thing into a begotten thing, of passing over from the temporary biological life into timeless "spiritual" life, has been done for us. Humanity is already "saved" in principle. We individuals have to appropriate that salvation. But the really tough work—the bit we could not have done for ourselves—has been done for us. We have not got to try to climb up into spiritual life by our own efforts; it has already come down into the human race. If we will only lay ourselves open to the one Man in whom it was fully present, and who, in spite of being God, is also a real man, He will do it in us and for us. Remember what I said about "good infection." One of our own race has this new life: if we get close to Him we shall catch it from Him.

Of course, you can express this in all sorts of different ways. You can say that Christ died for our sins. You may say that the Father has forgiven us because Christ has done for us what we ought to have done. You may say that we are washed in the blood of the Lamb. You may say that Christ has defeated death. They are all true. If any of them do not appeal to you, leave it alone and get on with the formula that does. And, whatever you do, do not start quarrelling with other people because they use a different formula from yours.

6.

TWO NOTES

In order to avoid misunderstanding I here add notes on two points arising out of the last chapter.

(1) One sensible critic wrote asking me why, if God wanted sons instead of "toy soldiers," He did not *beget* many sons at the outset instead of first *making* toy soldiers and then bringing them to life by such a difficult and painful process. One part of the answer to this question is fairly easy: the other part is probably beyond all human knowledge. The easy part is this. The process of being turned from a creature into a son would not have been difficult or painful if the human race had not turned away from God centuries ago. They were able to do this because He gave them free will: He gave them free will because a world of mere automata could never love and therefore never know infinite happiness. The difficult part is this. All Christians are agreed that there is, in the full and original sense, only one "Son of God." If we insist on asking "But could there have been many?" we find ourselves in very deep water. Have the words "Could have been" any sense at all when applied to God? You can say that one particular finite thing "could have been" different from what it is, because it would have been different if something else had been different, and the something else would have been different if some third thing had been different, and so on. (The letters on this page would have been red if the printer had used red ink, and he would have used red ink if he had been instructed to, and so on.) But when you are talking about God—i.e. about the rock bottom, irreducible Fact on which all other facts depend—it is nonsensical to ask if It could have been otherwise. It is what It is, and there is an end of the matter. But quite apart from this,

I find a difficulty about the very idea of the Father begetting many sons from all eternity. In order to be many they would have to be somehow different from one another. Two pennies have the same shape. How are they two? By occupying different places and containing different atoms. In other words, to think of them as different, we have had to bring in space and matter; in fact we have had to bring in "Nature" or the created universe. I can understand the distinction between the Father and the Son without bringing in space or matter, because the one begets and the other is begotten. The Father's relation to the Son is not the same as the Son's relation to the Father. But if there were several sons they would all be related to one another and to the Father in the same way. How would they differ from one another? One does not notice the difficulty at first, of course. One thinks one can form the idea of several "sons." But when I think closely, I find that the idea seemed possible only because I was vaguely imagining them as human forms standing about together in some kind of space. In other words, though I pretended to be thinking about something that exists before any universe was made, I was really smuggling in the picture of a universe and putting that something *inside* it. When I stop doing that and still try to think of the Father begetting many sons "before all worlds" I find I am not really thinking of anything. The idea fades away into mere words. (Was Nature—space and time and matter—created precisely in order to make many-ness possible? Is there perhaps no other way of getting many eternal spirits except by first making many natural creatures, in a universe, and then spiritualising them? But of course all this is guesswork.)

(2) The idea that the whole human race is, in a sense, one thing —one huge organism, like a tree—must not be confused with the idea that individual differences do not matter or that real people, Tom and Nobby and Kate, are somehow less important than collective things like classes, races, and so forth. Indeed the two ideas are opposites. Things which are parts of a single organism may be very different from one another: things which are not, may be very alike. Six pennies are quite separate and very alike: my nose and my lungs are very different but they are only alive at all because they are parts of my body and share its common life. Christianity thinks of human individuals not as mere members of a

group or items in a list, but as organs in a body—different from one another and each contributing what no other could. When you find yourself wanting to turn your children, or pupils, or even your neighbours, into people exactly like yourself, remember that God probably never meant them to be that. You and they are different organs, intended to do different things. On the other hand, when you are tempted not to bother about someone else's troubles because they are "no business of yours," remember that though he is different from you he is part of the same organism as you. If you forget that he belongs to the same organism as yourself you will become an Individualist. If you forget that he is a different organ from you, if you want to suppress differences and make people all alike, you will become a Totalitarian. But a Christian must not be either a Totalitarian or an Individualist.

I feel a strong desire to tell you—and I expect you feel a strong desire to tell me—which of these two errors is the worse. That is the devil getting at us. He always sends errors into the world in pairs—pairs of opposites. And he always encourages us to spend a lot of time thinking which is the worse. You see why, of course? He relies on your extra dislike of the one error to draw you gradually into the opposite one. But do not let us be fooled. We have to keep our eyes on the goal and go straight through between both errors. We have no other concern than that with either of them.

7·

LET'S PRETEND

May I once again start by putting two pictures, or' two stories rather, into your minds? One is the story you have all read called *Beauty and the Beast*. The girl, you remember, had to marry a monster for some reason. And she did. She kissed it as if it were a man. And then, much to her relief, it really turned into a man and all went well. The other story is about someone who had to wear a mask; a mask which made him look much nicer than he really was. He had to wear it for years. And when he took it off he found his own face had grown to fit it. He was now really beautiful. What had begun as disguise had become a reality. I think both these stories may (in a fanciful way, of course) help to illustrate what I have to say in this chapter. Up till now, I have been trying to describe facts—what God is and what He has done. Now I want to talk about practice—what do we do next? What difference does all this theology make? It can start making a difference to-night. If you are interested enough to have read thus far you are probably interested enough to make a shot at saying your prayers: and, whatever else you say, you will probably say the Lord's Prayer.

Its very first words are *Our Father*. Do you now see what those words mean? They mean quite frankly, that you are putting yourself in the place of a son of God. To put it bluntly, you are *dressing up as Christ*. If you like, you are pretending. Because, of course, the moment you realise what the words mean, you realise that you are not a son of God. You are not being like The Son of God, whose will and interests are at one with those of the Father: you are a bundle of self-centred fears, hopes, greeds, jealousies, and self-conceit, all doomed to death. So that, in a way, this dressing up as

Christ is a piece of outrageous cheek. But the odd thing is that He has ordered us to do it.

Why? What is the good of pretending to be what you are not? Well, even on the human level, you know, there are two kinds of pretending. There is a bad kind, where the pretence is there instead of the real thing; as when a man pretends he is going to help you instead of really helping you. But there is also a good kind, where the pretence leads up to the real thing. When you are not feeling particularly friendly but know you ought to be, the best thing you can do, very often, is to put on a friendly manner and behave as if you were a nicer person than you actually are. And in a few minutes, as we have all noticed, you will be really feeling friendlier than you were. Very often the only way to get a quality in reality is to start behaving as if you had it already. That is why children's games are so important. They are always pretending to be grown-ups—playing soldiers, playing shop. But all the time, they are hardening their muscles and sharpening their wits, so that the pretence of being grown-up helps them to grow up in earnest.

Now, the moment you realise "Here I am, dressing up as Christ," it is extremely likely that you will see at once some way in which at that very moment the pretence could be made less of a pretence and more of a reality. You will find several things going on in your mind which would not be going on there if you were really a son of God. Well, stop them. Or you may realise that, instead of saying your prayers, you ought to be downstairs writing a letter, or helping your wife to wash-up. Well, go and do it.

You see what is happening. The Christ Himself, the Son of God who is man (just like you) and God (just like His Father) is actually at your side and is already at that moment beginning to turn your pretence into a reality. This is not merely a fancy way of saying that your conscience is telling you what to do. If you simply ask your conscience, you get one result: if you remember that you are dressing up as Christ, you get a different one. There are lots of things which your conscience might not call definitely wrong (specially things in your mind) but which you will see at once you cannot go on doing if you are seriously trying to be like Christ. For you are no longer thinking simply about right and wrong; you are trying to catch the good infection from a Person. It is more like painting a portrait than like obeying a set of rules. And the odd thing is that while in one way it is much harder than keeping rules, in another way it is far easier.

The real Son of God is at your side. He is beginning to turn you into the same kind of thing as Himself. He is beginning, so to speak, to "inject" His kind of life and thought, His *Zoe,* into you; beginning to turn the tin soldier into a live man. The part of you that does not like it is the part that is still tin.

Some of you may feel that this is very unlike your own experience. You may say "I've never had the sense of being helped by an invisible Christ, but I often have been helped by other human beings." That is rather like the woman in the first war who said that if there were a bread shortage it would not bother her house because they always ate toast. If there is no bread there will be no toast. If there were no help from Christ, there would be no help from other human beings. He works on us in all sorts of ways: not only through what we think our "religious life." He works through Nature, through our own bodies, through books, sometimes through experiences which seem (at the time) *anti*-Christian. When a young man who has been going to church in a routine way honestly realises that he does not believe in Christianity and stops going—provided he does it for honesty's sake and not just to annoy his parents—the spirit of Christ is probably nearer to him then than it ever was before. But above all, He works on us through each other.

Men are mirrors, or "carriers" of Christ to other men. Sometimes unconscious carriers. This "good infection" can be carried by those who have not got it themselves. People who were not Christians themselves helped me to Christianity. But usually it is those who know Him that bring Him to others. That is why the Church, the whole body of Christians showing Him to one another, is so important. You might say that when two Christians are following Christ together there is not twice as much Christianity as when they are apart, but sixteen times as much.

But do not forget this. At first it is natural for a baby to take its mother's milk without knowing its mother. It is equally natural for us to see the man who helps us without seeing Christ behind him. But we must not remain babies. We must go on to recognise the real Giver. It is madness not to. Because, if we do not, we shall be relying on human beings. And that is going to let us down. The best of them will make mistakes; all of them will die. We must be thankful to all the people who have helped us, we must honour them and love them. But never, never pin your whole faith on any human being: not if he is the best and wisest in the whole world. There are lots of nice things you can do with sand; but do not try building a house on it.

And now we begin to see what it is that the New Testament is always talking about. It talks about Christians "being born again"; it talks about them "putting on Christ"; about Christ "being formed in us"; about our coming to "have the mind of Christ."

Put right out of your head the idea that these are only fancy ways of saying that Christians are to read what Christ said and try to carry it out—as a man may read what Plato or Marx said and try to carry it out. They mean something much more than that. They mean that a real Person, Christ, here and now, in that very room where you are saying your prayers, is doing things to you. It is not a question of a good man who died two thousand years ago. It is a living Man, still as much a man as you, and still as much God as He was when He created the world, really coming and interfering with your very self; killing the old natural self in you and replacing it with the kind of self He has. At first, only for moments. Then for longer periods. Finally, if all goes well, turning you permanently into a different sort of thing; into a new little Christ, a being which, in its own small way, has the same kind of life as God; which shares in His power, joy, knowledge and eternity. And soon we make two other discoveries.

(1) We begin to notice, besides our particular sinful acts, our sinfulness; begin to be alarmed not only about what we do, but about what we are. This may sound rather difficult, so I will try to make it clear from my own case. When I come to my evening prayers and try to reckon up the sins of the day, nine times out of ten the most obvious one is some sin against charity; I have sulked or snapped or sneered or snubbed or stormed. And the excuse that immediately springs to my mind is that the provocation was so sudden and unexpected: I was caught off my guard, I had not time

to collect myself. Now that may be an extenuating circumstance as regards those particular acts: they would obviously be worse if they had been deliberate and premeditated. On the other hand, surely what a man does when he is taken off his guard is the best evidence for what sort of a man he is? Surely what pops out before the man has time to put on a disguise is the truth? If there are rats in a cellar you are most likely to see them if you go in very suddenly. But the suddenness does not create the rats: it only prevents them from hiding. In the same way the suddenness of the provocation does not make me an ill-tempered man: it only shows me what an ill-tempered man I am. The rats are always there in the cellar, but if you go in shouting and noisily they will have taken cover before you switch on the light. Apparently the rats of resentment and vindictiveness are always there in the cellar of my soul. Now that cellar is out of reach of my conscious will. I can to some extent control my acts: I have no direct control over my temperament. And if (as I said before) what we are matters even more than what we do—if, indeed, what we do matters chiefly as evidence of what we are—then it follows that the change which I most need to undergo is a change that my own direct, voluntary efforts cannot bring about. And this applies to my good actions too. How many of them were done for the right motive? How many for fear of public opinion, or a desire to show off? How many from a sort of obstinacy or sense of superiority which, in different circumstances, might equally had led to some very bad act? But I cannot, by direct moral effort, give myself new motives. After the first few steps in the Christian life we realise that everything which really needs to be done in our souls can be done only by God. And that brings us to something which has been very misleading in my language up to now.

(2) I have been talking as if it were we who did everything. In reality, of course, it is God who does everything. We, at most, allow it to be done to us. In a sense you might even say it is God who does the pretending. The Three-Personal God, so to speak, sees before Him in fact a self-centred, greedy, grumbling, rebellious human animal. But He says "Let us pretend that this is not a mere creature, but our Son. It is like Christ in so far as it is a Man, for He became Man. Let us pretend that it is also like Him in Spirit.

Let us treat it as if it were what in fact it is not. Let us pretend in order to make the pretence into a reality." God looks at you as if you were a little Christ: Christ stands beside you to turn you into one. I daresay this idea of a divine make-believe sounds rather strange at first. But, is it so strange really? Is not that how the higher thing always raises the lower? A mother teaches her baby to talk by talking to it as if it understood long before it really does. We treat our dogs as if they were "almost human": that is why they really become "almost human" in the end.

8.

IS CHRISTIANITY HARD OR EASY?

In the last chapter we were considering the Christian idea of "putting on Christ," or first "dressing up" as a son of God in order that you may finally become a real son. What I want to make clear is that this is not one among many jobs a Christian has to do; and it is not a sort of special exercise for the top class. It is the whole of Christianity. Christianity offers nothing else at all. And I should like to point out how it differs from ordinary ideas of "morality" and "being good."

The ordinary idea which we all have before we become Christians is this. We take as starting point our ordinary self with its various desires and interests. We then admit that something else —call it "morality" or "decent behaviour," or "the good of society" —has claims on this self: claims which interfere with its own desires. What we mean by "being good" is giving in to those claims. Some of the things the ordinary self wanted to do turn out to be what we call "wrong": well, we must give them up. Other things, which the self did not want to do, turn out to be what we call "right": well, we shall have to do them. But we are hoping all the time that when all the demands have been met, the poor natural self will still have some chance, and some time, to get on with its own life and do what it likes. In fact, we are very like an honest man paying his taxes. He pays them all right, but he does hope that there will be enough left over for him to live on. Because we are still taking our natural self as the starting point.

As long as we are thinking that way, one or other of two results is likely to follow. Either we give up trying to be good, or else we become very unhappy indeed. For, make no mistake: if you are really going to try to meet all the demands made on the natural self, it will not have enough left over to live on. The more you obey your conscience, the more your conscience will demand of you. And your natural self, which is thus being starved and hampered and worried at every turn, will get angrier and angrier. In the end, you will either give up trying to be good, or else become one of those people who, as they say, "live for others" but always in a discontented, grumbling way—always wondering why the others do not notice it more and always making a martyr of yourself. And once you have become that you will be a far greater pest to anyone who has to live with you than you would have been if you had remained frankly selfish.

The Christian way is different: harder, and easier. Christ says "Give me All. I don't want so much of your time and so much of your money and so much of your work: I want You. I have not come to torment your natural self, but to kill it. No half-measures are any good. I don't want to cut off a branch here and a branch there, I want to have the whole tree down. I don't want to drill the tooth, or crown it, or stop it, but to have it out. Hand over the whole natural self, all the desires which you think innocent as well as the ones you think wicked—the whole outfit. I will give you a new self instead. In fact, I will give you Myself: my own will shall become yours."

Both harder and easier than what we are all trying to do. You have noticed, I expect, that Christ Himself sometimes describes the Christian way as very hard, sometimes as very easy. He says, "Take up your Cross"—in other words, it is like going to be beaten to death in a concentration camp. Next minute he says, "My yoke is easy and my burden light." He means both. And one can just see why both are true.

Teachers will tell you that the laziest boy in the class is the one who works hardest in the end. They mean this. If you give two boys, say, a proposition in geometry to do, the one who is prepared to take trouble will try to understand it. The lazy boy will try to learn it by heart because, for the moment, that needs less effort. But six months later, when they are preparing for an exam., that lazy boy is doing hours and hours of miserable drudgery over things the other boy understands, and positively enjoys, in a few minutes. Laziness means more work in the long run. Or look at it this way. In a battle, or in mountain climbing, there is often one thing which it takes a lot of pluck to do; but it is also, in the long run, the safest thing to do. If you funk it, you will find yourself, hours later, in far worse danger. The cowardly thing is also the most dangerous thing.

It is like that here. The terrible thing, the almost impossible thing, is to hand over your whole self—all your wishes and precautions—to Christ. But it is far easier than what we are all trying to do instead. For what we are trying to do is to remain what we call "ourselves," to keep personal happiness as our great aim in life, and yet at the same time be "good." We are all trying to let our mind and heart go their own way—centred on money or pleasure or ambition—and hoping, in spite of this, to behave honestly and chastely and humbly. And that is exactly what Christ warned us you could not do. As He said, a thistle cannot produce figs. If I am a field that contains nothing but grass-seed, I cannot produce wheat. Cutting the grass may keep it short: but I shall still produce grass and no wheat. If I want to produce wheat, the change must go deeper than the surface. I must be ploughed up and re-sown.

That is why the real problem of the Christian life comes where people do not usually look for it. It comes the very moment you wake up each morning. All your wishes and hopes for the day rush at you like wild animals. And the first job each morning consists simply in shoving them all back; in listening to that other voice, taking that other point of view, letting that other larger, stronger, quieter life come flowing in. And so on, all day. Standing back from all your natural fussings and frettings; coming in out of the wind.

We can only do it for moments at first. But from those moments the new sort of life will be spreading through our system: because now we are letting Him work at the right part of us. It is the difference between paint, which is merely laid on the surface, and a dye or stain which soaks right through. He never talked vague, idealistic gas. When he said, "Be perfect," He meant it. He meant that we must go in for the full treatment. It is hard; but the sort of compromise we are all hankering after is harder—in fact, it is impossible. It may be hard for an egg to turn into a bird: it would be a jolly sight harder for it to learn to fly while remaining an egg. We are like eggs at present. And you cannot go on indefinitely being just an ordinary, decent egg. We must be hatched or go bad.

May I come back to what I said before? This is the whole of Christianity. There is nothing else. It is so easy to get muddled about that. It is easy to think that the Church has a lot of different objects—education, building, missions, holding services. Just as it is easy to think the State has a lot of different objects—military, political, economic, and what not. But in a way things are much simpler than that. The State exists simply to promote and to protect the ordinary happiness of human beings in this life. A husband and wife chatting over a fire, a couple of friends having a game of darts in a pub, a man reading a book in his own room or digging in his own garden—that is what the State is there for. And unless they are helping to increase and prolong and protect such moments, all the laws, parliaments, armies, courts, police, economics, etc., are simply a waste of time. In the same way the Church exists for nothing else but to draw men into Christ, to make them little Christs. If they are not doing that, all the cathedrals, clergy, missions, sermons, even the Bible itself, are simply a waste of time. God became Man for no other purpose. It is even doubtful, you know, whether the whole universe was created for any other purpose. It says in the Bible that the whole universe was made for Christ and that everything is to be gathered together in Him. I do not suppose any of us can understand how this will happen as regards the whole universe. We do not know what (if anything) lives in the parts of it that are millions of miles away from this Earth. Even on this Earth we do not know how it applies to things other than men. After all, that is what you would expect. We have been shown the plan only in so far as it concerns ourselves.

I sometimes like to imagine that I can just see how it might apply to other things. I think I can see how the higher animals are in a sense drawn into Man when he loves them and makes them (as he does) much more nearly human than they would otherwise be. I can even see a sense in which the dead things and plants are drawn into Man as he studies them and uses and appreciates them. And if there were intelligent creatures in other worlds they might do the same with their worlds. It might be that when intelligent creatures entered into Christ they would, in that way, bring all the other things in along with them. But I do not know: it is only a guess.

What we have been told is how we men can be drawn into Christ —can become part of that wonderful present which the young Prince of the universe wants to offer to His Father—that present which is Himself and therefore us in Him. It is the only thing we were made for. And there are strange, exciting hints in the Bible that when we are drawn in, a great many other things in Nature will begin to come right. The bad dream will be over: it will be morning.

9.

COUNTING THE COST

I find a good many people have been bothered by what I said in the last chapter about Our Lord's words, "Be ye perfect." Some people seem to think this means "Unless you are perfect, I will not help you"; and as we cannot be perfect, then, if He meant that, our position is hopeless. But I do not think He did mean that. I think He meant "The only help I will give is help to become perfect. You may want something less: but I will give you nothing less."

Let me explain. When I was a child I often had toothache, and I knew that if I went to my mother she would give me something which would deaden the pain for that night and let me get to sleep. But I did not go to my mother—at least, not till the pain became very bad. And the reason I did not go was this. I did not doubt she would give me the aspirin; but I knew she would also do something else. I knew she would take me to the dentist next morning. I could not get what I wanted out of her without getting something more, which I did not want. I wanted immediate relief from pain: but I could not get it without having my teeth set permanently right. And I knew those dentists; I knew they started fiddling about with all sorts of other teeth which had not yet begun to ache. They would not let sleeping dogs lie; if you gave them an inch they took an ell.

Now, if I may put it that way, Our Lord is like the dentists. If you give Him an inch, He will take an ell. Dozens of people go to Him to be cured of some one particular sin which they are ashamed of (like masturbation or physical cowardice) or which is obviously spoiling daily life (like bad temper or drunkenness). Well, He will cure it all right: but He will not stop there. That may be all you asked; but if once you call Him in, He will give you the full treatment.

That is why He warned people to "count the cost" before becoming Christians. "Make no mistake," He says, "if you let me, I will make you perfect. The moment you put yourself in My hands, that is what you are in for. Nothing less, or other, than that. You have free will, and if you choose, you can push Me away. But if you do not push Me away, understand that I am going to see this job through. Whatever suffering it may cost you in your earthly life, whatever inconceivable purification it may cost you after death, whatever it costs Me, I will never rest, nor let you rest, until you are literally perfect—until my Father can say without reservation that He is well pleased with you, as He said He was well pleased with me. This I can do and will do. But I will not do anything less."

And yet—this is the other and equally important side of it— this Helper who will, in the long run, be satisfied with nothing less than absolute perfection, will also be delighted with the first feeble, stumbling effort you make tomorrow to do the simplest duty. As a great Christian writer (George MacDonald) pointed out, every father is pleased at the baby's first attempt to walk: no father would be satisfied with anything less than a firm, free, manly walk in a grown-up son. In the same way, he said, "God is easy to please, but hard to satisfy."

The practical upshot is this. On the one hand, God's demand for perfection need not discourage you in the least in your present attempts to be good, or even in your present failures. Each time you fall He will pick you up again. And He knows perfectly well that your own efforts are never going to bring you anywhere near perfection. On the other hand, you must realise from the outset that the goal towards which He is beginning to guide you is absolute perfection; and no power in the whole universe, except you yourself, can prevent Him from taking you to that goal. That is what you are in for. And it is very important to realise that. If we do not, then we are very likely to start pulling back and resisting Him after a certain point. I think that many of us, when Christ has enabled us to overcome one or two sins that were an obvious nuisance, are inclined to feel (though we do not put it into words) that we are now good enough. He has done all we wanted Him to do, and we should be obliged if He would now leave us alone. As we say "I never expected to be a saint, I only wanted to be a decent ordinary chap." And we imagine when we say this that we are being humble.

But this is the fatal mistake. Of course we never wanted, and never asked, to be made into the sort of creatures He is going to make us into. But the question is not what we intended ourselves to be, but what He intended us to be when He made us. He is the inventor, we are only the machine. He is the painter, we are only the picture. How should we know what He means us to be like? You see, He has already made us something very different from what we were. Long ago, before we were born, when we were inside our mothers' bodies, we passed through various stages. We were once rather like vegetables, and once rather like fish; it was only at a later stage that we became like human babies. And if we had been conscious at those earlier stages, I daresay we should have been quite contented to stay as vegetables or fish—should not have wanted to be made into babies. But all the time He knew His plan for us and was determined to carry it out. Something the same is now happening at a higher level. We may be content to remain what we call "ordinary people": but He is determined to carry out a quite different plan. To shrink back from that plan is not humility; it is laziness and cowardice. To submit to it is not conceit or megalomania; it is obedience.

Here is another way of putting the two sides of the truth. On the one hand we must never imagine that our own unaided efforts can be relied on to carry us even through the next twenty-four hours as "decent" people. If He does not support us, not one of us is safe from some gross sin. On the other hand, no possible degree of holiness or heroism which has ever been recorded of the greatest saints is beyond what He is determined to produce in every one of us in the end. The job will not be completed in this life: but He means to get us as far as possible before death.

That is why we must not be surprised if we are in for a rough time. When a man turns to Christ and seems to be getting on pretty well (in the sense that some of his bad habits are now corrected), he often feels that it would now be natural if things went fairly smoothly. When troubles come along—illnesses, money troubles, new kinds of temptation—he is disappointed. These things, he feels, might have been necessary to rouse him and make him repent in his bad old days; but why now? Because God is forcing him on, or up, to a higher level: putting him into situations where he will have to be very much braver, or more patient, or more loving, than he ever dreamed of being before. It seems to us all unnecessary: but that is because we have not yet had the slightest notion of the tremendous thing He means to make of us.

I find I must borrow yet another parable from George MacDonald. Imagine yourself as a living house. God comes in to rebuild that house. At first, perhaps, you can understand what He is doing. He is getting the drains right and stopping the leaks in the roof and so on: you knew that those jobs needed doing and so you are not surprised. But presently he starts knocking the house about in a way that hurts abominably and does not seem to make sense. What on earth is He up to? The explanation is that He is building quite a different house from the one you thought of—throwing out a new wing here, putting on an extra floor there, running up towers, making courtyards. You thought you were going to be made into a decent little cottage: but He is building a palace. He intends to come and live in it Himself.

The command *Be ye perfect* is not idealistic gas. Nor is it a command to do the impossible. He is going to make us into creatures that can obey that command. He said (in the Bible) that we were "gods" and He is going to make good His words. If we let Him—for we can prevent Him, if we choose—He will make the feeblest and filthiest of us into a god or goddess, a dazzling, radiant, immortal creature, pulsating all through with such energy and joy and wisdom and love as we cannot now imagine, a bright stainless mirror which reflects back to God perfectly (though, of course, on a smaller scale) His own boundless power and delight and goodness. The process will be long and in parts very painful; but that is what we are in for. Nothing less. He meant what He said.

IO.

NICE PEOPLE OR NEW MEN

He meant what He said. Those who put themselves in His hands will become perfect, as He is perfect—perfect in love, wisdom, joy, beauty, and immortality. The change will not be completed in this life, for death is an important part of the treatment. How far the change will have gone before death in any particular Christian is uncertain.

I think this is the right moment to consider a question which is often asked: If Christianity is true why are not all Christians obviously nicer than all non-Christians? What lies behind that question is partly something very reasonable and partly something that is not reasonable at all. The reasonable part is this. If conversion to Christianity makes no improvement in a man's outward actions —if he continues to be just as snobbish or spiteful or envious or ambitious as he was before—then I think we must suspect that his "conversion" was largely imaginary; and after one's original conversion, every time one thinks one has made an advance, that is the test to apply. Fine feelings, new insights, greater interest in "religion" mean nothing unless they make our actual behaviour better; just as in an illness "feeling better" is not much good if the thermometer shows that your temperature is still going up. In that sense the outer world is quite right to judge Christianity by its results. Christ told us to judge by results. A tree is known by its fruit; or, as we say, the proof of the pudding is in the eating. When we Christians behave badly, or fail to behave well, we are making Christianity unbelievable to the outside world. The war-time posters told us that Careless Talk costs Lives. It is equally true that Careless Lives cost Talk. Our careless lives set the outer world talking; and we give them grounds for talking in a way that throws doubt on the truth of Christianity itself.

But there is another way of demanding results in which the outer world may be quite illogical. They may demand not merely that each man's life should improve if he becomes a Christian: they may also demand before they believe in Christianity that they should see the whole world neatly divided into two camps —Christian and non-Christian—and that all the people in the first camp at any given moment should be obviously nicer than all the people in the second. This is unreasonable on several grounds.

(1) In the first place the situation in the actual world is much more complicated than that. The world does not consist of 100 per cent Christians and 100 per cent non-Christians. There are people (a great many of them) who are slowly ceasing to be Christians but who still call themselves by that name: some of them are clergymen. There are other people who are slowly becoming Christians though they do not yet call themselves so. There are people who do not accept the full Christian doctrine about Christ but who are so strongly attracted by Him that they are His in a much deeper sense than they themselves understand. There are people in other religions who are being led by God's secret influence to concentrate on those parts of their religion which are in agreement with Christianity, and who thus belong to Christ without knowing it. For example, a Buddhist of good will may be led to concentrate more and more on the Buddhist teaching about mercy and to leave in the background (though he might still say he believed) the Buddhist teaching on certain other points. Many of the good Pagans long before Christ's birth may have been in this position. And always, of course, there are a great many people who are just confused in mind and have a lot of inconsistent beliefs all jumbled up together. Consequently, it is not much use trying to make judgments about Christians and non-Christians in the mass. It is some use comparing cats and dogs, or even men and women, in the mass, because there one knows definitely which is which. Also, an animal does not turn (either slowly or suddenly) from a dog into a cat. But when we are comparing Christians in general with non-Christians in general, we are usually not thinking

about real people whom we know at all, but only about two vague ideas which we have got from novels and newspapers. If you want to compare the bad Christian and the good Atheist, you must think about two real specimens whom you have actually met. Unless we come down to brass tacks in that way, we shall only be wasting time.

(2) Suppose we have come down to brass tacks and are now talking not about an imaginary Christian and an imaginary non-Christian, but about two real people in our own neighbourhood. Even then we must be careful to ask the right question. If Christianity is true then it ought to follow (*a*) That any Christian will be nicer than the same person would be if he were not a Christian. (*b*) That any man who becomes a Christian will be nicer than he was before. Just in the same way, if the advertisements of Whitesmile's toothpaste are true it ought to follow (*a*) That anyone who uses it will have better teeth than the same person would have if he did not use it. (*b*) That if anyone begins to use it his teeth will improve. But to point out that I, who use Whitesmile's (and also have inherited bad teeth from both my parents), have not got as fine a set as some healthy young Negro who never used toothpaste at all, does not, by itself, prove that the advertisements are untrue. Christian Miss Bates may have an unkinder tongue than unbelieving Dick Firkin. That, by itself, does not tell us whether Christianity works. The question is what Miss Bates's tongue would be like if she were not a Christian and what Dick's would be like if he became one. Miss Bates and Dick, as a result of natural causes and early upbringing, have certain temperaments: Christianity professes to put both temperaments under new management if they will allow it to do so. What you have a right to ask is whether that management, if allowed to take over, improves the concern. Everyone knows that what is being managed in Dick Firkin's case is much "nicer" than what is being managed in Miss Bates's. That is not the point. To judge the management of a factory, you must consider not only the output but the plant. Considering the plant at Factory A it may be a wonder that it turns out anything at all; considering the first-class outfit at Factory B its output, though high, may be a great deal lower than it ought to be. No doubt the

good manager at Factory A is going to put in new machinery as soon as he can, but that takes time. In the meantime low output does not prove that he is a failure.

(3) And now, let us go a little deeper. The manager is going to put in new machinery: before Christ has finished with Miss Bates, she is going to be very "nice" indeed. But if we left it at that, it would sound as though Christ's only aim was to pull Miss Bates up to the same level on which Dick had been all along. We have been talking, in fact, as if Dick were all right; as if Christianity was something nasty people needed and nice ones could afford to do without; and as if niceness was all that God demanded. But this would be a fatal mistake. The truth is that in God's eyes Dick Firkin needs "saving" every bit as much as Miss Bates. In one sense (I will explain what sense in a moment) niceness hardly comes into the question.

You cannot expect God to look at Dick's placid temper and friendly disposition exactly as we do. They result from natural causes which God Himself creates. Being merely temperamental, they will all disappear if Dick's digestion alters. The niceness, in fact, is God's gift to Dick, not Dick's gift to God. In the same way, God has allowed natural causes, working in a world spoiled by centuries of sin, to produce in Miss Bates the narrow mind and jangled nerves which account for most of her nastiness. He intends, in His own good time, to set that part of her right. But that is not, for God, the critical part of the business. It presents no difficulties. It is not what He is anxious about. What He is watching and waiting and working for is something that is not easy even for God, because, from the nature of the case, even He cannot produce it by a mere act of power. He is waiting and watching for it both in Miss Bates and in Dick Firkin. It is something they can freely give Him or freely refuse to Him. Will they, or will they not, turn to Him and thus fulfil the only purpose for which they were created? Their free will is trembling inside them like the needle of a compass. But this is a needle that can choose. It *can* point to its true North; but it need not. Will the needle swing round, and settle, and point to God?

He can help it to do so. He cannot force it. He cannot, so to speak, put out His own hand and pull it into the right position, for then it would not be free will any more. Will it point North? That is the question on which all hangs. Will Miss Bates and Dick offer their natures to God? The question whether the natures they offer or withhold are, at that moment, nice or nasty ones, is of secondary importance. God can see to that part of the problem.

Do not misunderstand me. Of course God regards a nasty nature as a bad and deplorable thing. And, of course, He regards a nice nature as a good thing—good like bread, or sunshine, or water. But these are the good things which He gives and we receive. He created Dick's sound nerves and good digestion, and there is plenty more where they came from. It costs God nothing, so far as we know, to create nice things: but to convert rebellious wills cost Him crucifixion. And because they are wills they can—in nice people just as much as in nasty ones—refuse His request. And then, because that niceness in Dick was merely part of nature, it will all go to pieces in the end. Nature herself will all pass away. Natural causes come together in Dick to make a pleasant psychological pattern, just as they come together in a sunset to make a pleasant pattern of colours. Presently (for that is how nature works) they will fall apart again and the pattern in both cases will disappear. Dick has had the chance to turn (or rather, to allow God to turn) that momentary pattern into the beauty of an eternal spirit: and he has not taken it.

There is a paradox here. As long as Dick does not turn to God, he thinks his niceness is his own, and just as long as he thinks that, it is not his own. It is when Dick realises that his niceness is not his own but a gift from God, and when he offers it back to God— it is just then that it begins to be really his own. For now Dick is beginning to take a share in his own creation. The only things we can keep are the things we freely give to God. What we try to keep for ourselves is just what we are sure to lose.

We must, therefore, not be surprised if we find among the Christians some people who are still nasty. There is even, when you come to think it over, a reason why nasty people might be expected to turn to Christ in greater numbers than nice ones. That was what people objected to about Christ during His life on earth: He seemed to attract "such awful people." That is what people still object to, and always will. Do you not see why? Christ said

"'Blessed are the poor" and "How hard it is for the rich to enter the Kingdom," and no doubt He primarily meant the economically rich and economically poor. But do not His words also apply to another kind of riches and poverty? One of the dangers of having a lot of money is that you may be quite satisfied with the kinds of happiness money can give and so fail to realise your need for God. If everything seems to come simply by signing checks, you may forget that you are at every moment totally dependent on God. Now quite plainly, natural gifts carry with them a similar danger. If you have sound nerves and intelligence and health and popularity and a good upbringing, you are likely to be quite satisfied with your character as it is. "Why drag God into it?" you may ask. A certain level of good conduct comes fairly easily to you. You are not one of those wretched creatures who are always being tripped up by sex, or dipsomania, or nervousness, or bad temper. Everyone says you are a nice chap and (between ourselves) you agree with them. You are quite likely to believe that all this niceness is your own doing: and you may easily not feel the need for any better kind of goodness. Often people who have all these natural kinds of goodness cannot be brought to recognise their need for Christ at all until, one day, the natural goodness lets them down and their self-satisfaction is shattered. In other words, it is hard for those who are "rich" in this sense to enter the Kingdom.

It is very different for the nasty people—the little, low, timid, warped, thin-blooded, lonely people, or the passionate, sensual, unbalanced people. If they make any attempt at goodness at all, they learn, in double quick time, that they need help. It is Christ or nothing for them. It is taking up the cross and following—or else despair. They are the lost sheep; He came specially to find them. They are (in one very real and terrible sense) the "poor": He blessed them. They are the "awful set" he goes about with—and of course the Pharisees say still, as they said from the first, "If there were anything in Christianity those people would not be Christians."

There is either a warning or an encouragement here for every one of us. If you are a nice person—if virtue comes easily to you —beware! Much is expected from those to whom much is given.

If you mistake for your own merits what are really God's gifts to you through nature, and if you are contented with simply being nice, you are still a rebel: and all those gifts will only make your fall more terrible, your corruption more complicated, your bad example more disastrous. The Devil was an archangel once; his natural gifts were as far above yours as yours are above those of a chimpanzee.

But if you are a poor creature—poisoned by a wretched up-bringing in some house full of vulgar jealousies and senseless quarrels—saddled, by no choice of your own, with some loath-some sexual perversion—nagged day in and day out by an inferi-ority complex that makes you snap at your best friends—do not despair. He knows all about it. You are one of the poor whom He blessed. He knows what a wretched machine you are trying to drive. Keep on. Do what you can. One day (perhaps in another world, but perhaps far sooner than that) he will fling it on the scrap-heap and give you a new one. And then you may astonish us all—not least yourself: for you have learned your driving in a hard school. (Some of the last will be first and some of the first will be last.)

"Niceness"—wholesome, integrated personality—is an excellent thing. We must try by every medical, educational, economic, and political means in our power, to produce a world where as many people as possible grow up "nice"; just as we must try to produce a world where all have plenty to eat. But we must not suppose that even if we succeeded in making everyone nice we should have saved their souls. A world of nice people, content in their own niceness, looking no further, turned away from God, would be just as desperately in need of salvation as a miserable world—and might even be more difficult to save.

For mere improvement is not redemption, though redemption always improves people even here and now and will, in the end, improve them to a degree we cannot yet imagine. God became man to turn creatures into sons: not simply to produce better men of the old kind but to produce a new kind of man. It is not like teach-ing a horse to jump better and better but like turning a horse into a winged creature. Of course, once it has got its wings, it will soar over fences which could never have been jumped and thus beat the natural horse at its own game. But there may be a period, while the wings are just beginning to grow, when it cannot do so: and at that stage the lumps on the shoulders—no one could tell by looking at them that they are going to be wings—may even give it an awkward appearance.

But perhaps we have already spent too long on this question. If what you want is an argument against Christianity (and I well remember how eagerly I looked for such arguments when I began to be afraid it was true) you can easily find some stupid and unsatisfactory Christian and say, "So there's your boasted new man! Give me the old kind." But if once you have begun to see that Christianity is on other grounds probable, you will know in your heart that this is only evading the issue. What can you ever really know of other people's souls—of their temptations, their opportunities, their struggles? One soul in the whole creation you do know: and it is the only one whose fate is placed in your hands. If there is a God, you are, in a sense, alone with Him. You cannot put Him off with speculations about your next door neighbours or memories of what you have read in books. What will all that chatter and hearsay count (will you even be able to remember it?) when the anæsthetic fog which we call "nature" or "the real world" fades away and the Presence in which you have always stood becomes palpable, immediate, and unavoidable?

I I.

THE NEW MEN

In the last chapter I compared Christ's work of making New Men to the process of turning a horse into a winged creature. I used that extreme example in order to emphasise the point that it is not mere improvement but Transformation. The nearest parallel to it in the world of nature is to be found in the remarkable transformations we can make in insects by applying certain rays to them. Some people think this is how Evolution worked. The alterations in creatures on which it all depends may have been produced by rays coming from outer space. (Of course once the alterations are there, what they call "Natural Selection" gets to work on them: i.e., the useful alterations survive and the other ones get weeded out.)

Perhaps a modern man can understand the Christian idea best if he takes it in connection with Evolution. Everyone now knows about Evolution (though, of course, some educated people disbelieve it): everyone has been told that man has evolved from lower types of life. Consequently, people often wonder "What is the next step? When is the thing beyond man going to appear?" Imaginative writers try sometimes to picture this next step—the "Superman" as they call him; but they usually only succeed in picturing someone a good deal nastier than man as we know him and then try to make up for that by sticking on extra legs or arms. But supposing the next step was to be something even more different from the earlier steps than they ever dreamed of? And is it not very likely it would be? Thousands of centuries ago huge, very heavily armoured creatures were evolved. If anyone had at that time been watching the course of Evolution he would probably have expected that it was going to go on to heavier and heavier

armour. But he would have been wrong. The future had a card
up its sleeve which nothing at that time would have led him to
expect. It was going to spring on him little, naked, unarmoured
animals which had better brains: and with those brains they were
going to master the whole planet. They were not merely going to
have more power than the prehistoric monsters, they were going
to have a new kind of power. The next step was not only going to
be different, but different with a new kind of difference. The
stream of Evolution was not going to flow on in the direction in
which he saw it flowing: it was in fact going to take a sharp bend.

Now it seems to me that most of the popular guesses at the
Next Step are making just the same sort of mistake. People see
(or at any rate they think they see) men developing greater brains
and getting greater mastery over nature. And because they think
the stream is flowing in that direction, they imagine it will go on
flowing in that direction. But I cannot help thinking that the Next
Step will be really new; it will go off in a direction you could never
have dreamed of. It would hardly be worth calling a New Step
unless it did. I should expect not merely difference but a new kind
of difference. I should expect not merely change but a new method
of producing the change. Or, to make an Irish bull, I should expect
the next stage in Evolution not to be a stage in Evolution at all:
should expect the Evolution itself as a method of producing
change, will be superseded. And finally, I should not be surprised
if, when the thing happened, very few people noticed that it was
happening.

Now, if you care to talk in these terms, the Christian view is
precisely that the Next Step has already appeared. And it is really
new. It is not a change from brainy men to brainier men: it is a
change that goes off in a totally different direction—a change
from being creatures of God to being sons of God. The first
instance appeared in Palestine two thousand years ago. In a sense,
the change is not "Evolution" at all, because it is not something
arising out of the natural process of events but something coming
into nature from outside. But that is what I should expect. We
arrived at our idea of "Evolution" from studying the past. If there
are real novelties in store then of course our idea, based on the
past, will not really cover them. And in fact this New Step differs

from all previous ones not only in coming from outside nature but in several other ways as well.

(1) It is not carried on by sexual reproduction. Need we be surprised at that? There was a time before sex had appeared; development used to go on by different methods. Consequently, we might have expected that there would come a time when sex disappeared, or else (which is what is actually happening) a time when sex, though it continued to exist, ceased to be the main channel of development.

(2) At the earlier stages living organisms have had either no choice or very little choice about taking the new step. Progress was, in the main, something that happened to them, not something that they did. But the new step, the step from being creatures to being sons, is voluntary. At least, voluntary in one sense. It is not voluntary in the sense that we, of ourselves, could have chosen to take it or could even have imagined it; but it is voluntary in the sense that when it is offered to us we can refuse it. We can, if we please, shrink back: we can dig in our heels and let the new Humanity go on without us.

(3) I have called Christ the "first instance" of the new man. But of course He is something much more than that. He is not merely a new man, one specimen of the species, but *the* new man. He is the origin and centre and life of all the new men. He came into the created universe, of His own will, bringing with Him the *Zoe,* the new life. (I mean new to us, of course: in its own place *Zoe* has existed for ever and ever.) And He transmits it not by heredity but by what I have called "good infection." Everyone who gets it gets it by personal contact with Him. Other men become "new" by being "in Him."

(4) This step is taken at a different speed from the previous ones. Compared with the development of man on this planet, the diffusion of Christianity over the human race seems to go like a flash of lightning—for two thousand years is almost nothing in the history of the universe. (Never forget that we are all still "the early Christians." The present wicked and wasteful divisions between us are, let us hope, a disease of infancy: we are still teething. The outer world, no doubt, thinks just the opposite. It thinks we are dying of old age. But it has thought that so often before!

Again and again it has thought Christianity was dying, dying by persecutions from without or corruptions from within, by the rise of Mohammedanism, the rise of the physical sciences, the rise of great anti-Christian revolutionary movements. But every time the world has been disappointed. Its first disappointment was over the crucifixion. The Man came to life again. In a sense—and I quite realise how frightfully unfair it must seem to them—that has been happening ever since. They keep on killing the thing that He started: and each time, just as they are patting down the earth on its grave, they suddenly hear that it is still alive and has even broken out in some new place. No wonder they hate us.)

(5) The stakes are higher. By falling back at the earlier steps a creature lost, at the worst, its few years of life on this earth: very often it did not lose even that. By falling back at this step we lose a prize which is (in the strictest sense of the word) infinite. For now the critical moment has arrived. Century by century God has guided nature up to the point of producing creatures which can (if they will) be taken right out of nature, turned into "gods." Will they allow themselves to be taken? In a way, it is like the crisis of birth. Until we rise and follow Christ we are still parts of Nature, still in the womb of our great mother. Her pregnancy has been long and painful and anxious, but it has reached its climax. The great moment has come. Everything is ready. The Doctor has arrived. Will the birth "go off all right"? But of course it differs from an ordinary birth in one important respect. In an ordinary birth the baby has not much choice: here it has. I wonder what an ordinary baby would do if it had the choice. It might prefer to stay in the dark and warmth and safety of the womb. For of course it would think the womb meant safety. That would be just where it was wrong; for if it stays there it will die.

On this view the thing has happened: the new step has been taken and is being taken. Already the new men are dotted here and there all over the earth. Some, as I have admitted, are still hardly recognisable: but others can be recognised. Every now and then one meets them. Their very voices and faces are different from ours; stronger, quieter, happier, more radiant. They begin where most of us leave off. They are, I say, recognisable; but you must know what to look for. They will not be very like the idea of "religious people" which you have formed from your general reading. They do not draw attention to themselves. You tend to think that you are being kind to them when they are really being kind to you. They love you more than other men do, but they need you less. (We must get over wanting to be needed: in some goodish people, specially women, that is the hardest of all temptations to resist.) They will usually seem to have a lot of time: you will wonder where it comes from. When you have recognised one of them, you will recognise the next one much more easily. And I strongly suspect (but how should I know?) that they recognise one another immediately and infallibly, across every barrier of colour, sex, class, age, and even of creeds. In that way, to become holy is rather like joining a secret society. To put it at the very lowest, it must be great *fun*.

But you must not imagine that the new men are, in the ordinary sense, all alike. A good deal of what I have been saying in this last book might make you suppose that that was bound to be so. To become new men means losing what we now call "ourselves." Out of ourselves, into Christ, we must go. His will is to become ours and we are to think His thoughts, to "have the mind of Christ" as the Bible says. And if Christ is one, and if He is thus to be "in" us all, shall we not be exactly the same? It certainly sounds like it; but in fact it is not so.

It is difficult here to get a good illustration; because, of course, no other two things are related to each other just as the Creator is related to one of His creatures. But I will try two very imperfect illustrations which may give a hint of the truth. Imagine a lot of people who have always lived in the dark. You come and try to describe to them what light is like. You might tell them that if they come into the light that same light would fall on them all and they would all reflect it and thus become what we call visible. Is it not quite possible that they would imagine that, since they were all receiving the same light, and all reacting to it in the same way (i.e., all reflecting it), they would all look alike? Whereas you and I know that the light will in fact bring out, or show up, how different they are. Or again, suppose a person who knew nothing about salt. You give him a pinch to taste and he experiences a particular strong, sharp taste. You then tell him that in your country people use salt in all their cookery. Might he not reply "In that case I suppose all your dishes taste exactly the same: because the taste of that stuff you have just given me is so strong that it will kill the taste of everything else." But you and I know that the real effect of salt is exactly the opposite. So far from killing the taste of the egg and the tripe and the cabbage, it actually brings it out. They do not show their real taste till you have added the salt. (Of course, as I warned you, this is not really a very good illustration, because you can, after all, kill the other tastes by putting in too much salt, whereas you cannot kill the taste of a human personality by putting in too much Christ. I am doing the best I can.)

It is something like that with Christ and us. The more we get what we now call "ourselves" out of the way and let Him take us over, the more truly ourselves we become. There is so much of Him that millions and millions of "little Christs," all different, will still be too few to express Him fully. He made them all. He invented—as an author invents characters in a novel—all the different men that you and I were intended to be. In that sense our real selves are all waiting for us in Him. It is no good trying to "be myself" without Him. The more I resist Him and try to live on my own, the more I become dominated by my own heredity and upbringing and surroundings and natural desires. In fact what I so proudly call "Myself" becomes merely the meeting place for trains of events which I never started and which I cannot stop. What I call "My wishes" become merely the desires thrown up by my physical organism or pumped into me by other men's thoughts or even suggested to me by devils. Eggs and alcohol and a good night's sleep will be the real origins of what I flatter myself by regarding as my own highly personal and discriminating decision to make love to the girl opposite to me in the railway carriage. Propaganda will be the real origin of what I regard as my own personal political ideals, I am not, in my natural state, nearly so much of a person as I like to believe: most of what I call "me" can be very easily explained. It is when I turn to Christ, when I give myself up to His Personality, that I first begin to have a real personality of my own.

At the beginning I said there were Personalities in God. I will go further now. There are no real personalities anywhere else.

Until you have given up your self to Him you will not have a real self. Sameness is to be found most among the most "natural" men, not among those who surrender to Christ. How monotonously alike all the great tyrants and conquerors have been: how gloriously different are the saints.

But there must be a real giving up of the self. You must throw it away "blindly" so to speak. Christ will indeed give you a real personality: but you must not go to Him for the sake of that. As long as your own personality is what you are bothering about you are not going to Him at all. The very first step is to try to forget about the self altogether. Your real, new self (which is Christ's and also yours, and yours just because it is His) will not come as long as you are looking for it. It will come when you are looking for Him. Does that sound strange? The same principle holds, you know, for more everyday matters. Even in social life, you will never make a good impression on other people until you stop thinking about what sort of impression you are making. Even in literature and art, no man who bothers about originality will ever be original: whereas if you simply try to tell the truth (without caring twopence how often it has been told before) you will, nine times out of ten, become original without ever having noticed it. The principle runs through all life from top to bottom. Give up your self, and you will find your real self. Lose your life and you will save it. Submit to death, death of your ambitions and favourite wishes every day and death of your whole body in the end: submit with every fibre of your being, and you will find eternal life. Keep back nothing. Nothing that you have not given away will ever be really yours. Nothing in you that has not died will ever be raised from the dead. Look for yourself, and you will find in the long run only hatred, loneliness, despair, rage, ruin, and decay. But look for Christ and you will find Him, and with Him everything else thrown in.

SURPRISED BY JOY

THE SHAPE OF MY EARLY LIFE

Surprised by joy—impatient as the wind
—Wordsworth

TO
DOM BEDE GRIFFITHS, O.S.B.

Preface

This book is written partly in answer to requests that I would tell how I passed from Atheism to Christianity and partly to correct one or two false notions that seem to have got about. How far the story matters to anyone but myself depends on the degree to which others have experienced what I call "joy." If it is at all common, a more detailed treatment of it than has (I believe) been attempted before may be of some use. I have been emboldened to write of it because I notice that a man seldom mentions what he had supposed to be his most idiosyncratic sensations without receiving from at least one (often more) of those present the reply, "What! Have *you* felt that too? I always thought I was the only one."

The book aims at telling the story of my conversion and is not a general autobiography, still less "Confessions" like those of St. Augustine or Rousseau. This means in practice that it gets less like a general autobiography as it goes on. In the earlier chapters the net has to be spread pretty wide in order that, when the explicitly spiritual crisis arrives, the reader may understand what sort of person my childhood and adolescence had made me. When the "build-up" is complete, I confine myself strictly to business and omit everything (however important by ordinary biographical standards) which seems, at that stage, irrelevant. I do not think there is much loss; I never read an autobiography in which the parts devoted to the earlier years were not far the most interesting.

The story is, I fear, suffocatingly subjective; the kind of thing I have never written before and shall probably never write again. I have tried so to write the first chapter that those who can't bear such a story will see at once what they are in for and close the book with the least waste of time.

C. S. L.

Contents

I

THE FIRST YEARS

Happy, but for so happy ill secured.

MILTON

I WAS BORN in the winter of 1898 at Belfast, the son of a so-
licitor and of a clergyman's daughter. My parents had only
two children, both sons, and I was the younger by about
three years. Two very different strains had gone to our making. My father belonged to the first generation of his family
that reached professional station. His grandfather had been a
Welsh farmer; his father, a self-made man, had begun life as
a workman, emigrated to Ireland, and ended as a partner in
the firm of Macilwaine and Lewis, "Boiler-makers, Engineers,
and Iron Ship Builders." My mother was a Hamilton with
many generations of clergymen, lawyers, sailors, and the like
behind her; on her mother's side, through the Warrens, the
blood went back to a Norman knight whose bones lie at
Battle Abbey. The two families from which I spring were as
different in temperament as in origin. My father's people
were true Welshmen, sentimental, passionate, and rhetorical,
easily moved both to anger and to tenderness; men who
laughed and cried a great deal and who had not much of the
talent for happiness. The Hamiltons were a cooler race. Their
minds were critical and ironic and they had the talent for
happiness in a high degree—went straight for it as experienced
travelers go for the best seat in a train. From my earliest years

3

I was aware of the vivid contrast between my mother's cheerful and tranquil affection and the ups and downs of my father's emotional life, and this bred in me long before I was old enough to give it a name a certain distrust or dislike of emotion as something uncomfortable and embarrassing and even dangerous.

Both my parents, by the standards of that time and place, were bookish or "clever" people. My mother had been a promising mathematician in her youth and a B.A. of Queen's College, Belfast, and before her death was able to start me both in French and Latin. She was a voracious reader of good novels, and I think the Merediths and Tolstoys which I have inherited were bought for her. My father's tastes were quite different. He was fond of oratory and had himself spoken on political platforms in England as a young man; if he had had independent means he would certainly have aimed at a political career. In this, unless his sense of honor, which was fine to the point of being Quixotic, had made him unmanageable, he might well have succeeded, for he had many of the gifts once needed by a Parliamentarian—a fine presence, a resonant voice, great quickness of mind, eloquence, and memory. Trollope's political novels were very dear to him; in following the career of Phineas Finn he was, as I now suppose, vicariously gratifying his own desires. He was fond of poetry provided it had elements of rhetoric or pathos, or both; I think *Othello* was his favorite Shakespearean play. He greatly enjoyed nearly all humorous authors, from Dickens to W. W. Jacobs, and was himself, almost without rival, the best *raconteur* I have ever heard; the best, that is, of his own type, the type that acts all the characters in turn with a free use of grimace, gesture, and pantomime. He was never happier than when closeted for an hour or so with one or two of my uncles exchanging "wheezes" (as anecdotes were oddly called in our family). What neither he nor my mother had the least taste for was that kind of literature to which my allegiance was given the moment I could choose books for myself. Neither had ever listened for the horns of elfland. There was no copy either of Keats or Shelley in the house, and the copy of Coleridge was never (to my knowledge) opened. If I am a romantic my parents bear no responsibility for it. Tennyson, indeed, my father liked, but it was the Tennyson of *In Memoriam* and *Locksley Hall*. I never heard from him of the *Lotus Eaters* or the *Morte d'Arthur*. My mother, I have been told, cared for no poetry at all.

In addition to good parents, good food, and a garden (which then seemed large) to play in, I began life with two other blessings. One was our nurse, Lizzie Endicott, in whom even the exacting memory of childhood can discover no flaw —nothing but kindness, gaiety, and good sense. There was no nonsense about "lady nurses" in those days. Through Lizzie we struck our roots into the peasantry of County Down. We were thus free of two very different social worlds. To this I owe my lifelong immunity from the false identification which some people make of refinement with virtue. From before I can remember I had understood that certain jokes could be shared with Lizzie which were impossible in the drawing room; and also that Lizzie was, as nearly as a human can be, simply good.

The other blessing was my brother. Though three years my senior, he never seemed to be an elder brother: we were allies, not to say confederates, from the first. Yet we were very different. Our earliest pictures (and I can remember no time when we were not incessantly drawing) reveal it. His were of ships and trains and battles; mine, when not imitated from his, were of what we both called "dressed animals"—the anthropomorphized beasts of nursery literature. His earliest story—as my elder he preceded me in the transition from drawing to writing—was called *The Young Rajah*. He had already made India "his country"; Animal-Land was mine. I do not think any of the surviving drawings date from the first six years of my life which I am now describing, but I have plenty of them that cannot be much later. From them it appears to me that I had the better talent. From a very early age I could draw movement—figures that looked as if they were really running or fighting—and the perspective is good. But nowhere, either in my brother's work or my own, is there a single line drawn in obedience to an idea, however crude, of beauty. There is action, comedy, invention; but there is not even the germ of a feeling for design, and there is a shocking ignorance of natural form. Trees appear as balls of cotton wool stuck on posts, and there is nothing to show that either of us knew the shape of any leaf in the garden where we played almost daily. This absence of beauty, now that I come to think of it, is characteristic of our childhood. No picture on the walls of my father's house ever attracted—and indeed none deserved—our attention. We never saw a beautiful building nor imagined that a building could be beautiful. My

6

earliest aesthetic experiences, if indeed they were aesthetic, were not of that kind; they were already incurably romantic, not formal. Once in those very early days my brother brought into the nursery the lid of a biscuit tin which he had covered with moss and garnished with twigs and flowers so as to make it a toy garden or a toy forest. That was the first beauty I ever knew. What the real garden had failed to do, the toy garden did. It made me aware of nature—not, indeed, as a storehouse of forms and colors but as something cool, dewy, fresh, exuberant. I do not think the impression was very important at the moment, but it soon became important in memory. As long as I live my imagination of Paradise will retain something of my brother's toy garden. And every day there were what we called "the Green Hills"; that is, the low line of the Castlereagh Hills which we saw from the nursery windows. They were not very far off but they were, to children, quite unattainable. They taught me longing—*Sehnsucht*; made me for good or ill, and before I was six years old, a votary of the Blue Flower.

If aesthetic experiences were rare, religious experiences did not occur at all. Some people have got the impression from my books that I was brought up in strict and vivid Puritanism, but this is quite untrue. I was taught the usual things and made to say my prayers and in due time taken to church. I naturally accepted what I was told but I cannot remember feeling much interest in it. My father, far from being specially Puritanical, was, by nineteenth-century and Church of Ireland standards, rather "high," and his approach to religion, as to literature, was at the opposite pole from what later became my own. The charm of tradition and the verbal beauty of Bible and Prayer Book (all of them for me late and acquired tastes) were his natural delight, and it would have been hard to find an equally intelligent man who cared so little for metaphysics. Of my mother's religion I can say almost nothing from my own memory. My childhood, at all events, was not in the least other-worldly. Except for the toy garden and the Green Hills it was not even imaginative; it lives in my memory mainly as a period of humdrum, prosaic happiness and awakes none of the poignant nostalgia with which I look back on my much less happy boyhood. It is not settled happiness but momentary joy that glorifies the past.

To this general happiness there was one exception. I remember nothing earlier than the terror of certain dreams. It is a very common trouble at that age, yet it still seems to me odd that petted and guarded childhood should so often have in it a window opening on what is hardly less than Hell. My bad dreams were of two kinds, those about specters and those about insects. The second were, beyond comparison, the worse; to this day I would rather meet a ghost than a tarantula. And to this day I could almost find it in my heart to rationalize and justify my phobia. As Owen Barfield once said to me, "The trouble about insects is that they are like French locomotives—they have all the works on the outside." *The works*—that is the trouble. Their angular limbs, their jerky movements, their dry, metallic noises, all suggest either machines that have come to life or life degenerating into mechanism. You may add that in the hive and the anthill we see fully realized the two things that some of us most dread for our own species—the dominance of the female and the dominance of the collective. One fact about the history of this phobia is perhaps worth recording. Much later, in my teens, from reading Lubbock's *Ants, Bees and Wasps*, I developed for a short time a genuinely scientific interest in insects. Other studies soon crowded it out; but while my entomological period lasted my fear almost vanished, and I am inclined to think a real objective curiosity will usually have this cleansing effect.

I am afraid the psychologists will not be content to explain my insect fears by what a simpler generation would diagnose as their cause—a certain detestable picture in one of my nursery books. In it a midget child, a sort of Tom Thumb, stood on a toadstool and was threatened from below by a stag beetle very much larger than himself. This was bad enough; but there is worse to come. The horns of the beetle were strips of cardboard separate from the plate and working on a pivot. By moving a devilish contraption on the *verso* you could make them open and shut like pincers: snip-snap—snip-snap— I can see it while I write. How a woman ordinarily so wise as my mother could have allowed this abomination into the nursery is difficult to understand. Unless, indeed (for now a doubt assails me), unless that picture itself is a product of nightmare. But I think not.

In 1905, my seventh year, the first great change in my life took place. We moved house. My father, growing, I suppose, in prosperity, decided to leave the semidetached villa in which I had been born and build himself a much larger house, further out into what was then the country. The "New

House," as we continued for years to call it, was a large one even by my present standards; to a child it seemed less like a house than a city. My father, who had more capacity for being cheated than any man I have ever known, was badly cheated by his builders; the drains were wrong, the chimneys were wrong, and there was a draft in every room. None of this, however, mattered to a child. To me, the important thing about the move was that the background of my life became larger. The New House is almost a major character in my story. I am a product of long corridors, empty sunlit rooms, upstairs indoor silences, attics explored in solitude, distant noises of gurgling cisterns and pipes, and the noise of wind under the tiles. Also, of endless books. My father bought all the books he read and never got rid of any of them. There were books in the study, books in the drawing room, books in the cloakroom, books (two deep) in the great bookcase on the landing, books in a bedroom, books piled as high as my shoulder in the cistern attic, books of all kinds reflecting every transient stage of my parents' interest, books readable and unreadable, books suitable for a child and books most emphatically not. Nothing was forbidden me. In the seemingly endless rainy afternoons I took volume after volume from the shelves. I had always the same certainty of finding a book that was new to me as a man who walks into a field has of finding a new blade of grass. Where all these books had been before we came to the New House is a problem that never occurred to me until I began writing this paragraph. I have no idea of the answer.

Out of doors was "the view" for which, no doubt, the site

had principally been chosen. From our front door we looked down over wide fields to Belfast Lough and across it to the long mountain line of the Antrim shore—Divis, Colin, Cave Hill. This was in the far-off days when Britain was the world's carrier and the Lough was full of shipping; a delight to both us boys, but most to my brother. The sound of a steamer's horn at night still conjures up my whole boyhood. Behind the house, greener, lower, and nearer than the Antrim mountains, were the Holywood Hills, but it was not till much later that they won my attention. The northwestern prospect was what mattered at first; the interminable summer sunsets behind the blue ridges, and the rooks flying home. In these surroundings the blows of change began to fall.

First of all, my brother was packed off to an English boarding school and thus removed from my life for the greater part of every year. I remember well the rapture of his homecomings for the holidays but have no recollection of any corresponding anguish at his departures. His new life made no difference to the relations between us. I, meanwhile, was going on with my education at home; French and Latin from my mother and everything else from an excellent governess, Annie Harper. I made rather a bugbear of this mild and modest little lady at the time, but all that I can remember assures me that I was unjust. She was a Presbyterian; and a longish lecture which she once interpolated between sums and copies is the first thing I can remember that brought the other world to my mind with any sense of reality. But there were many things that I thought about more. My real life—or what memory reports as my real life—was increasingly one of solitude. I had indeed plenty of people to talk to: my parents, my grandfather Lewis, prematurely old and deaf, who lived with us; the maids; and a somewhat bibulous old gardener. I was, I believe, an intolerable chatterbox. But solitude was nearly always at my command, somewhere in the garden or somewhere in the house. I had now learned both to read and to write; I had a dozen things to do.

What drove me to write was the extreme manual clumsiness from which I have always suffered. I attribute it to a physical defect which my brother and I both inherit from our father; we have only one joint in the thumb. The upper joint (that furthest from the nail) is visible, but it is a mere sham; we cannot bend it. But whatever the cause, nature laid on me from birth an utter incapacity to make anything. With pencil and pen I was handy enough, and I can still tie as good a bow as ever lay on a man's collar; but with a tool or a bat or a gun, a sleeve link or a corkscrew, I have always been unteachable. It was this that forced me to write. I longed to make things, ships, houses, engines. Many sheets of cardboard and pairs of scissors I spoiled, only to turn from my hopeless failures in tears. As a last resource, as a *pis aller*, I was driven to write stories instead; little dreaming to what a world of happiness I was being admitted. You can do more with a castle in a story than with the best cardboard castle that ever stood on a nursery table.

I soon staked out a claim to one of the attics and made it "my study." Pictures, of my own making or cut from the brightly colored Christmas numbers of magazines, were nailed on the walls. There I kept my pen and inkpot and writing books and paintbox; and there

What more felicity can fall to creature
Than to enjoy delight with liberty?

Here my first stories were written, and illustrated, with enormous satisfaction. They were an attempt to combine my two chief literary pleasures—"dressed animals" and "knights in armor." As a result, I wrote about chivalrous mice and rabbits who rode out in complete mail to kill not giants but cats. But already the mood of the systematizer was strong in me; the mood which led Trollope so endlessly to elaborate his Barsetshire. The Animal-Land which came into action in the holidays when my brother was at home was a modern Animal-Land; it had to have trains and steamships if it was to be a country shared with him. It followed, of course, that the medieval Animal-Land about which I wrote my stories must be the same country at an earlier period; and of course the two periods must be properly connected. This led me from romancing to historiography; I set about writing a full history of Animal-Land. Though more than one version of this instructive work is extant, I never succeeded in bringing it down to modern times; centuries take a deal of filling when all the events have to come out of the historian's head. But there is one touch in the *History* that I still recall with some pride. The chivalric adventures which filled my stories were in it alluded to very lightly and the reader was warned that they might be "only legends." Somehow—but heaven knows how —I realized even then that a historian should adopt a critical attitude toward epic material. From history it was only a step to geography. There was soon a map of Animal-Land—several maps, all tolerably consistent. Then Animal-Land had to be geographically related to my brother's India, and India consequently lifted out of its place in the real world. We made it an island, with its north coast running along the back of the Himalayas; between it and Animal-Land my brother rapidly invented the principal steamship routes. Soon there was a whole world and a map of that world which used every color in my paintbox. And those parts of that world which we regarded as our own—Animal-Land and India—were increasingly peopled with consistent characters.

Of the books that I read at this time very few have quite faded from memory, but not all have retained my love. Conan Doyle's *Sir Nigel,* which first set my mind upon "knights in armor," I have never felt inclined to reread. Still less would I now read Mark Twain's *A Connecticut Yankee in King Arthur's Court,* which was then my only source for the Arthurian story, blissfully read for the sake of the romantic elements that came through and with total disregard of the vulgar ridicule directed against them. Much better than either of these was E. Nesbit's trilogy, *Five Children and It, The Phoenix and the Wishing Carpet,* and *The Amulet.* The last did most for me. It first opened my eyes to antiquity, the "dark backward and abysm of time." I can still reread it with delight. *Gulliver* in an unexpurgated and lavishly illustrated edition was one of my favorites, and I pored endlessly over an almost complete set of old *Punches* which stood in my father's study. Tenniel gratified my passion for "dressed animals" with his Russian Bear, British Lion, Egyptian Crocodile and the rest, while his slovenly and perfunctory treatment of vegetation confirmed my own deficiencies. Then came the Beatrix Potter books, and here at last beauty.

It will be clear that at this time—at the age of six, seven, and eight—I was living almost entirely in my imagination; or at least that the imaginative experience of those years now seems to me more important than anything else. Thus I pass over a holiday in Normandy (of which, nevertheless, I retain very clear memories) as a thing of no account; if it could be cut out of my past I should still be almost exactly the man I am. But imagination is a vague word and I must make some distinctions. It may mean the world of reverie, daydream, wish-fulfilling fantasy. Of that I knew more than enough. I often pictured myself cutting a fine figure. But I must insist that this was a totally different activity from the invention of Animal-Land. Animal-Land was not (in that sense) a fantasy at all. I was not one of the characters it contained. I was its creator, not a candidate for admission to it. Invention is essentially different from reverie; if some fail to recognize the difference that is because they have not themselves experienced both. Anyone who has will understand me. In my daydreams I was training myself to be a fool; in mapping and chronicling Animal-Land I was training myself to be a novelist. Note well, a novelist; not a poet. My invented world was full (for me) of interest, bustle, humor, and character; but there was no poetry, even no romance, in it. It was almost astonishingly prosaic.[1] Thus if we use the word imagination

[1] For readers of my children's books, the best way of putting this would be to say that Animal-Land had nothing whatever in common with Narnia except the anthropomorphic beasts. Animal-Land, by its whole quality, excluded the least hint of wonder.

in a third sense, and the highest sense of all, this invented world was not imaginative. But certain other experiences were, and I will now try to record them. The thing has been much better done by Traherne and Wordsworth, but every man must tell his own tale.

The first is itself the memory of a memory. As I stood beside a flowering currant bush on a summer day there suddenly arose in me without warning, and as if from a depth not of years but of centuries, the memory of that earlier morning at the Old House when my brother had brought his toy garden into the nursery. It is difficult to find words strong enough for the sensation which came over me; Milton's "enormous bliss" of Eden (giving the full, ancient meaning to "enormous") comes somewhere near it. It was a sensation, of course, of desire; but desire for what? not, certainly, for a biscuit tin filled with moss, nor even (though that came into it) for my own past. Ἰουλίανποθῶ[2]—and before I knew what I desired, the desire itself was gone, the whole glimpse withdrawn, the world turned commonplace again, or only stirred by a longing for the longing that had just ceased. It had taken only a moment of time; and in a certain sense everything else that had ever happened to me was insignificant in comparison.

The second glimpse came through *Squirrel Nutkin;* through it only, though I loved all the Beatrix Potter books. But the rest of them were merely entertaining; it administered the shock, it was a trouble. It troubled me with what I can only describe as the Idea of Autumn. It sounds fantastic to say that one can be enamored of a season, but that is something

[2] Oh, I desire too much.

like what happened; and, as before, the experience was one of intense desire. And one went back to the book, not to gratify the desire (that was impossible—how can one *possess* Autumn?) but to reawake it. And in this experience also there was the same surprise and the same sense of incalculable importance. It was something quite different from ordinary life and even from ordinary pleasure; something, as they would now say, "in another dimension."

The third glimpse came through poetry. I had become fond of Longfellow's *Saga of King Olaf:* fond of it in a casual, shallow way for its story and its vigorous rhythms. But then, and quite different from such pleasures, and like a voice from far more distant regions, there came a moment when I idly turned the pages of the book and found the unrhymed translation of *Tegner's Drapa* and read

> *I heard a voice that cried,*
> *Balder the beautiful*
> *Is dead, is dead——*

I knew nothing about Balder; but instantly I was uplifted into huge regions of northern sky, I desired with almost sickening intensity something never to be described (except that it is cold, spacious, severe, pale, and remote) and then, as in the other examples, found myself at the very same moment already falling out of that desire and wishing I were back in it.

The reader who finds these three episodes of no interest need read this book no further, for in a sense the central story of my life is about nothing else. For those who are still disposed to proceed I will only underline the quality common to the three experiences; it is that of an unsatisfied desire which is itself more desirable than any other satisfaction. I call it Joy, which is here a technical term and must be sharply distinguished both from Happiness and from Pleasure. Joy (in my sense) has indeed one characteristic, and one only, in common with them; the fact that anyone who has experienced it will want it again. Apart from that, and considered only in its quality, it might almost equally well be called a particular kind of unhappiness or grief. But then it is a kind we want. I doubt whether anyone who has tasted it would ever, if both were in his power, exchange it for all the pleasures in the world. But then Joy is never in our power and pleasure often is.

I cannot be absolutely sure whether the things I have just been speaking of happened before or after the great loss which befell our family and to which I must now turn. There came a night when I was ill and crying both with headache and toothache and distressed because my mother did not come to me. That was because she was ill too; and what was odd was that there were several doctors in her room, and voices and comings and goings all over the house and doors shutting and opening. It seemed to last for hours. And then my father, in tears, came into my room and began to try to convey to my terrified mind things it had never conceived before. It was in fact cancer and followed the usual course; an operation (they operated in the patient's house in those days), an apparent convalescence, a return of the disease, increasing pain, and death. My father never fully recovered from this loss.

Children suffer not (I think) less than their elders, but differently. For us boys the real bereavement had happened before our mother died. We lost her gradually as she was gradually withdrawn from our life into the hands of nurses and delirium and morphia, and as our whole existence changed into something alien and menacing, as the house became full of strange smells and midnight noises and sinister whispered conversations. This had two further results, one very evil and one very good. It divided us from our father as well as our mother. They say that a shared sorrow draws people closer together; I can hardly believe that it often has that effect when those who share it are of widely different ages. If I may trust my own experience, the sight of adult misery and adult terror has an effect on children which is merely paralyzing and alienating. Perhaps it was our fault. Perhaps if we had been better children we might have lightened our father's sufferings at this time. We certainly did not. His nerves had never been of the steadiest and his emotions had always been uncontrolled. Under the pressure of anxiety his temper became incalculable; he spoke wildly and acted unjustly. Thus by a peculiar cruelty of fate, during those months the unfortunate man, had he but known it, was really losing his sons as well as his wife. We were coming, my brother and I, to rely more and more exclusively on each other for all that made life bearable; to have confidence only in each other. I expect that we (or at any rate I) were already learning to lie to him. Everything that had made the house a home had failed us; everything except one another. We drew daily closer together (that was the good result)—two frightened urchins huddled for warmth in a bleak world.

Grief in childhood is complicated with many other miseries. I was taken into the bedroom where my mother lay dead; as they said, "to see her," in reality, as I at once knew, "to see it." There was nothing that a grown-up would call disfigurement—except for that total disfigurement which is death itself. Grief was overwhelmed in terror. To this day I do not know what they mean when they call dead bodies beautiful. The ugliest man alive is an angel of beauty compared with the loveliest of the dead. Against all the subsequent paraphernalia of coffin, flowers, hearse, and funeral I reacted with horror. I even lectured one of my aunts on the absurdity of mourning clothes in a style which would have seemed to most adults both heartless and precocious; but this was our dear Aunt Annie, my maternal uncle's Canadian wife, a woman almost as sensible and sunny as my mother herself. To my hatred for what I already felt to be all the fuss and flummery of the funeral I may perhaps trace something in me which I now recognize as a defect but which I have never fully overcome—a distaste for all that is public, all that belongs to the collective; a boorish inaptitude for formality.

My mother's death was the occasion of what some (but not I) might regard as my first religious experience. When her case was pronounced hopeless I remembered what I had been taught; that prayers offered in faith would be granted. I accordingly set myself to produce by will power a firm belief that my prayers for her recovery would be successful; and, as I thought, I achieved it. When nevertheless she died I shifted my ground and worked myself into a belief that there was to be a miracle. The interesting thing is that my disappointment produced no results beyond itself. The thing hadn't worked, but I was used to things not working, and I thought no more about it. I think the truth is that the belief into which I had hypnotized myself was itself too irreligious for its failure to cause any religious revolution. I had approached God, or my idea of God, without love, without awe, even without fear. He was, in my mental picture of this miracle, to appear neither as Savior nor as Judge, but merely as a magician; and when He had done what was required of Him I supposed He would simply—well, go away. It never crossed my mind that the tremendous contact which I solicited should have any consequences beyond restoring the *status quo*. I imagine that a "faith" of this kind is often generated in children and that its disappointment is of no religious importance; just as the things believed in, if they could happen and be only as the child pictures them, would be of no religious importance either.

With my mother's death all settled happiness, all that was tranquil and reliable, disappeared from my life. There was to be much fun, many pleasures. many stabs of Joy; but no more of the old security. It was sea and islands now; the great continent had sunk like Atlantis.

II

CONCENTRATION CAMP

Arithmetic with Coloured Rods.
TIMES EDUCATIONAL SUPPLEMENT,
Nov. 19, 1954

CLOP-CLOP-CLOP-CLOP . . . we are in a four-wheeler rattling over the uneven squaresets of the Belfast streets through the damp twilight of a September evening, 1908; my father, my brother, and I. I am going to school for the first time. We are in low spirits. My brother, who has most reason to be so, for he alone knows what we are going to, shows his feelings least. He is already a veteran. I perhaps am buoyed up by a little excitement, but very little. The most important fact at the moment is the horrible clothes I have been made to put on. Only this morning—only two hours ago—I was running wild in shorts and blazer and sand shoes. Now I am choking and sweating, itching too, in thick dark stuff, throttled by an Eton collar, my feet already aching with unaccustomed boots. I am wearing knickerbockers that button at the knee. Every night for some forty weeks of every year and for many a year I am to see the red, smarting imprint of those buttons in my flesh when I undress. Worst of all is the bowler hat, apparently made of iron, which grasps my head. I have read of boys in the same predicament who welcomed such things as signs of growing up; I had no such feeling. Nothing in my experience had ever suggested to me that it was nicer to be a schoolboy than a child or nicer to be a man than a schoolboy. My brother never talked much about school in the holidays. My father, whom I implicitly believed, represented adult life as one of incessant drudgery under the continual threat of financial ruin. In this he did not mean to deceive us. Such was his temperament that when he exclaimed, as he frequently did, "There'll soon be nothing for it but the workhouse," he momentarily believed, or at least felt, what he said. I took it all literally and had the gloomiest anticipation of adult life. In the meantime, the putting on of the school clothes was, I well knew, the assumption of a prison uniform.

We reach the quay and go on board the old "Fleetwood boat"; after some miserable strolling about the deck my father bids us good-by. He is deeply moved; I, alas, am mainly embarrassed and self-conscious. When he has gone ashore we almost, by comparison, cheer up. My brother begins to show me over the ship and tell me about all the other shipping in sight. He is an experienced traveler and a complete man of the world. A certain agreeable excitement steals over me. I like the reflected port and starboard lights on the oily water, the rattle of winches, the warm smell from the engine-room skylight. We cast off. The black space widens between us and the quay; I feel the throb of screws underneath me. Soon we are dropping down the Lough and there is a taste of salt on one's lips, and that cluster of lights astern, receding from us, is everything I have known. Later, when we have gone to our bunks, it begins to blow. It is a rough night and my brother is seasick. I absurdly envy him this accomplishment. He is behaving as experienced travelers should. By great efforts I succeed in vomiting; but it is a poor affair—I was, and am, an obstinately good sailor.

No Englishman will be able to understand my first impressions of England. When we disembarked, I suppose at about six next morning (but it seemed to be midnight), I found myself in a world to which I reacted with immediate hatred. The flats of Lancashire in the early morning are in reality a dismal sight; to me they were like the banks of Styx. The strange English accents with which I was surrounded seemed like the voices of demons. But what was worst was the English landscape from Fleetwood to Euston. Even to my adult eye that main line still appears to run through the dullest and most unfriendly strip in the island. But to a child who had always lived near the sea and in sight of high ridges it appeared as I suppose Russia might appear to an English boy. The flatness! The interminableness! The miles and miles of featureless land, shutting one in from the sea, imprisoning, suffocating! Everything was wrong; wooden fences instead of stone walls and hedges, red brick farmhouses instead of white cottages, the fields too big, haystacks the wrong shape. Well does the *Kalevala* say that in the stranger's house the floor is full of knots. I have made up the quarrel since; but at that moment I conceived a hatred for England which took many years to heal.

Our destination was the little town of—let us call it Belsen—in Hertfordshire. "Green Hertfordshire," Lamb calls it; but it was not green to a boy bred in County Down. It was flat Hertfordshire, flinty Hertfordshire, Hertfordshire of the yellow soil. There is the same difference between the climate of Ireland and of England as between that of England and the Continent. There was far more weather at Belsen than I had ever met before; there I first knew bitter frost and stinging fog, sweltering heat and thunderstorms on the great scale. There, through the curtainless dormitory windows, I first came to know the ghastly beauty of the full moon.

The school, as I first knew it, consisted of some eight or nine boarders and about as many day boys. Organized games, except for endless rounders in the flinty playground, had long been moribund and were finally abandoned not very long after my arrival. There was no bathing except one's weekly bath in the bathroom. I was already doing Latin exercises (as taught by my mother) when I went there in 1908, and I was still doing Latin exercises when I left there in 1910; I had never got in sight of a Roman author. The only stimulating element in the teaching consisted of a few well-used canes which hung on the green iron chimney piece of the single schoolroom. The teaching staff consisted of the headmaster and proprietor (we called him Oldie), his grown-up son (Wee Wee), and an usher. The ushers succeeded one another with great rapidity; one lasted for less than a week. Another was dismissed in the presence of the boys, with a rider from Oldie to the effect that if he were not in Holy Orders he would kick him downstairs. This curious scene took place in the dormitory, though I cannot remember why. All these ushers (except the one who stayed less than a week) were obviously as much in awe of Oldie as we. But there came a time when there were no more ushers, and Oldie's youngest daughter taught the junior pupils. By that time there were only five boarders, and Oldie finally gave up his school and sought a cure of souls. I was one of the last survivors, and left the ship only when she went down under us.

Oldie lived in a solitude of power, like a sea captain in the days of sail. No man or woman in that house spoke to him as an equal. No one except Wee Wee initiated conversation with him at all. At meal times we boys had a glimpse of his family life. His son sat on his right hand; they two had separate food. His wife and three grown-up daughters (silent), the usher (silent), and the boys (silent) munched their inferior messes. His wife, though I think she never addressed Oldie, was allowed to make something of a reply to him; the girls—three tragic figures, dressed summer and winter in the same shabby black—never went beyond an almost whispered "Yes, Papa," or "No, Papa," on the rare occasions when they were addressed. Few visitors entered the house. Beer, which Oldie and Wee Wee drank regularly at dinner, was offered to the usher but he was expected to refuse; the one who accepted got his pint, but was taught his place by being asked a few moments later in a voice of thunderous irony, "Perhaps you would like a little *more* beer, Mr. N.?" Mr. N., a man of spirit, replied casually, "Well, thank you, Mr. C., I think I would." He was the one who did not stay till the end of his first week; and the rest of that day was a black one for us boys.

I myself was rather a pet or mascot of Oldie's—a position which I swear I never sought and of which the advantages were purely negative. Even my brother was not one of his favorite victims. For he had his favorite victims, boys who could do nothing right. I have known Oldie enter the schoolroom after breakfast, cast his eyes round, and remark, "Oh, there you are, Rees, you horrid boy. If I'm not too tired I shall give you a good drubbing this afternoon." He was not angry, nor was he joking. He was a big, bearded man with full lips like an Assyrian king on a monument, immensely strong, physically dirty. Everyone talks of sadism nowadays but I question whether his cruelty had any erotic element in it. I half divined then, and seem to see clearly now, what all his whipping boys had in common. They were the boys who fell below a certain social status, the boys with vulgar accents. Poor P.—dear, honest, hard-working, friendly, healthily pious P.—was flogged incessantly, I now think, for one offense only; he was the son of a dentist. I have seen Oldie make that child bend down at one end of the schoolroom and then take a run of the room's length at each stroke; but P. was the trained sufferer of countless thrashings and no sound escaped him until, toward the end of the torture, there came a noise quite unlike a human utterance. That peculiar croaking or rattling cry, that, and the gray faces of all the other boys, and their deathlike stillness, are among the memories I could willingly dispense with.[1]

The curious thing is that despite all this cruelty we did surprisingly little work. This may have been partly because the cruelty was irrational and unpredictable; but it was partly because of the curious methods employed. Except at geometry (which he really liked) it might be said that Oldie did not

---

[1] This punishment was for a mistake in a geometrical proof.

teach at all. He called his class up and asked questions. When the replies were unsatisfactory he said in a low, calm voice, "Bring me my cane. I see I shall need it." If a boy became confused Oldie flogged the desk, shouting in a crescendo, "Think —Think—THINK!!" Then, as the prelude to execution, he muttered, "Come out, come out, come out." When really angry he proceeded to antics; worming for wax in his ear with his little finger and babbling, "Aye, aye, aye, aye . . ." I have seen him leap up and dance round and round like a performing bear. Meanwhile, almost in whispers, Wee Wee or the usher, or (later) Oldie's youngest daughter, was questioning us juniors at another desk. "Lessons" of this sort did not take very long; what was to be done with the boys for the rest of the time? Oldie had decided that they could, with least trouble to himself, be made to do arithmetic. Accordingly, when you entered school at nine o'clock you took your slate and began doing sums. Presently you were called up to "say a lesson." When that was finished you went back to your place and did more sums—and so forever. All the other arts and sciences thus appeared as islands (mostly rocky and dangerous islands)

> *Which like to rich and various gems inlaid*
> *The unadorned bosom of the deep*

—the deep being a shoreless ocean of arithmetic. At the end of the morning you had to say how many sums you had done; and it was not quite safe to lie. But supervision was slack and very little assistance was given. My brother—I have told you that he was already a man of the world—soon found the proper solution. He announced every morning with perfect truth that he had done five sums; he did not add that they were the same five every day. It would be interesting to know how many thousand times he did them.

I must restrain myself. I could continue to describe Oldie for many pages; some of the worst is unsaid. But perhaps it would be wicked, and it is certainly not obligatory, to do so. One good thing I can tell of him. Impelled by conscience, a boy once confessed to him an otherwise undetectable lie. The ogre was touched; he only patted the terrified boy's back and said, "Always stick to the truth." I can also say that though he taught geometry cruelly, he taught it well. He forced us to reason, and I have been the better for those geometry lessons all my life. For the rest, there is a possible explanation of his behavior which renders it more forgivable. Years after, my brother met a man who had grown up in the house next door to Oldie's school. That man and his family, and (I think) the neighbors in general, believed Oldie to be insane. Perhaps they were right. And if he had fairly recently become so, it would explain a thing which puzzles me. At that school as I knew it most boys learned nothing and no boy learned much. But Oldie could boast an impressive record of scholarships in the past. His school cannot always have been the swindle it was in our time.

You may ask how our father came to send us there. Certainly not because he made a careless choice. The surviving correspondence shows that he had considered many other schools before fixing on Oldie's; and I know him well enough to be sure that in such a matter he would never have been guided by his first thoughts (which would probably have been right) nor even by his twenty-first (which would at least have been explicable). Beyond doubt he would have prolonged deliberation till his hundred-and-first; and they would be infallibly and invincibly wrong. This is what always happens to the deliberations of a simple man who thinks he is a subtle one. Like Earle's *Scepticke in Religion* he "is always too hard for himself." My father piqued himself on what he called "reading between the lines." The obvious meaning of any fact or document was always suspect: the true and inner meaning, invisible to all eyes except his own, was unconsciously created by the restless fertility of his imagination. While he thought he was interpreting Oldie's prospectus, he was really composing a school story in his own mind. And all this, I doubt not, with extreme conscientiousness and even some anguish. It might, perhaps, have been expected that this story of his would presently be blown away by the real story which we had to tell after we had gone to Belsen. But this did not happen. I believe it rarely happens. If the parents in each generation always or often knew what really goes on at their sons' schools, the history of education would be very different. At any rate, my brother and I certainly did not succeed in impressing the truth on our father's mind. For one thing (and this will become clearer in the sequel) he was a man not easily informed. His mind was too active to be an accurate receiver. What he thought he had heard was never exactly what you had said. We did not even try very hard. Like other children, we had no standard of comparison; we supposed the miseries of Belsen to be the common and unavoidable miseries of all schools. Vanity helped to tie our tongues. A boy home from school (especially during that first week when the holidays seem eternal) likes to cut a dash. He would rather represent his master as a buffoon than an ogre. He would hate to be thought a coward and a crybaby, and he cannot paint the true picture of his concentration camp without admitting himself to have been for the last thirteen weeks a pale, quivering, tear-stained, obsequious slave. We all like showing scars received in battle; the wounds of the *ergastulum*, less. My father must not bear the blame for our wasted and miserable years at Oldie's; and now, in Dante's words, "to treat of the good that I found there."

First, I learned, if not friendship, at least gregariousness. There had been bullying at the school when my brother first went there. I had my brother's protection for my first few terms (after which he left to go to a school we may call Wyvern) but I doubt if it was necessary. During those last declining years of the school we boarders were too few and too badly treated to do or suffer much in that way. Also, after a certain time, there were no new boys. We had our quarrels, which seemed serious enough at the time; but long before the end we had known one another too long and suffered too much together not to be, at the least, very old acquaintance. That, I think, is why Belsen did me, in the long run, so little harm. Hardly any amount of oppression from above takes the heart out of a boy like oppression from his fellows. We had many pleasant hours alone together, we five remaining boarders. The abandonment of organized games, though a wretched preparation for the public-school life to which most

of us were destined, was at the time a great blessing. We were
sent out for walks alone on half holidays. We did not do
much walking. We bought sweets in drowsy village shops
and pottered about on the canal bank or sat at the brow of a
railway cutting watching a tunnel mouth for trains. Hertfordshire came to look less hostile. Our talk was not bound
down to the narrow interests which satisfy public-school
boys; we still had the curiosity of children. I can even remember from those days what must have been the first metaphys-
ical argument I ever took part in. We debated whether the
future was like a line you can't see or like a line that is not
yet drawn. I have forgotten which side I took though I
know that I took it with great zeal. And always there was
what Chesterton calls "the slow maturing of old jokes."

The reader will notice that school was thus coming to reflect a pattern I had already encountered in my home life.
At home, the bad times had drawn my brother and me closer
together; here, where the times were always bad, the fear
and hatred of Oldie had something the same effect upon us
all. His school was in some ways very like Dr. Grimstone's
school in *Vice Versa;* but unlike Dr. Grimstone's it contained
no informer. We stood foursquare against the common
enemy. I suspect that this pattern, occurring twice and so
early in my life, has unduly biased my whole outlook. To
this day the vision of the world which comes most naturally
to me is one in which "we two" or "we few" (and in a sense
"we happy few") stand together against something stronger
and larger. England's position in 1940 was to me no surprise;
it was the sort of thing that I always expect. Hence while

friendship has been by far the chief source of my happiness, acquaintance or general society has always meant little to me, and I cannot quite understand why a man should wish to know more people than he can make real friends of. Hence, too, a very defective, perhaps culpably defective, interest in large impersonal movements, causes and the like. The concern aroused in me by a battle (whether in story or in reality) is almost in an inverse ratio to the number of the combatants.

In another way too Oldie's school presently repeated my home experience. Oldie's wife died; and in term time. He reacted to bereavement by becoming more violent than before; so much so that Wee Wee made a kind of apology for him to the boys. You will remember that I had already learned to fear and hate emotion; here was a fresh reason to do so.

But I have not yet mentioned the most important thing that befell me at Oldie's. There first I became an effective believer. As far as I know, the instrument was the church to which we were taken twice every Sunday. This was high "Anglo-Catholic." On the conscious level I reacted strongly against its peculiarities—was I not an Ulster Protestant, and were not these unfamiliar rituals an essential part of the hated English atmosphere? Unconsciously, I suspect, the candles and incense, the vestments and the hymns sung on our knees, may have had a considerable, and opposite, effect on me. But I do not think they were the important thing. What really mattered was that I here heard the doctrines of Christianity (as distinct from general "uplift") taught by men who obviously believed them. As I had no skepticism, the effect was to bring to life what I would already have said that I believed. In this experience there was a great deal of fear. I do not think there was more than was wholesome or even necessary; but if in my books I have spoken too much of Hell, and if critics want a historical explanation of the fact, they must seek it not in the supposed Puritanism of my Ulster childhood but in the Anglo-Catholicism of the church at Belsen. I feared for my soul; especially on certain blazing moonlit nights in that curtainless dormitory—how the sound of other boys breathing in their sleep comes back! The effect, so far as I can judge, was entirely good. I began seriously to pray and to read my Bible and to attempt to obey my conscience. Religion was among the subjects which we often discussed; discussed, if my memory serves me, in an entirely healthy and profitable way, with great gravity and without hysteria, and without the shamefacedness of older boys. How I went back from this beginning you shall hear later.

Intellectually, the time I spent at Oldie's was almost entirely wasted; if the school had not died, and if I had been left there two years more, it would probably have sealed my fate as a scholar for good. Geometry and some pages in West's *English Grammar* (but even those I think I found for myself) are the only items on the credit side. For the rest, all that rises out of the sea of arithmetic is a jungle of dates, battles, exports, imports and the like, forgotten as soon as learned and perfectly useless had they been remembered. There was also a great decline in my imaginative life. For many years Joy (as I have defined it) was not only absent but forgotten. My reading was now mainly rubbish; but as there was no library at the school we must not make Oldie responsible for that. I read twaddling school stories in *The Captain*. The pleasure here was, in the proper sense, mere wish fulfillment and fantasy; one enjoyed vicariously the triumphs of the hero. When the boy passes from nursery literature to school stories he is going down, not up. *Peter Rabbit* pleases a disinterested imagination, for the child does not want to be a rabbit, though he may like pretending to be a rabbit as he may later like acting Hamlet; but the story of the unpromising boy who became captain of the First Eleven exists precisely to feed his real ambitions. I also developed a great taste for all the fiction I could get about the ancient world: *Quo Vadis, Darkness and Dawn, The Gladiators, Ben Hur*. It might be expected that this arose out of my new concern for my religion, but I think not. Early Christians came into many of these stories, but they were not what I was after. I simply wanted sandals, temples, togas, slaves, emperors, galleys, amphitheaters; the attraction, as I now see, was erotic, and erotic in rather a morbid way. And they were mostly, as literature, rather bad books. What has worn better, and what I took to at the same time, is the work of Rider Haggard; and also the "scientifiction" of H. G. Wells. The idea of other planets exercised upon me then a peculiar, heady attraction, which was quite different from any other of my literary interests. Most emphatically it was not the romantic spell of *Das Ferne*. "Joy" (in my technical sense) never darted from Mars or the Moon. This was something coarser and stronger. The interest, when the fit was upon me, was ravenous, like a lust. This particular coarse strength I have come to accept as a mark that the interest which has it is psychological, not spiritual;

behind such a fierce tang there lurks, I suspect, a psycho-analytical explanation. I may perhaps add that my own planetary romances have been not so much the gratification of that fierce curiosity as its exorcism. The exorcism worked by reconciling it with, or subjecting it to, the other, the more elusive, and genuinely imaginative, impulse. That the ordinary interest in scientifiction is an affair for psychoanalysts is borne out by the fact that all who like it, like it thus ravenously, and equally by the fact that those who do not, are often nauseated by it. The repulsion of the one sort has the same coarse strength as the fascinated interest of the other and is equally a telltale.

So much for Oldie's; but the year was not all term. Life at a vile boarding school is in this way a good preparation for the Christian life, that it teaches one to live by hope. Even, in a sense, by faith; for at the beginning of each term, home and the holidays are so far off that it is as hard to realize them as to realize heaven. They have the same pitiful unreality when confronted with immediate horrors. Tomorrow's geometry blots out the distant end of term as tomorrow's operation may blot out the hope of Paradise. And yet, term after term, the unbelievable happened. Fantastical and astronomical figures like "this time six weeks" shrank into practicable figures like "this time next week," and then "this time tomorrow," and the almost supernatural bliss of the Last Day punctually appeared. It was a delight that almost demanded to be stayed with flagons and comforted with apples; a delight that tingled down the spine and troubled the belly and at moments went near to stopping the breath. Of course this had a terrible and equally relevant reverse side. In the first week of the holidays we might acknowledge that term would come again—as a young man, in peacetime, in full health, acknowledges that he will one day die. But like him we could not even by the grimmest *memento mori* be brought to realize it. And there too, each time, the unbelievable happened. The grinning skull finally peered through all disguises; the last hour, held at bay by every device our will and imaginations knew, came in the end, and once more it was the bowler hat, the Eton collar, the knickerbockers, and (clop-clop-clop-clop) the evening drive to the quay. In all seriousness I think that the life of faith is easier to me because of these memories. To think, in sunny and confident times, that I shall die and rot, or to think that one day all this universe will slip away and become memory (as Oldie slipped away into memory three times a year, and with him the canes and the disgusting food, the stinking sanitation and the cold beds)—this is easier to us if we have seen just that sort of thing happening before. We have learned not to take present things at their face value.

In attempting to give an account of our home life at this time I am troubled by doubts about chronology. School affairs can to some extent be dated by surviving records, but the slow, continuous unfolding of family life escapes them. Our slight alienation from our father imperceptibly increased. In part no one was to blame; in a very great part we were to blame. A temperamental widower, still prostrated by the loss of his wife, must be a very good and wise man indeed if he makes no mistakes in bringing up two noisy and mischievous schoolboys who reserve their confidence wholly for each other. And my father's good qualities as well as his weaknesses incapacitated him for the task. He was far too manly and generous to strike a child for the gratification of his anger; and he was too impulsive ever to punish a child in cold blood and on principle. He therefore relied wholly on his tongue as the instrument of domestic discipline. And here that fatal bent toward dramatization and rhetoric (I speak of it the more freely since I inherit it) produced a pathetic yet comic result. When he opened his mouth to reprove us he no doubt intended a short well-chosen appeal to our common sense and conscience. But alas, he had been a public speaker long before he became a father. He had for many years been a public prosecutor. Words came to him and intoxicated him as they came. What actually happened was that a small boy who had walked on damp grass in his slippers or left a bathroom in a pickle found himself attacked with something like Cicero on Catiline, or Burke on Warren Hastings; simile piled on simile, rhetorical question on rhetorical question, the flash of an orator's eye and the thundercloud of an orator's brow, the gestures, the cadences and the pauses. The pauses might be the chief danger. One was so long that my brother, quite innocently supposing the denunciation to have ended, humbly took up his book and resumed his reading; a gesture which my father (who had after all only made a rhetorical miscalculation of about a second and a half) not unnaturally took for "cool, premeditated insolence." The ludicrous disproportion between such harangues and their occasions puts me in mind of the advocate in Martial who thun-

ders about all the villains of Roman history while meantime
lis est de tribus capellis—

> *This case, I beg the court to note,*
> *Concerns a trespass by a goat.*

My poor father, while he spoke, forgot not only the offense,
but the capacities, of his audience. All the resources of his
immense vocabulary were poured forth. I can still remember
such words as "abominable," "sophisticated," and "surreptitious." You will not get the full flavor unless you know an
angry Irishman's energy in explosive consonants and the rich
growl of his r's. A worse treatment could hardly have been
applied. Up to a certain age these invectives filled me with
boundless terror and dismay. From the wilderness of the
adjectives and the welter of the unintelligible, emerged ideas
which I thought I understood only too well, as I heard with
implicit and literal belief that our Father's ruin was approaching, that we should all soon beg our bread in the streets, that he
would shut up the house and keep us at school all the year
round, that we should be sent to the colonies and there end in
misery the career of crime on which we had, it seemed, already embarked. All security seemed to be taken from me;
there was no solid ground beneath my feet. It is significant
that at this time if I woke in the night and did not immediately
hear my brother's breathing from the neighboring bed, I
often suspected that my father and he had secretly risen while
I slept and gone off to America—that I was finally abandoned.
Such was the effect of my father's rhetoric up to a certain
age; then, quite suddenly, it became ridiculous. I can even

remember the moment of the change, and the story well illustrates both the justice of my father's anger and the unhappy way in which he expressed it. One day my brother decided it would be a good thing to make a tent. Accordingly we procured a dust sheet from one of the attics. The next step was to find uprights; the stepladder in the wash house suggested itself. For a boy with a hatchet it was the work of a moment to reduce this to a number of disconnected poles. Four of these were then planted in the earth and the sheet draped over them. To make sure that the whole structure was really reliable my brother then tried sitting on the top of it. We remembered to put away the ragged remains of the sheet but quite forgot about the uprights. That evening, when my father had come home from work and dined, he went for a stroll in the garden, accompanied by us. The sight of four slender wooden posts rising from the grass moved in him a pardonable curiosity. Interrogation followed; on this occasion we told the truth. Then the lightnings flashed and the thunder roared; and all would have gone now as it had gone on a dozen previous occasions, but for the climax—"Instead of which I find you have cut up the stepladder. And what for, forsooth? To make a thing like an abortive Punch-and-Judy show." At that moment we both hid our faces; not, alas, to cry.

As will be seen from this anecdote one dominant factor in our life at home was the daily absence of our father from about nine in the morning till six at night. For the rest of the day we had the house to ourselves, except for the cook and housemaid with whom we were sometimes at war and sometimes in alliance. Everything invited us to develop a life that had no connection with our father. The most important of our activities was the endless drama of Animal-Land and India, and this of itself isolated us from him.

But I must not leave the reader under the impression that all the happy hours of the holidays occurred during our father's absence. His temperament was mercurial, his spirits rose as easily as they fell, and his forgiveness was as thoroughgoing as his displeasure. He was often the most jovial and companionable of parents. He could "play the fool" as well as any of us, and had no regard for his own dignity, "conned no state." I could not, of course, at that age see what good company (by adult standards) he was, his humor being of the sort that requires at least some knowledge of life for its full appreciation; I merely basked in it as in fine weather. And all the time there was the sensuous delight of being at home, the delight of luxury—"civilization," as we called it. I spoke just now of *Vice Versa*. Its popularity was surely due to something more than farce. It is the only truthful school story in existence. The machinery of the Garuda Stone really serves to bring out in their true colors (which would otherwise seem exaggerated) the sensations which every boy had on passing from the warmth and softness and dignity of his home life to the privations, the raw and sordid ugliness, of school. I say "had" not "has"; for perhaps homes have gone down in the world and schools gone up since then.

It will be asked whether we had no friends, no neighbors, no relatives. We had. To one family in particular our debt is so great that it had better be left, with some other matters, to the next chapter.

III

MOUNTBRACKEN AND CAMPBELL

For all these fair people in hall were in their first age;
none happier under the heaven; their king, the man of
noblest temper. It would be a hard task to-day to find so
brave a fellowship in any castle.

GAWAIN AND THE GREEN KNIGHT

To SPEAK of my nearer relatives is to remind myself how the contrast of Lewis and Hamilton dominated my whole early life. It began, for me, with the grandparents. Grandfather Lewis, deaf, slow-moving, humming his psalm chants, much concerned for his health and prone to remind the family that he would not be with them long, is contrasted with Grandmother Hamilton, the sharp-tongued, sharp-witted widow, full of heterodox opinions (even, to the scandal of the whole connection, a Home Ruler), every inch a Warren, indifferent to convention as only an old Southern Irish aristocrat could be, living alone in a large tumble-down house with half a hundred cats for company. To how many an innocent conversational gambit did she reply, "You're talking great nonsense"? Born a little later, she would, I think, have been a Fabian. She met vague small talk with ruthless statements of ascertainable fact and well-worn maxims with a tart demand for evidence. Naturally, people called her eccentric. Coming down a generation I find the same opposi-

42

tion. My father's elder brother "Uncle Joe," with his family of two boys and three girls, lived very close to us while we were at the Old House. His younger son was my earliest friend, but we drifted apart as we grew older. Uncle Joe was both a clever man and a kind, and especially fond of me. But I remember nothing that was said by our elders in that house; it was simply "grown-up" conversation—about people, business, politics, and health, I suppose. But "Uncle Gussie"—my mother's brother, A. W. Hamilton—talked to me as if we were of an age. That is, he talked about Things. He told me all the science I could then take in, clearly, eagerly, without silly jokes and condescensions, obviously liking it as much as I did. He thus provided the intellectual background for my reading of H. G. Wells. I do not suppose he cared for me as a person half so much as Uncle Joe did; and that (call it an injustice or not) was what I liked. During these talks our attention was fixed not on one another but on the subject. His Canadian wife I have already mentioned. In her also I found what I liked best—an unfailing, kindly welcome without a hint of sentimentality, unruffled good sense, the unobtrusive talent for making all things at all times as cheerful and comfortable as circumstances allowed. What one could not have one did without and made the best of it. The tendency of the Lewises to reopen wounds and to rouse sleeping dogs was unknown to her as to her husband.

But we had other kin who mattered to us far more than our aunts and uncles. Less than a mile from our home stood the largest house I then knew, which I will here call Mountbracken, and there lived Sir W. E. Lady E. was my mother's first cousin and perhaps my mother's dearest friend, and it was no doubt for my mother's sake that she took upon herself the heroic work of civilizing my brother and me. We had a standing invitation to lunch at Mountbracken whenever we were at home; to this, almost entirely, we owe it that we did not grow up savages. The debt is not only to Lady E. ("Cousin Mary") but to her whole family; walks, motor drives (in those days an exciting novelty), picnics, and invitations to the theater were showered on us, year after year, with a kindness which our rawness, our noise, and our unpunctuality never seemed to weary. We were at home there almost as much as in our own house, but with this great difference, that a certain standard of manners had to be kept up. Whatever I know (it is not much) of courtesy and *savoir faire* I learned at Mountbracken.

Sir W. ("Cousin Quartus") was the eldest of several brothers who owned between them one of the most important industrial concerns in Belfast. He belonged in fact to just that class and generation of which the modern man gets his impressions through Galsworthy's Forsytes. Unless Cousin Quartus was very untrue to type (as he may well have been) that impression is grossly unjust. No one less like a Galsworthian character ever existed. He was gracious, childlike, deeply and religiously humble, and abounding in charity. No man could feel more fully his responsibility to dependants. He had a good deal of boyish gaiety about him; at the same time I always felt that the conception of duty dominated his life. His stately figure, his gray beard, and his strikingly handsome profile make up one of the most venerable images in my memory. Physical beauty was indeed common to most of the family. Cousin Mary was the very type of the beautiful old lady, with her silver hair and her sweet Southern Irish voice; foreigners must be warned that this resembles what they call a "brogue" about as little as the speech of a Highland gentle-man resembles the jargon of the Glasgow slums. But it was the three daughters whom we knew best. All three were "grown up" but in fact much nearer to us in age than any other grown-ups we knew, and all three were strikingly handsome. H., the eldest and the gravest, was a Juno, a dark queen who at certain moments looked like a Jewess. K. was more like a Valkyrie (though all, I think, were good horse-women) with her father's profile. There was in her face something of the delicate fierceness of a thoroughbred horse, an indignant fineness of nostril, the possibility of an excellent disdain. She had what the vanity of my own sex calls a "masculine" honesty; no man ever was a truer friend. As for the youngest, G., I can only say that she was the most beauti-ful woman I have ever seen, perfect in shape and color and voice and every movement—but who can describe beauty? The reader may smile at this as the far-off echo of a pre-cocious calf love, but he will be wrong. There are beauties so unambiguous that they need no lens of that kind to reveal them; they are visible even to the careless and objective eyes of a child. (The first woman who ever spoke to my blood was a dancing mistress at a school that will come in a later chapter.)

In some ways Mountbracken was like our father's house. There too we found the attics, the indoor silences, the end-

45

less bookshelves. In the early days, when we were still only a quarter tamed, we often neglected our hostesses and rummaged on our own; it was there that I found Lubbock's *Ants, Bees and Wasps*. But it was also very different. Life there was more spacious and considered than with us, glided like a barge where ours bumped like a cart.

Friends of our own age—boy and girl friends—we had none. In part this is a natural result of boarding school; children grow up strangers to their next-door neighbors. But much more it was the result of our own obstinate choice. One boy who lived near us attempted every now and then to get to know us. We avoided him by every means in our power. Our lives were already full, and the holidays too short for all the reading, writing, playing, cycling, and talking that we wanted to get through. We resented the appearance of any third party as an infuriating interruption. We resented even more bitterly all attempts (excepting the great and successful attempt made by Mountbracken) to show us hospitality. At the period that I am now speaking of this had not yet become a serious nuisance, but as it became gradually and steadily more serious throughout our schooldays I may be allowed to say a word about it here and to get the subject out of our way. It was the custom of the neighborhood to give parties which were really dances for adults but to which, none the less, mere schoolboys and schoolgirls were asked. One sees the advantages of this arrangement from the hostess's point of view; and when the junior guests know each other well and are free from self-consciousness perhaps they enjoy themselves. To me these dances were a torment—of which ordinary shyness made only a part. It was the false position (which I was well able to realize) that tormented me; to know that one was regarded as a child and yet be forced to take part in an essentially grown-up function, to feel that all the adults present were being half-mockingly kind and pretending to treat you as what you were not. Add to this the discomfort of one's Eton suit and stiff shirt, the aching feet and burning head, and the mere weariness of being kept up so many hours after one's usual bedtime. Even adults, I fancy, would not find an evening party very endurable without the attraction of sex and the attraction of alcohol; and how a small boy who can neither flirt nor drink should be expected to enjoy prancing about on a polished floor till the small hours of the morning, is beyond my conception. I had of course no notion of the social nexus. I never realized that certain people were in civility obliged to ask me because they knew my father or had known my mother. To me it was all inexplicable, unprovoked persecution; and when, as often happened, such engagements fell in the last week of the holidays and wrested from us a huge cantle of hours in which every minute was worth gold, I positively felt that I could have torn my hostess limb from limb. Why should she thus pester me? I had never done her any harm, never asked *her* to a party.

My discomforts were aggravated by the totally unnatural behavior which I thought it my duty to adopt at a dance; and that had come about in a sufficiently amusing way. Reading much and mixing little with children of my own age, I had, before I went to school, developed a vocabulary which must (I now see) have sounded very funny from the lips of a chubby urchin in an Eton jacket. When I brought out my "long words" adults not unnaturally thought I was showing off. In this they were quite mistaken. I used the only words I knew. The position was indeed the exact reverse of what they supposed; my pride would have been gratified by using such schoolboy slang as I possessed, not at all by using the bookish language which (inevitably in my circumstances) came naturally to my tongue. And there were not lacking adults who would egg me on with feigned interest and feigned seriousness—on and on till the moment at which I suddenly knew I was being laughed at. Then, of course, my mortification was intense; and after one or two such experiences I made it a rigid rule that at "social functions" (as I secretly called them) I must never on any account speak of any subject in which I felt the slightest interest nor in any words that naturally occurred to me. And I kept my rule only too well; a giggling and gurgling imitation of the vapidest grown-up chatter, a deliberate concealment of all that I really thought and felt under a sort of feeble jocularity and enthusiasm, was henceforth my party manner, assumed as consciously as an actor assumes his role, sustained with unspeakable weariness, and dropped with a groan of relief the moment my brother and I at last tumbled into our cab and the drive home (the only pleasure of the evening) began. It took me years to make the discovery that any real human intercourse could take place at a mixed assembly of people in their good clothes.

I am here struck by the curious mixture of justice and injustice in our lives. We are blamed for our real faults but usually not on the right occasions. I was, no doubt, and was blamed for being, a conceited boy; but the blame was usually attached to something in which no conceit was present. Adults often accuse a child of vanity without pausing to discover on what points children in general, or that child in particular, are likely to be vain. Thus it was for years a complete mystery to me that my father should stigmatize as "affectation" my complaints about the itching and tickling of new underclothes. I see it all now; he had in mind a social legend associating delicacy of skin with refinement and supposed that I was claiming to be unusually refined. In reality I was in simple ignorance of that social legend, and if vanity had come into the matter would have been much prouder of having a skin like a sailor. I was being accused of an offense which I lacked resources to commit. I was on another occasion called "affected" for asking what "stirabout" was. It is, in fact, a "low" Irish word for porridge. To certain adults it seems obvious that he who claims not to know the Low must be pretending to be High. Yet the real reason why I asked was that I had never happened to hear the word; had I done so I should have piqued myself on using it.

Oldie's school, you will remember, sank unlamented in summer 1910; new arrangements had to be made for my education. My father now hit upon a plan which filled me with delight. About a mile from the New House rose the large red-brick walls and towers of Campbell College, which had been founded for the express purpose of giving Ulster boys all the advantages of a public-school education without the trouble of crossing the Irish Sea. My clever cousin, Uncle Joe's boy, was already there and doing well. It was decided that I should go as a boarder, but I could get an *exeat* to come home every Sunday. I was enchanted. I did not believe that anything Irish, even a school, could be bad; certainly not so bad as all I yet knew of England. To "Campbell" I accordingly went.

I was at this school for so short a time that I shall attempt no criticism of it. It was very unlike any English public school that I have ever heard of. It had indeed prefects, but the prefects were of no importance. It was nominally divided into "houses" on the English pattern, but they were mere legal fictions; except for purposes of games (which were not compulsory) no one took any notice of them. The population was socially much more "mixed" than at most English schools; I rubbed shoulders there with farmers' sons. The boy I most nearly made a friend of was the son of a tradesman who had recently been going the rounds with his father's van because the driver was illiterate and could not keep "the books." I much envied him this pleasant occupation, and he, poor fellow, looked back on it as a golden age. "This time last month, Lewis," he used to say, "I wouldn't have been going in to Preparation. I'd have been coming home from my rounds and a wee tea cloth laid for me at one end of the table and sausages to my tea."

I am always glad, as a historian, to have known Campbell, for I think it was very much what the great English schools had been before Arnold. There were real fights at Campbell, with seconds, and (I think) betting, and a hundred or more roaring spectators. There was bullying, too, though no serious share of it came my way, and there was no trace of the rigid hierarchy which governs a modern English school; every boy held just the place which his fists and mother wit could win for him. From my point of view the great drawback was that one had, so to speak, no home. Only a few very senior boys had studies. The rest of us, except when seated at table for meals or in a huge "preparation room" for evening "Prep," belonged nowhere. In out-of-school hours one spent one's time either evading or conforming to all those inexplicable movements which a crowd exhibits as it thins here and thickens there, now slackens its pace and now sets like a tide in one particular direction, now seems about to disperse and then clots again. The bare brick passages echoed to a continual tramp of feet, punctuated with catcalls, scrimmages, gusty laughter. One was always "moving on" or "hanging about"—in lavatories, in storerooms, in the great hall. It was very like living permanently in a large railway station.

The bullying had this negative merit that it was honest bullying; not bullying conscience-salved and authorized in the *maison tolérée* of the prefectorial system. It was done mainly by gangs; parties of eight or ten boys each who scoured those interminable corridors for prey. Their sorties, though like a whirlwind, were not perceived by the victim till too late; the general, endless confusion and clamor, I suppose, masked them. Sometimes capture involved serious consequences; two boys whom I knew were carried off and flogged in some backwater—flogged in the most disinterested fashion, for their captors had no personal acquaintance with them; art for art's sake. But on the only occasion when I was caught myself my fate was much milder and perhaps odd enough to be worth recording. When I had come to myself after being dragged at headlong speed through a labyrinth of passages which took me beyond all usual landmarks, I found that I was one of several prisoners in a low, bare room, half-lit (I think) by a single gas jet. After a pause to recover their breath two of the brigands led out the first captive. I now noticed that a horizontal row of pipes ran along the opposite wall, about three feet from the floor. I was alarmed but not surprised when the prisoner was forced into a bending position under the lowest pipe, in the very posture for execution. But I was very much surprised a moment later. You will remember that the room was half dark. The two gangsters gave their victim a shove; and instantly no victim was there. He vanished; without trace, without sound. It appeared to be sheer black magic. Another victim was led out; again the posture for a flogging was assumed; again, instead of flogging —dissolution, atomization, annihilation. At last my own turn came. I too received the shove from behind, and found myself falling through a hole or hatch in the wall into what turned out to be a coal cellar. Another small boy came hurtling in after me, the door was slammed and bolted behind us, and our captors with a joyous whoop rushed away for more booty. They were, no doubt, playing against a rival gang with whom they would presently compare "bags." We were let out again presently, very dirty and rather cramped, but otherwise none the worse.

Much the most important thing that happened to me at Campbell was that I there read *Sohrab and Rustum* in form under an excellent master whom we called Octie. I loved the poem at first sight and have loved it ever since. As the wet fog, in the first line, rose out of the Oxus stream, so out of the whole poem there rose and wrapped me round an exquisite, silvery coolness, a delightful quality of distance and calm, a grave melancholy. I hardly appreciated then, as I have since learned to do, the central tragedy; what enchanted me was the artist in Pekin with his ivory forehead and pale hands, the cypress in the queen's garden, the backward glance at Rustum's youth, the pedlars from Khabul, the hushed Chorasmian waste. Arnold gave me at once (and the best of Arnold gives me still) a sense, not indeed of passionless vision, but of a passionate, silent gazing at things a long way off. And here observe how literature actually works. Parrot critics say that *Sohrab* is a poem for classicists, to be enjoyed only by those who recognize the Homeric echoes. But I, in Octie's form room (and on Octie be peace) knew nothing of Homer. For me the relation between Arnold and Homer worked the other way; when I came, years later, to read the *Iliad* I liked it partly because it was for me reminiscent of *Sohrab*. Plainly, it does not matter at what point you first break into the system of European poetry. Only keep your ears open and your mouth shut and everything will lead you to everything else in the end—*ogni parte ad ogni parte splende.*

About halfway through my first and only term at Campbell I fell ill and was taken home. My father, for reasons I do not quite know, had become dissatisfied with the school. He had also been attracted by accounts of a preparatory school in the town of Wyvern, though quite unconnected with Wyvern College; especially by the convenience that if I went there my brother and I could still do the journey together. Accordingly I had a blessed six weeks at home, with the Christmas holidays to look forward to at the end and, after that, a new adventure. In a surviving letter my father writes to my brother that I think myself lucky but he "fears I shall be very lonely before the end of the week." It is strange that having known me all my life he should have known me so little. During these weeks I slept in his room and was thus freed from solitude during most of those dark hours in which alone solitude was dreadful to me. My brother being absent, he and I could not lead one another into mischief; there was therefore no friction between my father and myself. I remember no other time in my life of such untroubled affection; we were famously snug together. And in the days, when he was out, I entered with complete satisfaction into a deeper solitude than I had ever known. The empty house, the empty, silent rooms, were like a refreshing bath after the crowded noise of Campbell. I could read, write, and draw to my heart's content. Curiously enough it is at this time, not in earlier childhood, that I chiefly remember delighting in fairy tales. I fell deeply under the spell of Dwarfs —the old bright-hooded, snowy-bearded dwarfs we had in those days before Arthur Rackham sublimed, or Walt Disney vulgarized, the earthmen. I visualized them so intensely that I came to the very frontiers of hallucination; once, walking in the garden, I was for a second not quite sure that a little man had not run past me into the shrubbery. I was faintly alarmed, but it was not like my night fears. A fear that guarded the road to Faerie was one I could face. No one is a coward at all points.

IV

I BROADEN MY MIND

I struck the board, and cry'd, 'No more;
I will abroad.'
What? shall I ever sigh and pine?
My lines and life are free: free as the rode,
Loose as the winde, as large as store.

HERBERT

IN JANUARY, 1911, just turned thirteen, I set out with my brother to Wyvern, he for the College and I for a preparatory school which we will call Chartres. Thus began what may be called the classic period of our schooldays, the thing we both think of first when boyhood is mentioned. The joint journeys back to school with a reluctant parting at Wyvern station, the hilarious reunion at the same station for the joint journey home, were now the great structural pillars of each year. Growing maturity is marked by the increasing liberties we take with our traveling. At first, on being landed early in the morning at Liverpool, we took the next train south; soon we learned that it was pleasanter to spend the whole morning in the lounge of the Lime Street Hotel with our magazines and cigarettes and to proceed to Wyvern by an afternoon train which brought us there at the latest permitted moment. Soon too we gave up the magazines; we made the discovery (some people never make it) that real books can be taken on a journey and that hours of golden reading can so be added to its other delights. (It is important to acquire early in life the power of reading sense wherever you happen to be. I first read *Tamburlaine* while traveling from Larne to Belfast in a thunderstorm, and first read Browning's *Paracelsus* by a candle which went out and had to be relit whenever a big battery fired in a pit below me, which I think it did every four minutes all that night.) The homeward journey was even more festal. It had an invariable routine: first the supper at a restaurant—it was merely poached eggs and tea but to us the tables of the gods—then the visit to the old Empire (there were still music halls in those days)—and after that the journey to the Landing Stage, the sight of great and famous ships, the departure, and once more the blessed salt on our lips.

The smoking was of course, as my father would have said, "surreptitious"; not so the visit to the Empire. He was no Puritan about such matters, and often of a Saturday night would take us to the Belfast Hippodrome. I recognize now that I never had the taste for vaudeville which he shared with my brother. At the time I supposed myself to be enjoying the show, but I was mistaken. All those antics lie dead in my memory and are incapable of rousing the least vibration even of reminiscent pleasure; whereas the pain of sympathy and vicarious humiliation which I felt when a "turn" failed is still vivid. What I enjoyed was merely the et cetera of the show, the bustle and lights, the sense of having a night out, the good spirits of my father in his holiday mood, and—above all—the admirable cold supper to which we came back at about ten o'clock. For this was also the classical age of our domestic cookery, the age of one Annie Strahan. There were certain "raised pies" set on that table of which a modern English boy has no conception, and which even then would have astonished those who knew only the poor counterfeits sold in shops.

Chartres, a tall, white building further up the hill than the College, was a smallish school with less than twenty boarders; but it was quite unlike Oldie's. Here indeed my education really began. The Headmaster, whom we called Tubbs, was a clever and patient teacher; under him I rapidly found my feet in Latin and English and even began to be looked on as a promising candidate for a scholarship at the College. The food was good (though of course we grumbled at it) and we were well cared for. On the whole I got on well with my school fellows, though we had our full share of those lifelong friendships and irreconcilable factions and deadly quarrels and final settlements and glorious revolutions which made up so much of the life of a small boy, and in which I came out sometimes at the bottom and sometimes at the top.

Wyvern itself healed my quarrel with England. The great blue plain below us and, behind, those green, peaked hills, so mountainous in form and yet so manageably small in size, became almost at once my delight. And Wyvern Priory was the first building that I ever perceived to be beautiful. And at Chartres I made my first real friends. But there, too, something far more important happened to me: I ceased to be a Christian.

The chronology of this disaster is a little vague, but I know for certain that it had not begun when I went there and that the process was complete very shortly after I left. I will try to set down what I know of the conscious causes and what I suspect of the unconscious.

Most reluctantly, venturing no blame, and as tenderly as I would at need reveal some error in my own mother, I must begin with dear Miss C., the Matron. No school ever had a better Matron, more skilled and comforting to boys in sickness, or more cheery and companionable to boys in health. She was one of the most selfless people I have ever known. We all loved her; I, the orphan, especially. Now it so happened that Miss C., who seemed old to me, was still in her spiritual immaturity, still hunting, with the eagerness of a soul that had a touch of angelic quality in it, for a truth and a way of life. Guides were even rarer then than now. She was (as I should now put it) floundering in the mazes of Theosophy, Rosicrucianism, Spiritualism; the whole Anglo-American Occultist tradition. Nothing was further from her intention than to destroy my faith; she could not tell that the room into which she brought this candle was full of gunpowder. I had never heard of such things before; never, except in a nightmare or a fairy tale, conceived of spirits other than God and men. I had loved to read of strange sights and other worlds and unknown modes of being, but never with the slightest belief; even the phantom dwarf had only flashed on my mind for a moment. It is a great mistake to suppose that children believe the things they imagine; and I, long familiar with the whole imaginary world of Animal-Land and India (which I could not possibly believe in since I knew I was one of its creators) was as little likely as any child to make that mistake. But now, for the first time, there burst upon me the idea that there might be real marvels all about us, that the visible world might be only a curtain to conceal huge realms uncharted by my very simple theology. And that started in me something with which, on and off, I have had plenty of trouble since—the desire for the preternatural, simply as such, the passion for the Occult. Not everyone has this disease; those who have will know what I mean. I once tried to describe it in a novel. It is a spiritual lust; and like the lust of the body it has the fatal power of making everything else in the world seem uninteresting while it lasts. It is probably this passion, more even than the desire for power, which makes magicians. But the result of Miss C.'s conversation did not stop there. Little by little, unconsciously, unintentionally, she loosened the whole framework, blunted all the sharp edges, of my belief. The vagueness, the merely speculative character, of all this Occultism began to spread—yes, and to spread *deliciously*—to the stern truths of the creed. The whole thing became a matter of speculation: I was soon (in the famous words) "altering 'I believe' to 'one does feel.'" And oh, the relief of it! Those moonlit nights in the dormitory at Belsen faded far away. From the tyrannous noon of revelation I passed into the cool evening of Higher Thought, where there was nothing to be obeyed, and nothing to be believed except what was either comforting or exciting. I do not mean that Miss C. did this; better say that the Enemy did this in me, taking occasion from things she innocently said.

One reason why the Enemy found this so easy was that,

without knowing it, I was already desperately anxious to get rid of my religion; and that for a reason worth recording. By a sheer mistake—and I still believe it to have been an honest mistake—in spiritual technique I had rendered my private practice of that religion a quite intolerable burden. It came about in this way. Like everyone else I had been told as a child that one must not only say one's prayers but think about what one was saying. Accordingly, when (at Oldie's) I came to a serious belief, I tried to put this into practice. At first it seemed plain sailing. But soon the false conscience (St. Paul's "Law," Herbert's "prattler") came into play. One had no sooner reached "Amen" than it whispered, "Yes. But are you sure you were really thinking about what you said?"; then, more subtly, "Were you, for example, thinking about it as well as you did last night?" The answer, for reasons I did not then understand, was nearly always No. "Very well," said the voice, "hadn't you, then, better try it over again?" And one obeyed; but of course with no assurance that the second attempt would be any better.

To these nagging suggestions my reaction was, on the whole, the most foolish I could have adopted. I set myself a standard. No clause of my prayer was to be allowed to pass muster unless it was accompanied by what I called a "realization," by which I meant a certain vividness of the imagination and the affections. My nightly task was to produce by sheer will power a phenomenon which will power could never produce, which was so ill-defined that I could never say with absolute confidence whether it had occurred, and which, even when it did occur, was of very mediocre spiritual value. If only someone had read to me old Walter Hilton's warning that we must never in prayer strive to extort "by maistry" what God does not give! But no one did; and night after night, dizzy with desire for sleep and often in a kind of despair, I endeavored to pump up my "realizations." The thing threatened to become an infinite regress. One began of course by praying for good "realizations." But had that preliminary prayer itself been "realized"? This question I think I still had enough sense to dismiss; otherwise it might have been as difficult to begin my prayers as to end them. How it all comes back! The cold oilcloth, the quarters chiming, the night slipping past, the sickening, hopeless weariness. This was the burden from which I longed with soul and body to escape. It had already brought me to such a pass that the nightly torment projected its gloom over the whole evening, and I dreaded bedtime as if I were a chronic sufferer from insomnia. Had I pursued the same road much further I think I should have gone mad.

This ludicrous burden of false duties in prayer provided, of course, an unconscious motive for wishing to shuffle off the Christian faith; but about the same time, or a little later, conscious causes of doubt arose. One came from reading the classics. Here, especially in Virgil, one was presented with a mass of religious ideas; and all teachers and editors took it for granted from the outset that these religious ideas were sheer illusion. No one ever attempted to show in what sense Christianity fulfilled Paganism or Paganism prefigured Christianity. The accepted position seemed to be that religions were normally a mere farrago of nonsense, though our own, by a fortunate exception, was exactly true. The other religions were not even explained, in the earlier Christian fashion, as the work of devils. That I might, conceivably, have been brought to believe. But the impression I got was that religion in general, though utterly false, was a natural growth, a kind of endemic nonsense into which humanity tended to blunder. In the midst of a thousand such religions stood our own, the thousand and first, labeled True. But on what grounds could I believe in this exception? It obviously was in some general sense the same kind of thing as all the rest. Why was it so differently treated? Need I, at any rate, continue to treat it differently? I was very anxious not to.

In addition to this, and equally working against my faith, there was in me a deeply ingrained pessimism; a pessimism, by that time, much more of intellect than of temper. I was now by no means unhappy; but I had very definitely formed the opinion that the universe was, in the main, a rather regrettable institution. I am well aware that some will feel disgust and some will laugh, at the idea of a loutish, well-fed boy in an Eton collar, passing an unfavorable judgment on the cosmos. They may be right in either reaction, but no more right because I wore an Eton collar. They are forgetting what boyhood felt like from within. Dates are not so important as people believe. I fancy that most of those who think at all have done a great deal of their thinking in the first fourteen years. As to the sources of my pessimism, the reader will remember that, though in many ways most fortunate, yet I had very early in life met a great dismay. But I am now inclined to think that the seeds of pessimism were sown be-

fore my mother's death. Ridiculous as it may sound, I believe
that the clumsiness of my hands was at the root of the matter.
How could this be? Not, certainly, that a child says, "I
can't cut a straight line with a pair of scissors, therefore the
universe is evil." Childhood has no such power of generalization and is not (to do it justice) so silly. Nor did my clumsiness produce what is ordinarily called an Inferiority Complex.
I was not comparing myself with other boys; my defeats
occurred in solitude. What they really bred in me was a deep
(and, of course, inarticulate) sense of resistance or opposition
on the part of inanimate things. Even that makes it too
abstract and adult. Perhaps I had better call it a settled expectation that everything would do what you did not want
it to do. Whatever you wanted to remain straight, would
bend; whatever you tried to bend would fly back to the
straight; all knots which you wished to be firm would come
untied; all knots you wanted to untie would remain firm. It
is not possible to put it into language without making it
comic, and I have indeed no wish to see it (now) except as
something comic. But it is perhaps just these early experiences
which are so fugitive and, to an adult, so grotesque, that give
the mind its earliest bias, its habitual sense of what is or is not
plausible.

There was another predisposing factor. Though the son
of a prosperous man—a man by our present tax-ridden standards almost incredibly comfortable and secure—I had heard
ever since I could remember, and believed, that adult life
was to be an unremitting struggle in which the best I could
hope for was to avoid the workhouse by extreme exertion.

My father's highly colored statements on such matters had sunk deeply into my mind; and I never thought to check them by the very obvious fact that most of the adults I actually knew seemed to be living very comfortable lives. I remember summing up what I took to be our destiny, in conversation with my best friend at Chartres, by the formula, "Term, holidays, term, holidays, till we leave school, and then work, work, work till we die." Even if I had been free from this delusion, I think I should still have seen grounds for pessimism. One's views, even at that age, are not wholly determined by one's own momentary situation; even a boy can recognize that there is desert all round him though he, for the nonce, sits in an oasis. I was, in my ineffective way, a tenderhearted creature; perhaps the most murderous feelings I ever entertained were toward an under master at Chartres who forbade me to give to a beggar at the school gate. Add to this that my early reading—not only Wells but Sir Robert Ball—had lodged very firmly in my imagination the vastness and cold of space, the littleness of Man. It is not strange that I should feel the universe to be a menacing and unfriendly place. Several years before I read Lucretius I felt the force of his argument (and it is surely the strongest of all) for atheism—

Nequaquam nobis divinitus esse paratam
Naturam rerum; tanta stat praedita culpa
Had God designed the world, it would not be
A world so frail and faulty as we see.

You may ask how I combined this directly Atheistical thought, this great "Argument from Undesign" with my

Occultist fancies. I do not think I achieved any logical connection between them. They swayed me in different moods, and had only this in common, that both made against Christianity. And so, little by little, with fluctuations which I cannot now trace, I became an apostate, dropping my faith with no sense of loss but with the greatest relief.

My stay at Chartres lasted from the spring term of 1911 till the end of the summer term 1913, and, as I have said, I cannot give an accurate chronology, between those dates, of my slow apostasy. In other respects the period is divided into two; about halfway through it a much loved under master, and the even more loved Matron, left at the same time. From that day onward there was a sharp decline; not, indeed, in apparent happiness but in solid good. Dear Miss C. had been the occasion of much good to me as well as of evil. For one thing, by awakening my affections, she had done something to defeat that antisentimental inhibition which my early experience had bred in me. Nor would I deny that in all her "Higher Thought," disastrous though its main effect on me was, there were elements of real and disinterested spirituality by which I benefited. Unfortunately, once her presence was withdrawn, the good effects withered and the bad ones remained. The change of masters was even more obviously for the worse. "Sirrah," as we called him, had been an admirable influence. He was what I would now describe as a wise madcap: a boisterous, boyish, hearty man, well able to keep his authority while yet mixing with us almost as one of ourselves, an untidy, rollicking man without a particle of affectation. He communicated (what I very much needed) a sense of the gusto with which life ought, wherever possible, to be taken. I fancy it was on a run with him in the sleet that I first discovered how bad weather is to be treated—as a rough joke, a romp. He was succeeded by a young gentleman just down from the University whom we may call Pogo. Pogo was a very minor edition of a Saki, perhaps even a Wodehouse, hero. Pogo was a wit, Pogo was a dressy man, Pogo was a man about town, Pogo was even a lad. After a week or so of hesitation (for his temper was uncertain) we fell at his feet and adored. Here was sophistication, glossy all over, and (dared one believe it?) ready to impart sophistication to us.

We became—at least I became—dressy. It was the age of the "knut": of "spread" ties with pins in them, of very low cut coats and trousers worn very high to show startling socks, and brogue shoes with immensely wide laces. Something of all this had already trickled to me from the College through my brother, who was now becoming sufficiently senior to aspire to knuttery. Pogo completed the process. A more piti-ful ambition for a lout of an overgrown fourteen-year-old with a shilling a week pocket money could hardly be imag-ined; the more so since I am one of those on whom Nature has laid the doom that whatever they buy and whatever they wear they will always look as if they had come out of an old clothes shop. I cannot even now remember without embar-rassment the concern that I then felt about pressing my trou-sers and (filthy habit) plastering my hair with oil. A new element had entered my life: Vulgarity. Up till now I had committed nearly every other sin and folly within my power, but I had not yet been flashy.

These hobbledehoy fineries were, however, only a small part of our new sophistication. Pogo was a great theatrical authority. We soon knew all the latest songs. We soon knew all about the famous actresses of that age—Lily Elsie, Gertie Millar, Zena Dare. Pogo was a fund of information about their private lives. We learned from him all the latest jokes; where we did not understand he was ready to give us help. He explained many things. After a term of Pogo's society one had the feeling of being not twelve weeks but twelve years older.

How gratifying, and how edifying, it would be if I could trace to Pogo all my slips from virtue and wind up by pointing the moral; how much harm a loose-talking young man can do to innocent boys! Unfortunately this would be false. It is quite true that at this time I underwent a violent, and wholly successful, assault of sexual temptation. But this is amply accounted for by the age I had then reached and by my recent, in a sense my deliberate, withdrawal of myself from Divine protection. I do not believe Pogo had anything to do with it. The mere facts of generation I had learned long ago, from another boy, when I was too young to feel much more than a scientific interest in them. What attacked me through Pogo was not the Flesh (I had that of my own) but the World: the desire for glitter, swagger, distinction, the desire to be in the know. He gave little help, if any, in destroying my chastity, but he made sad work of certain humble and childlike and self-forgetful qualities which (I think) had remained with me till that moment. I began to labor very hard to make myself into a fop, a cad, and a snob.

Pogo's communications, however much they helped to

vulgarize my mind, had no such electric effect on my senses as the dancing mistress, nor as Bekker's *Charicles*, which was given me for a prize. I never thought that dancing mistress as beautiful as my cousin G., but she was the first woman I ever "looked upon to lust after her"; assuredly through no fault of her own. A gesture, a tone of the voice, may in these matters have unpredictable results. When the schoolroom on the last night of the winter term was decorated for a dance, she paused, lifted a flag, and, remarking, "I love the smell of bunting," pressed it to her face—and I was undone.

You must not suppose that this was a romantic passion. The passion of my life, as the next chapter will show, belonged to a wholly different region. What I felt for the dancing mistress was sheer appetite; the prose and not the poetry of the Flesh. I did not feel at all like a knight devoting himself to a lady; I was much more like a Turk looking at a Circassian whom he could not afford to buy. I knew quite well what I wanted. It is common, by the way, to assume that such an experience produces a feeling of guilt, but it did not do so in me. And I may as well say here that the feeling of guilt, save where a moral offense happened also to break the code of honor or had consequences which excited my pity, was a thing which at that time I hardly knew. It took me as long to acquire inhibitions as others (they say) have taken to get rid of them. That is why I often find myself at such cross-purposes with the modern world: I have been a converted Pagan living among apostate Puritans.

I would be sorry if the reader passed too harsh a judgment on Pogo. As I now see it, he was not too old to have charge of boys but too young. He was only an adolescent himself, still immature enough to be delightedly "grown up" and naïve enough to enjoy our greater naïveté. And there was a real friendliness in him. He was moved partly by that to tell us all he knew or thought he knew. And now, as Herodotus would say, "Good-by to Pogo."

Meanwhile, side by side with my loss of faith, of virtue, and of simplicity, something quite different was going on. It will demand a new chapter.

V

RENAISSANCE

So is there in us a world of love to somewhat, though
we know not what in the world that should be.

TRAHERNE

I DO NOT much believe in the Renaissance as generally described by historians. The more I look into the evidence the less trace I find of that vernal rapture which is supposed to have swept Europe in the fifteenth century. I half suspect that the glow in the historians' pages has a different source, that each is remembering, and projecting, his own personal Renaissance; that wonderful reawakening which comes to most of us when puberty is complete. It is properly called a rebirth not a birth, a reawakening not a wakening, because in many of us, besides being a new thing, it is also the recovery of things we had in childhood and lost when we became boys. For boyhood is very like the "dark ages" not as they were but as they are represented in bad, short histories. The dreams of childhood and those of adolescence may have much in common; between them, often, boyhood stretches like an alien territory in which everything (ourselves included) has been greedy, cruel, noisy, and prosaic, in which the imagination has slept and the most unideal senses and ambitions have been restlessly, even maniacally, awake.

In my own life it was certainly so. My childhood is at unity

71

with the rest of my life; my boyhood not so. Many of the books that pleased me as a child, please me still; nothing but necessity would make me reread most of the books that I read at Oldie's or at Campbell. From that point of view it is all a sandy desert. The authentic "Joy" (as I tried to describe it in an earlier chapter) had vanished from my life: so completely that not even the memory or the desire of it remained. The reading of *Sohrab* had not given it to me. Joy is distinct not only from pleasure in general but even from aesthetic pleasure. It must have the stab, the pang, the inconsolable longing.

This long winter broke up in a single moment, fairly early in my time at Chartres. Spring is the inevitable image, but this was not gradual like Nature's springs. It was as if the Arctic itself, all the deep layers of secular ice, should change not in a week nor in an hour, but instantly, into a landscape of grass and primroses and orchards in bloom, deafened with bird songs and astir with running water. I can lay my hand on the very moment; there is hardly any fact I know so well, though I cannot date it. Someone must have left in the schoolroom a literary periodical: *The Bookman*, perhaps, or the *Times Literary Supplement*. My eye fell upon a headline and a picture, carelessly, expecting nothing. A moment later, as the poet says, "The sky had turned round."

What I had read was the words *Siegfried and the Twilight of the Gods*. What I had seen was one of Arthur Rackham's illustrations to that volume. I had never heard of Wagner, nor of Siegfried. I thought the Twilight of the Gods meant the twilight in which the gods lived. How did I know, at once and beyond question, that this was no Celtic, or silvan, or terrestrial twilight? But so it was. Pure "Northernness" engulfed me: a vision of huge, clear spaces hanging above the Atlantic in the endless twilight of Northern summer, remoteness, severity . . . and almost at the same moment I knew that I had met this before, long, long ago (it hardly seems longer now) in *Tegner's Drapa*, that Siegfried (whatever it might be) belonged to the same world as Balder and the sunward-sailing cranes. And with that plunge back into my own past there arose at once, almost like heartbreak, the memory of Joy itself, the knowledge that I had once had what I had now lacked for years, that I was returning at last from exile and desert lands to my own country; and the distance of the Twilight of the Gods and the distance of my own past Joy, both unattainable, flowed together into a single, unendurable sense of desire and loss, which suddenly became one with the loss of the whole experience, which, as I now stared round that dusty schoolroom like a man recovering from unconsciousness, had already vanished, had eluded me at the very moment when I could first say *It is*. And at once I knew (with fatal knowledge) that to "have it again" was the supreme and only important object of desire.

After this everything played into my hands. One of my father's many presents to us boys had been a gramophone. Thus at the moment when my eyes fell on the words *Siegfried and the Twilight of the Gods*, gramophone catalogues were already one of my favorite forms of reading; but I had never remotely dreamed that the records from Grand Opera with their queer German or Italian names could have anything to do with me. Nor did I for a week or two think so now. But then I was assailed from a new quarter. A magazine called *The Soundbox* was doing synopses of great operas week by week, and it now did the whole *Ring*. I read in a rapture and discovered who Siegfried was and what was the "twilight" of the gods. I could contain myself no longer—I began a poem, a heroic poem on the Wagnerian version of the Niblung story. My only source was the abstracts in *The Soundbox*, and I was so ignorant that I made Alberich rhyme with *ditch* and Mime with *time*. My model was Pope's *Odyssey* and the poem began (with some mixture of mythologies)

> *Descend to earth, descend, celestial Nine*
> *And chant the ancient legends of the Rhine. . . .*

Since the fourth book had carried me only as far as the last scene of *The Rheingold*, the reader will not be surprised to hear that the poem was never finished. But it was not a waste of time, and I can still see just what it did for me and where it began to do it. The first three books (I may, perhaps, at this distance of time, say it without vanity) are really not at all bad for a boy. At the beginning of the unfinished fourth it goes all to pieces; and that is exactly the point at which I really began to try to make poetry. Up to then, if my lines rhymed and scanned and got on with the story I asked no more. Now, at the beginning of the fourth, I began to try to convey some of the intense excitement I was feeling, to look for expressions which would not merely state but suggest. Of course I failed, lost my prosaic clarity, spluttered, gasped, and presently fell silent; but I had learned what writing means.

74

All this time I had still not heard a note of Wagner's music, though the very shape of the printed letters of his name had become to me a magical symbol. Next holidays, in the dark, crowded shop of T. Edens Osborne (on whom be peace), I first heard a record of the *Ride of the Valkyries*. They laugh at it nowadays, and, indeed, wrenched from its context to make a concert piece, it may be a poor thing. But I had this in common with Wagner, that I was thinking not of concert pieces but of heroic drama. To a boy already crazed with "the Northernness," whose highest musical experience had been Sullivan, the *Ride* came like a thunderbolt. From that moment Wagnerian records (principally from the *Ring*, but also from *Lohengrin* and *Parsifal*) became the chief drain on my pocket money and the presents I invariably asked for. My general appreciation of music was not, at first, much altered. "Music" was one thing, "Wagnerian music" quite another, and there was no common measure between them; it was not a new pleasure but a new kind of pleasure, if indeed "pleasure" is the right word, rather than trouble, ecstasy, astonishment, "a conflict of sensations without name."

That summer our cousin H. (you remember, I hope, Cousin Quartus's eldest daughter, the dark Juno, the queen of Olympus), who was now married, asked us to spend some weeks with her on the outskirts of Dublin, in Dundrum. There, on her drawing-room table, I found the very book which had started the whole affair and which I had never dared to hope I should see, *Siegfried and the Twilight of the Gods* illustrated by Arthur Rackham. His pictures, which seemed to me then to be the very music made visible, plunged

75

me a few fathoms deeper into my delight. I have seldom coveted anything as I coveted that book; and when I heard that there was a cheaper edition at fifteen shillings (though the sum was to me almost mythological) I knew I could never rest till it was mine. I got it in the end, largely because my brother went shares with me, purely through kindness, as I now see and then more than half suspected, for he was not enslaved by the Northernness. With a generosity which I was even then half ashamed to accept, he sank in what must have seemed to him a mere picture book seven and sixpence for which he knew a dozen better uses.

Although this affair will already seem to some readers undeserving of the space I have given it, I cannot continue my story at all without noting some of its bearings on the rest of my life.

First, you will misunderstand everything unless you realize that, at the time, Asgard and the Valkyries seemed to me incomparably more important than anything else in my experience—than the Matron Miss C., or the dancing mistress, or my chances of a scholarship. More shockingly, they seemed much more important than my steadily growing doubts about Christianity. This may have been—in part, no doubt was—penal blindness; yet that might not be the whole story. If the Northernness seemed then a bigger thing than my religion, that may partly have been because my attitude toward it contained elements which my religion ought to have contained and did not. It was not itself a new religion, for it contained no trace of belief and imposed no duties. Yet unless I am greatly mistaken there was in it something very like adoration, some kind of quite disinterested self-abandonment to an object which securely claimed this by simply being the object it was. We are taught in the Prayer Book to "give thanks to God for His great glory," as if we owed Him more thanks for being what He necessarily is than for any particular benefit He confers upon us; and so indeed we do and to know God is to know this. But I had been far from any such experience; I came far nearer to feeling this about the Norse gods whom I disbelieved in than I had ever done about the true God while I believed. Sometimes I can almost think that I was sent back to the false gods there to acquire some capacity for worship against the day when the true God should recall me to Himself. Not that I might not have learned this sooner and more safely, in ways I shall now never know, without apostasy, but that Divine punishments are also mercies, and particular good is worked out of particular evil, and the penal blindness made sanative.

Secondly, this imaginative Renaissance almost at once produced a new appreciation of external nature. At first, I think, this was parasitic on the literary and musical experiences. On that holiday at Dundrum, cycling among the Wicklow mountains, I was always involuntarily looking for scenes that might belong to the Wagnerian world, here a steep hillside covered with firs where Mime might meet Sieglinde, there a sunny glade where Siegfried might listen to the bird, or presently a dry valley of rocks where the lithe scaly body of Fafner might emerge from its cave. But soon (I cannot say how soon) nature ceased to be a mere reminder of the books, became herself the medium of the real joy. I do not say she ceased to be a reminder. All Joy reminds. It is never a possession, always a desire for something longer ago or further away or still "about to be." But Nature and the books now became equal reminders, joint reminders, of—well, of whatever it is. I came no nearer to what some would regard as the only genuine love of nature, the studious love which will make a man a botanist or an ornithologist. It was the mood of a scene that mattered to me; and in tasting that mood my skin and nose were as busy as my eyes.

Thirdly, I passed on from Wagner to everything else I could get hold of about Norse mythology, *Myths of the Norsemen*, *Myths and Legends of the Teutonic Race*, Mallet's *Northern Antiquities*. I became knowledgeable. From these books again and again I received the stab of Joy. I did not yet notice that it was, very gradually, becoming rarer. I did not yet reflect on the difference between it and the merely intellectual satisfaction of getting to know the Eddaic universe. If I could at this time have found anyone to teach me Old Norse I believe I would have worked at it hard.

And finally, the change I had undergone introduces a new difficulty into the writing of this present book. From that first moment in the schoolroom at Chartres my secret, imaginative life began to be so important and so distinct from my outer life that I almost have to tell two separate stories. The two lives do not seem to influence each other at all. Where there are hungry wastes, starving for Joy, in the one, the other may be full of cheerful bustle and success; or again, where the outer life is miserable, the other may be brimming over with ecstasy. By the imaginative life I here mean only my life as concerned with Joy—including in the outer life much that would ordinarily be called imagination, as, for example, much of my reading, and all my erotic or ambitious fantasies; for these are self-regarding. Even Animal-Land and India belong to the "Outer."

But they were no longer Animal-Land and India; some time in the late eighteenth century (their eighteenth century, not ours) they had been united into the single state of Boxen, which yields, oddly, an adjective *Boxonian*, not *Boxenian* as you might expect. By a wise provision they retained their separate kings but had a common legislative assembly, the Damerfesk. The electoral system was democratic, but this mattered very much less than in England, for the Damerfesk was never doomed to one fixed meeting place. The joint sovereigns could summon it anywhere, say at the tiny fishing village of Danphabel (the Clovelly of Northern Animal-Land, nestling at the foot of the mountains) or in the island of Piscia; and since the Court knew the sovereigns' choice earlier than anyone else, all local accommodation would be booked before a private member got wind of the matter, nor, if he reached the session, had he the least assurance that it would not be moved elsewhere as soon as he arrived. Hence we hear of a certain member who had never actually sat in the Damerfesk at all except on one fortunate occasion when it met in his home town. The records sometimes call this assembly the Parliament, but that is misleading. It had only a single chamber, and the kings presided. At the period which I know best the effective control, however, was not in their hands but in those of an all-important functionary known as the Littlemaster (you must pronounce this all as one word with the accent on the first syllable—like *Jerrybuilder*). The Littlemaster was a Prime Minister, a judge, and if not always Commander in Chief (the records waver on this point) certainly always a member of the General Staff. Such at least were the powers he wielded when I last visited Boxen. They may have been encroachments, for the office was held at that time by a man—or to speak more accurately, a Frog—of powerful personality. Lord Big brought to his task one rather unfair advantage; he had been the tutor of the two young kings and continued to hold over them a quasi-parental authority. Their spasmodic efforts to break his yoke were, unhappily, more directed to the evasion of his inquiry into their private pleasures than to any serious political end. As a result Lord Big, immense in size, resonant of voice, chivalrous (he was the hero of innumerable duels), stormy, eloquent, and impulsive, almost was the state. The reader will divine a certain resemblance between the life of the two kings under Lord Big and our own life under our father. He will be right. But Big was not, in origin, simply our father first batrachised and then caricatured in some directions and glorified in others. He was in many ways a prophetic portrait of Sir Winston Churchill as Sir Winston Churchill came to be during the last war; I have indeed seen photographs of that great statesman in which, to anyone who has known Boxen, the frog element was unmistakable. This was not our only anticipation of the real world. Lord Big's most consistent opponent, the gadfly that always got inside his armor, was a certain small brown bear, a lieutenant in the Navy; and believe me or believe me not, Lieutenant James Bar was almost exactly like Mr. John Betjeman, whose acquaintance I could not then have made. Ever since I have done so, I have been playing Lord Big to his James Bar.

The interesting thing about the resemblance between Lord Big and my father is that such reflections of the real world had not been the germ out of which Boxen grew. They were more numerous as it drew nearer to its end, a sign of over-ripeness or even the beginning of decay. Go back a little and you will not find them. The two sovereigns who allowed themselves to be dominated by Lord Big were King Benjamin VIII of Animal-Land and Rajah Hawki (I think, VI) of India. They had much in common with my brother and myself. But their fathers, the elder Benjamin and the elder Hawki, had not. The Fifth Hawki is a shadowy figure; but the Seventh Benjamin (a rabbit, as you will have guessed) is a rounded character. I can see him still—the heaviest-jowled and squarest-built of all rabbits, very fat in his later years, most shabbily and unroyally clad in his loose brown coat and baggy checked trousers, yet not without a certain dignity which could, on occasion, take disconcerting forms. His earlier life had been dominated by the belief that he could be both a king and an amateur detective. He never succeeded in the latter role, partly because the chief enemy whom he was pursuing (Mr. Baddlesmere) was not really a criminal at all but a lunatic—a complication which would have thrown out the plans of Sherlock Holmes himself. But he very often got himself kidnaped, sometimes for longish periods, and caused great anxiety to his court (we do not learn that his colleague,

Hawki V, shared this). Once, on his return from such a mis-adventure, he had great difficulty in establishing his identity; Baddlesmere had dyed him and the familiar brown figure re-appeared as a piebald rabbit. Finally (what will not boys think of?) he was a very early experimenter with what has since been called artificial insemination. The judgment of his-tory cannot pronounce him either a good rabbit or a good King; but he was not a nonentity. He ate prodigiously.

And now that I have opened the gate, all the Boxonians, like the ghosts in Homer, come clamoring for mention. But they must be denied it. Readers who have built a world would rather tell of their own than hear of mine; those who have not would perhaps be bewildered and repelled. Nor had Boxen any connection with Joy. I have mentioned it at all only because to omit it would have been to misrepresent this period of my life.

One caution must here be repeated. I have been describing a life in which, plainly, imagination of one sort or another played the dominant part. Remember that it never involved the least grain of belief; I never mistook imagination for reality. About the Northernness no such question could arise: it was essentially a desire and implied the absence of its object. And Boxen we never could believe in, for we had made it. No novelist (in that sense) believes in his own characters.

At the end of the Summer Term 1913 I won a classical entrance scholarship to Wyvern College.

VI

BLOODERY

Any way for Heaven sake
So I were out of your whispering.

WEBSTER

NOW THAT we have done with Chartres we may call Wyvern College simply Wyvern, or more simply still, as
Wyvernians themselves call it, the Coll.

Going to the Coll was the most exciting thing that had yet
happened in my outer life. At Chartres we had lived under
the shadow of the Coll. We were often taken there to see
matches or sports or the finish of the great Goldbury Run.
These visits turned our heads. The crowd of boys older than
oneself, their dazzling air of sophistication, scraps of their
esoteric talk overheard, were like Park Lane in the old "Season" to a girl who is to be a debutante next year. Above all,
the Bloods, the adored athletes and prefects, were an embodi-
ment of all worldly pomp, power, and glory. Beside them
Pogo shrank into insignificance; what is a Master compared
with a Blood? The whole school was a great temple for the
worship of these mortal gods; and no boy ever went there
more prepared to worship them than I.

If you have not been at such a school as Wyvern, you may
ask what a *Blood* is. He is a member of the school aristocracy.

Foreign readers must clearly understand that this aristocracy has nothing whatever to do with the social position of the boys in the outer world. Boys of good, or wealthy, family are no more likely to be in it than anyone else; the only nobleman in my House at Wyvern never became a Blood. Shortly before my time there the son of a very queer customer had been at least on the fringe of Bloodery. The qualifying condition for Bloodery is that one should have been at the school for a considerable time. This by itself will not get you in, but newness will certainly exclude you. The most important qualification is athletic prowess. Indeed if this is sufficiently brilliant it makes you a Blood automatically. If it is a little less brilliant, then good looks and personality will help. So, of course, will fashion, as fashion is understood at your school. A wise candidate for Bloodery will wear the right clothes, use the right slang, admire the right things, laugh at the right jokes. And of course, as in the outer world, those on the fringes of the privileged class can, and do, try to worm their way into it by all the usual arts of pleasing.

At some schools, I am told, there is a sort of dyarchy. An aristocracy of Bloods, supported or at least tolerated by popular sentiment, stands over against an official ruling class of prefects appointed by the Masters. I believe they usually appoint it from the highest form, so that it has some claim to be an intelligentsia. It was not so at the Coll. Those who were made prefects were nearly all Bloods and they did not have to be in any particular form. Theoretically (though I do not suppose this would ever happen) the dunce at the bottom of the lowest form could have been made the captain—in our language, the Head—of the Coll. We thus had only a single governing class, in whom every kind of power, privilege, and prestige were united. Those to whom the hero worship of their juniors would in any case have gone, and those whose astuteness and ambition would under any system have enabled them to rise, were the same whom the official power of the Masters supported. Their position was emphasized by special liberties, clothes, priorities, and dignities which affected every side of school life. This, you will see, makes a pretty strong class. But it was strengthened still further by a factor which distinguishes school from ordinary life. In a country governed by an oligarchy, huge numbers of people, and among them some very stirring spirits, know they can never hope to get into that oligarchy; it may therefore be worth their while to attempt a revolution. At the Coll the lowest social class of all were too young, therefore too weak, to dream of revolt. In the middle class—boys who were no longer fags but not yet Bloods—those who alone had physical strength and popularity enough to qualify them as leaders of a revolution were already beginning to hope for Bloodery themselves. It suited them better to accelerate their social progress by courting the existing Bloods than to risk a revolt which, in the unlikely event of its succeeding, would destroy the very prize they were longing to share. And if at last they despaired of ever doing so—why, by that time their school-days were nearly over. Hence the Wyvernian constitution was unbreakable. Schoolboys have often risen against their Masters; I doubt if there has ever been or ever can be a revolt against Bloods.

It is not, then, surprising if I went to the Coll prepared to worship. Can any adult aristocracy present the World to us in quite such an alluring form as the hierarchy of a public school? Every motive for prostration is brought to bear at once on the mind of the New Boy when he sees a Blood; the natural respect of the thirteen-year-old for the nineteen-year-old, the fan's feeling for a film star, the suburban woman's feeling for a duchess, the newcomer's awe in the presence of the Old Hand, the street urchin's dread of the police.

One's first hours at a public school are unforgettable. Our House was a tall, narrow stone building (and, by the way, the only house in the place which was not an architectural nightmare) rather like a ship. The deck on which we chiefly lived consisted of two very dark stone corridors at right angles to one another. The doors off them opened into the studies—little rooms about six feet square, each shared by two or three boys. The very sight of them was ravishing to a boy from a Prep school who had never before had a *pied-à-terre* of his own. As we were still living (culturally) in the Edwardian period, each study imitated as closely as possible the cluttered appearance of an Edwardian drawing room; the aim was to fill the tiny cell as full as it could hold with bookcases, corner cupboards, knickknacks, and pictures. There were two larger rooms on the same floor; one the "Pres' Room," the synod of Olympus, and the other the New Boys' Study. It was not like a study at all. It was larger, darker, and undecorated; an immovable bench ran round a clamped table. But we knew, we ten or twelve recruits, that not all of us would be left in the New Boys' Study. Some of us would be

86

given "real" studies; the residue would occupy the opprobrious place for a term or so. That was the great hazard of our first evening; one was to be taken and another left.

As we sat round our clamped table, silent for the most part and speaking in whispers when we spoke, the door would be opened at intervals; a boy would look in, smile (not at us but to himself) and withdraw. Once, over the shoulder of the smiler there came another face, and a chuckling voice said, "Ho-ho! I know what *you're* looking for." Only I knew what it was all about, for my brother had played Chesterfield to my Stanhope and instructed me in the manners of the Coll. None of the boys who looked in and smiled was a Blood; they were all quite young and there was something common to the faces of them all. They were, in fact, the reigning or fading Tarts of the House, trying to guess which of us were their destined rivals or successors.

It is possible that some readers will not know what a House Tart was. First, as to the adjective. All life at Wyvern was lived, so to speak, in the two concentric circles of Coll and House. You could be a Coll pre or merely a House pre. You could be a Coll Blood or merely a House Blood, a Coll Punt (*i. e.*, a pariah, an unpopular person) or merely a House Punt; and of course a Coll Tart or merely a House Tart. A Tart is[1] a pretty and effeminate-looking small boy who acts as a catamite to one or more of his seniors, usually Bloods. Usually, not always. Though our oligarchy kept most of the

[1] Here, and throughout this account, I sometimes use the "historic present." Heaven forfend I should be taken to mean that Wyvern is the same today.

amenities of life to themselves, they were, on this point, liberal; they did not impose chastity on the middle-class boy in addition to all his other disabilities. Pederasty among the lower classes was not "side," or at least not serious side; not like putting one's hands in one's pockets or wearing one's coat unbuttoned. The gods had a sense of proportion.

The Tarts had an important function to play in making school (what it was advertised to be) a preparation for public life. They were not like slaves, for their favors were (nearly always) solicited, not compelled. Nor were they exactly like prostitutes, for the liaison often had some permanence and, far from being merely sensual, was highly sentimentalized. Nor were they paid (in hard cash, I mean) for their services; though of course they had all the flattery, unofficial influence, favor, and privileges which the mistresses of the great have always enjoyed in adult society. That was where the Preparation for Public Life came in. It would appear from Mr. Arnold Lunn's *Harrovians* that the Tarts at his school acted as informers. None of ours did. I ought to know, for one of my friends shared a study with a minor Tart; and except that he was sometimes turned out of the study when one of the Tart's lovers came in (and that, after all, was only natural) he had nothing to complain of. I was not shocked by these things. For me, at that age, the chief drawback to the whole system was that it bored me considerably. For you will have missed the atmosphere of our House unless you picture the whole place from week's end to week's end buzzing, tittering, hinting, whispering about this subject. After games, gallantry was the principal topic of polite conversation; who had "a case with" whom, whose star was in the ascendant, who had whose photo, who and when and how often and what night and where. . . . I suppose it might be called the Greek Tradition. But the vice in question is one to which I had never been tempted, and which, indeed, I still find opaque to the imagination. Possibly, if I had only stayed longer at the Coll, I might, in this respect as in others, have been turned into a Normal Boy, as the system promises. As things were, I was bored.

Those first days, like your first days in the army, were spent in a frantic endeavor to find out what you had to do. One of my first duties was to find out what "Club" I was in. Clubs were the units to which we were assigned for compulsory games; they belonged to the Coll organization, not the House organization, so I had to go to a notice board "Up Coll" to get my facts. And first to find the place—and then to dare to squeeze oneself into the crowd of more important boys around the notice board—and then to begin reading through five hundred names, but always with one eye on your watch, for of course there is something else to be done within ten minutes. I was forced away from the board before I had found my name, and so, sweating, back to the House, in a flurry of anxiety, wondering how I could find time to do the job tomorrow and what unheard-of disaster might follow if I could not. (Why, by the way, do some writers talk as if care and worry were the special characteristics of adult life? It appears to me that there is more *atra cura* in an average schoolboy's week than in a grown man's average year.)

When I reached the House something gloriously unexpected happened. At the door of the Pres' Room stood one Fribble; a mere House Blood, it is true, even a minor House Blood, but to me a sufficiently exalted figure; a youth of the lean, laughing type. I could hardly believe it when he actually addressed me. "Oh, I say, Lewis," he bawled, "I can tell you your Club. You're in the same one as me, B6." What a transition from all but despair to elation I underwent! All my anxiety was laid to rest. And then the graciousness of Fribble, the condescension! If a reigning monarch had asked me to dine, I could hardly have been more flattered. But there was better to follow. On every half-holiday I went dutifully to the B6 notice board to see whether my name was down to play that afternoon or not. And it never was. This was pure joy, for of course I hated games. My native clumsiness, combined with the lack of early training for which Belsen was responsible, had ruled out all possibility of my ever playing well enough to amuse myself, let alone to satisfy other players. I accepted games (quite a number of boys do) as one of the necessary evils of life, comparable to Income Tax or the Dentist. And so, for a week or two, I was in clover.

Then the blow fell. Fribble had lied. I was in a totally different Club. My name had more than once appeared on a notice board I had never seen. I had committed the serious crime of "Skipping Clubs." The punishment was a flogging administered by the Head of the Coll in the presence of the assembled Coll Pres. To the Head of the Coll himself—a red-headed, pimply boy with a name like Borage or Porridge—I can bear no grudge; it was to him a routine matter. But I must give him a name because the real point of the story requires it. The emissary (some Blood a little lower than the Head himself) who summoned me to execution attempted to reveal to me the heinousness of my crime by the words, "Who are you? Nobody. Who is Porridge? THE MOST IMPORTANT PERSON THERE IS."

I thought then, and I still think, that this rather missed the point. There were two perfectly good morals he could have drawn. He might have said, "We are going to teach you never to rely on secondhand information when firsthand is available"—a very profitable lesson. Or he might have said, "What made you think that a Blood could not be a liar?" But, "Who are you? Nobody," however just, seems hardly relevant. The implication is that I have skipped Club in arrogance or defiance. And I puzzle endlessly over the question whether the speaker really believed that. Did he really think it likely that an utterly helpless stranger in a new society, a society governed by an irresistible class on whose favor all his hopes of happiness depended, had set himself in the first week to pull the nose of The Most Important Person There Is? It is a problem which has met me many times in later life. What does a certain type of examiner mean when he says, "To show up work like this is an insult to the examiners"? Does he really think that the plowed candidate has insulted him?

Another problem is Fribble's share in my little catastrophe. Was his lie to me a hoax, a practical joke? Was he paying off some old score against my brother? Or was he (as I now think most likely) simply what our ancestors called a Rattle, a man from whose mouth information, true and false, flows out all day long without consideration, almost without voli-tion? Some might think that, whatever his motive had origi-nally been, he might have come forward and confessed his part when he saw what I was in for. But that, you know, was hardly to be expected. He was a very minor Blood, still climbing up the social stair; Burradge was almost as far above Fribble as Fribble was above me. By coming forward he would have imperiled his social position, in a community where social advancement was the one thing that mattered; school is a preparation for public life.

In justice to Wyvern, I must add that Fribble was not, by our standards, quite a fair representative of Bloodery. He had offended against the rules of gallantry in a manner which (my brother tells me) would have been impossible in his day. I said just now that the Tarts were solicited, not compelled. But Fribble did use all his prefectorial powers for a whole term to persecute a boy called, let us say, Parsley who had refused his suit. This was quite easy for Fribble to do. The innumerable small regulations which a junior boy could break almost unawares enabled a prefect to make sure that a given boy was nearly always in trouble, while the fagging system made it easy to see that he had no leisure at all at any hour of any day. So Parsley learned what it was to refuse even a minor Blood. The story would be more impressive if Parsley had been a virtuous boy and had refused on moral grounds. Unfortunately he was "as common as a barber's chair," had been a reigning toast in my brother's day, and was now almost past his bloom. He drew the line at Fribble. But Fribble's attempt at coercion was the only instance of its kind I ever knew.

Indeed, taking them by and large, and considering the temptations of adolescents, so privileged, so flattered, our Bloods were not a bad lot. The Count was even kindly. The Parrot was nothing worse than a grave fool: "Yards-of-Face" they called him. Stopfish, whom some thought cruel, even had moral principles; in his younger days many (I'm told) had desired him as a Tart, but he had kept his virtue. "Pretty, but no good to anyone; he's *pie*," would be the Wyvernian comment. The hardest to defend, perhaps, is Tennyson. We did not much mind his being a shoplifter; some people thought it rather clever of him to come back from a tour of the town with more ties and socks than he had paid for. We minded more his favorite punishment for us rabble, "a clip." Yet he could truly have pleaded to the authorities that it meant merely a box on the ear. He would not have added that the patient was made to stand with his left ear, temple and cheek almost, but not quite, touching the jamb of a doorway, and then struck with full force on the right. We also grumbled a little in secret when he got up a tournament (either explicitly or virtually compulsory, I think) in a game called Yard Cricket, collected subscriptions, and neither held the tournament nor returned the cash. But you will remember that this happened in the Marconi period, and to be a prefect is a Preparation for Public Life. And for all of them, even Tennyson, one thing can be said; they were never drunk. I was told that their predecessors, a year before I came, were sometimes very drunk indeed in the House corridor at midday. In fact, odd as it would have sounded to an adult, I joined the House when it was in a stern mood of moral rearmament. That was the point of a series of speeches which the prefects addressed to us all in the House Library during my first week. It was explained with a wealth of threatenings that we were to be pulled Up or Together or wherever decadents are pulled by moral reformers. Tennyson was very great on that occasion. He had a fine bass voice and sang solos in the choir. I knew one of his Tarts.

Peace to them all. A worse fate awaited them than the most vindictive fag among us could have wished. Ypres and the Somme ate up most of them. They were happy while their good days lasted.

My flogging by pimply old Ullage was no unmerciful affair in itself. The real trouble was that I think I now became, thanks to Fribble, a marked man; the sort of dangerous New Boy who skips Clubs. At least I think that must have been the main reason why I was an object of dislike to Tennyson. There were probably others. I was big for my age, a great lout of a boy, and that sets one's seniors against one. I was also useless at games. Worst of all, there was my face. I am the kind of person who gets told, "And take that look off your face too." Notice, once more, the mingled justice and injustice of our lives. No doubt in conceit or ill temper I have often intended to look insolent or truculent; but on those occasions people don't appear to notice it. On the other hand, the moments at which I was told to "take that look off" were usually those when I intended to be most abject. Can there have been a freeman somewhere among my ancestors whose expression, against my will, looked out?

As I have hinted before, the fagging system is the chief medium by which the Bloods, without breaking any rule, can make a junior boy's life a weariness to him. Different schools have different kinds of fagging. At some of them, individual Bloods have individual fags. This is the system most often depicted in school stories; it is sometimes represented as—and, for all I know, sometimes really is—a fruitful relation as of knight and squire, in which service on the one part is rewarded with some degree of countenance and protection on the other. But whatever its merits may be, we never experienced them at Wyvern. Fagging with us was as impersonal as the labor market in Victorian England; in that way, too, the Coll was a preparation for public life. All boys under a certain seniority constituted a labor pool, the common property of all the Bloods. When a Blood wanted his O.T.C. kit brushed and polished, or his boots cleaned, or his study "done out," or his tea made, he shouted. We all came running, and of course the Blood gave the work to the boy he most disliked. The kit cleaning—it took hours, and then, when you had finished it, your own kit was still to do—was the most detested *corvée*. Shoe cleaning was a nuisance not so much in itself as in its attendant circumstances. It came at an hour which was vital for a boy like me who, having won a scholarship, had been placed in a high form and could hardly, by all his best efforts, keep up with the work. Hence the success of one's whole day in Form might depend on the precious forty minutes between breakfast and Morning School, when one went over the set passages of translation with other boys in the same Form. This could be done only if one escaped being fagged as a shoeblack. Not, of course, that it takes forty minutes to clean a pair of shoes. What takes the time is waiting in the queue of other fags in the "boot-hole" to get your turn at the brushes and blacking. The whole look of that cellar, the darkness, the smell, and (for most of the year) the freezing cold, are a vivid memory. You must not of course suppose that, in those spacious days, we lacked servants. There were two official "bootboys" paid by the Housemaster for cleaning all boots and shoes, and everyone, including us fags who had cleaned both our own shoes and the Bloods' shoes daily, tipped the bootboys at the end of each term for their services.

For a reason which all English readers will understand (others will hear something of it in the next chapter) I am humiliated and embarrassed at having to record that as time went on I came to dislike the fagging system. No true defender of the Public Schools will believe me if I say that I was tired. But I was—dog tired, cab-horse tired, tired (almost) like a child in a factory. Many things besides fagging contributed to it. I was big and had possibly outgrown my strength. My work in Form was almost beyond me. I was having a good deal of dental trouble at the time, and many nights of clamorous pain. Never, except in the front-line trenches (and not always there) do I remember such aching and continuous weariness as at Wyvern. Oh, the implacable day, the horror of waking, the endless desert of hours that separated one from bedtime! And remember that, even without fagging, a school day contains hardly any leisure for a boy who does not like games. For him, to pass from the form room to the playing field is simply to exchange work in which he can take some interest for work in which he can take none, in which failure is more severely punished, and in which (worst of all) he must feign an interest.

I think that this feigning, this ceaseless pretense of interest in matters to me supremely boring, was what wore me out more than anything else. If the reader will picture himself, unarmed, shut up for thirteen weeks on end, night and day, in a society of fanatical golfers—or, if he is a golfer himself, let him substitute fishermen, theosophists, bimetallists, Baconians, or German undergraduates with a taste for autobiography—who all carry revolvers and will probably shoot him if he ever seems to lose interest in their conversation, he will have an idea of my school life. Even the hardy Chowbok (in *Erewhon*) quailed at such a destiny. For games (and gallantry) were the only subjects, and I cared for neither. But I must seem to care for both, for a boy goes to a Public School precisely to be made a normal, sensible boy— a good mixer—to be taken out of himself; and eccentricity is severely penalized.

You must not, from this, hastily conclude that most boys liked *playing* games any better than I did. To escape Clubs was considered by dozens of boys an obvious good. Leave off Clubs required the Housemaster's signature, and that harmless Merovingian's signature was imitable. A competent forger (I knew one member of the profession) by manufacturing and selling forged signatures could make a steady addition to his pocket money. The perpetual talk about games depended on three things. First, on the same sort of genuine (though hardly practical) enthusiasm which sends the crowds to the League Football Matches. Few wanted to play, but many wanted to watch, to participate vicariously in the triumphs of the Coll, or the House, team. Secondly, this natural feeling had the vigilant backing of all the Bloods and nearly all the Masters. To be lukewarm on such matters was the supreme sin. Hence enthusiasm had to be exaggerated where it existed and simulated where it did not. At cricket matches minor Bloods patrolled the crowd of spectators to detect and punish any "slackness" in the applause; it reminds one of the precautions taken when Nero sang. For of course the whole structure of Bloodery would collapse if the Bloods played in the spirit of play, for their recreation; there must be audience and limelight. And this brings us to the third reason. For boys who were not yet Bloods but who had some athletic promise, Games were essentially a *moyen de parvenir*. There was nothing recreational about Clubs for them any more than for me. They went to the playing fields not as men go to the tennis club but as stagestruck girls go to an Audition; tense and anxious, racked with dazzling hopes and sickening fears, never in peace of mind till they had won some notice which would set their feet on the first rung of the social ladder. And not then at peace either; for not to advance is to fall back.

The truth is that organized and compulsory games had, in my day, banished the element of play from school life almost entirely. There was no time to play (in the proper sense of the word). The rivalry was too fierce, the prizes too glittering, the "hell of failure" too severe.

The only boy, almost, who "played" (but not at games) was our Irish earl. But then he was an exception to all rules; not because of his earldom but because he was an untamable

Irishman, anarch in grain, whom no society could iron out. He smoked a pipe in his first term. He went off by night on strange expeditions to a neighboring city; not, I believe, for women, but for harmless rowdyism, low life, and adventure. He always carried a revolver. I remember it well, for he had a habit of loading one chamber only, rushing into your study, and then firing off (if that is the right word) all the others at you, so that your life depended on his counting accurately. I felt at the time, and I feel still, that this (unlike the fagging) was the sort of thing no sensible boy could object to. It was done in defiance both of masters and Bloods, it was wholly useless, and there was no malice in it. I liked Ballygunnian; he, too, was killed in France. I do not think he ever became a Blood; if he had, he wouldn't have noticed it. He cared nothing for the limelight or for social success. He passed through the Coll without paying it any attention.

I suppose Popsy—the pretty redhead who was housemaid on "the Private side"—might also rank as an element making for "play." Popsy, when caught and carried bodily into our part of the House (I think by the Count), was all giggles and screams. She was too sensible a girl to surrender her "virtue" to any Blood; but it was rumored that those who found her in the right time and place might induce her to give certain lessons in anatomy. Perhaps they lied.

I have hardly mentioned a Master yet. One master, dearly loved and reverenced, will appear in the next chapter. But other masters are hardly worth speaking of. It is difficult for parents (and more difficult, perhaps, for schoolmasters) to realize the unimportance of most masters in the life of a school. Of the good and evil which is done to a schoolboy masters, in general, do little, and know less. Our own House-master must have been an upright man, for he fed us excellently. For the rest, he treated his House in a very gentle-manly, uninquisitive way. He sometimes walked round the dormitories of a night, but he always wore boots, trod heavily and coughed at the door. He was no spy and no kill-joy, honest man. Live and let live.

As I grew more and more tired, both in body and mind, I came to hate Wyvern. I did not notice the real harm it was doing to me. It was gradually teaching me to be a prig; that is, an intellectual prig or (in the bad sense) a Highbrow. But that subject must wait for another chapter. At the tail end of this I must repeat (for this is the over-all impression left by Wyvern) that I was tired. Consciousness itself was becoming the supreme evil; sleep, the prime good. To lie down, to be out of the sound of voices, to pretend and grimace ·and evade and slink no more, that was the object of all desire—if only there were not another morning ahead—if only sleep could last for ever!

VII

LIGHT AND SHADE

No situation, however wretched it seems, but has some sort of comfort attending it.

GOLDSMITH

HERE'S A fellow, you say, who used to come before us as a moral and religious writer, and now, if you please, he's written a whole chapter describing his old school as a very furnace of impure loves without one word on the heinousness of the sin. But there are two reasons. One you shall hear before this chapter ends. The other is that, as I have said, the sin in question is one of the two (gambling is the other) which I have never been tempted to commit. I will not indulge in futile philippics against enemies I never met in battle.

("This means, then, that all the other vices you have so largely written about . . ." Well, yes, it does, and more's the pity; but it's nothing to our purpose at the moment.)

I have now to tell you how Wyvern made me a prig. When I went there, nothing was further from my mind than the idea that my private taste for fairly good books, for Wagner, for mythology, gave me any sort of superiority to those who read nothing but magazines and listened to nothing but the (then fashionable) Ragtime. The claim might seem unbelievable if I did not add that I had been protected from this

sort of conceit by downright ignorance. Mr. Ian Hay somewhere draws a picture of the reading minority at a Public
School in his day as boys who talked about "G. B. S. and
G. K. C." in the same spirit in which other boys secretly
smoked; both sets were inspired by the same craving for forbidden fruit and the same desire to be grown up. And I
suppose boys such as he describes might come from Chelsea
or Oxford or Cambridge homes where they heard things
about contemporary literature. But my position was wholly
different. I was, for example, a great reader of Shaw about
the time I went to Wyvern, but I had never dreamed that
reading Shaw was anything to be proud of. Shaw was an
author on my father's shelves like any other author. I began
reading him because his *Dramatic Opinions* contained a good
deal about Wagner and Wagner's very name was then a lure
to me. Thence I went on to read most of the other Shaws we
had. But how his reputation stood in the literary world I
neither knew nor cared; I didn't know there was "a literary
world." My father told me Shaw was "a mountebank" but
that there were some laughs in *John Bull's Other Island*. It
was the same with all my other reading; no one (thank God)
had ever admired or encouraged it. (William Morris, for some
unfathomable reason, my father always referred to as "that
whistlepainter.") I might be—no doubt I was—conceited at
Chartres for being good at my Latin; this was something
recognized as meritorious. But "Eng. Lit." was blessedly absent from the official syllabus, so I was saved from any possibility of conceit about it. Never in my life had I read a
work of fiction, poetry, or criticism in my own language ex·

cept because, after trying the first few pages, I liked the taste of it. I could not help knowing that most other people, boys and grown-ups alike, did not care for the books I read. A very few tastes I could share with my father, a few more with my brother; apart from that, there was no point of contact, and this I accepted as a sort of natural law. If I reflected on it at all, it would have given me, I think, a slight feeling, not of superiority, but of inferiority. The latest popular novel was so obviously a more adult, a more normal, a more sophisticated taste than any of mine. A certain shame or bashfulness attached itself to whatever one deeply and privately enjoyed. I went to the Coll far more disposed to excuse my literary tastes than to plume myself on them.

But this innocence did not last. It was, from the first, a little shaken by all that I soon began to learn from my form master about the glories of literature. I was at last made free of the dangerous secret that others had, like me, found there "enormous bliss" and been maddened by beauty. Among the other New Bugs of my year, too, I met a pair of boys who came from the Dragon School at Oxford (where Naomi Mitchison in her teens had just produced her first play) and from them also I got the dim impression that there was a world I had never dreamed of, a world in which poetry, say, was a thing public and accepted, just as Games and Gallantry were accepted at Wyvern; nay, a world in which a taste for such things was almost meritorious. I felt as Siegfried felt when it first dawned on him that he was not Mime's son. What had been "my" taste was apparently "our" taste (if only I could ever meet the "we" to whom that "our" belonged). And if "our" taste, then—by a perilous transition—perhaps "good" taste or "the right taste." For that transition involves a kind of Fall. The moment good taste knows itself, some of its goodness is lost. Even then, however, it is not necessary to take the further downward step of despising the "philistines" who do not share it. Unfortunately I took it. Hitherto, though increasingly miserable at Wyvern, I had been half ashamed of my own misery, still ready (if I were only allowed) to admire the Olympians, still a little over-awed, cowed rather than resentful. I had, you see, no standing place against the Wyvernian *ethos*, no side for which I could play against it; it was a bare "I" against what seemed simply the world. But the moment that "I" became, however vaguely, a *we*—and Wyvern not *the* world but *a* world—the whole thing changed. It was now possible, at least in thought, to retaliate. I can remember what may well have been the precise moment of this transition. A prefect called Blugg or Glubb or some such name stood opposite me, belching in my face, giving me some order. The belching was not intended as an insult. You can't "insult" a fag any more than an animal. If Bulb had thought of my reactions at all, he would have expected me to find his eructations funny. What pushed me over the edge into pure priggery was his face—the puffy bloated cheeks, the thick, moist, sagging lower lip, the yokel blend of drowsiness and cunning. "The lout!" I thought. "The clod! The dull, crass clown! For all his powers and privileges, I would not be he." I had become a Prig, a High-brow.

The interesting thing is that the public-school system

had thus produced the very thing which it was advertised to prevent or cure. For you must understand (if you have not been dipped in that tradition yourself) that the whole thing was devised to "knock the nonsense" out of the smaller boys and "put them in their place." "If the junior boys weren't fagged," as my brother once said, "they would become insufferable." That is why I felt so embarrassed, a few pages ago, when I had to confess that I got rather tired of perpetual fagging. If you say this, every true defender of the system will diagnose your case at once, and they will all diagnose it in the same way. "Ho-ho!" they will cry, "so *that's* the trouble! Thought yourself too good to black your betters' boots, did you? That just shows how badly you needed to be fagged. It's to cure young prigs like you that the system exists." That any cause except "thinking yourself too good for it" might awaken discontent with a fag's lot will not be admitted. You have only to transfer the thing to adult life and you will, apparently, see the full logic of the position. If some neighboring V.I.P. had irresistible authority to call on you for any service he pleased at any hour when you were not in the office—if, when you came home on a summer evening, tired from work and with more work to prepare against the morrow, he could drag you to the links and make you his caddy till the light failed—if at last he dismissed you unthanked with a suitcase full of his clothes to brush and clean and return to him before breakfast, and a hamper full of his foul linen for your wife to wash and mend—and if, under this regime, you were not always perfectly happy and contented; where could the cause lie except in your own van-

ity? What else, after all, could it be? For, almost by definition, every offense a junior boy commits must be due to
"cheek" or "side"; and to be miserable, even to fall short of
rapturous enthusiasm, is an offense.

Obviously a certain grave danger was ever present to the
minds of those who built up the Wyvernian hierarchy. It
seemed to them self-evident that, if you left things to themselves, boys of nineteen who played rugger for the county
and boxed for the school would everywhere be knocked
down and sat on by boys of thirteen. And that, you know,
would be a very shocking spectacle. The most elaborate
mechanism, therefore, had to be devised for protecting the
strong against the weak, the close corporation of Old Hands
against the parcel of newcomers who were strangers to one
another and to everyone in the place, the poor, trembling
lions against the furious and ravening sheep.

There is, of course, some truth in it. Small boys can be
cheeky; and half an hour in the society of a French thirteen-
year-old makes most of us feel that there is something to be
said for fagging after all. Yet I cannot help thinking that the
bigger boys would have been able to hold their own without
all the complicated assurances, pattings on the back, and
encouragement which the authorities gave them. For, of
course, these authorities, not content with knocking the "nonsense" out of the sheep, were always coaxing and petting an
at least equal quantity of "nonsense" into the lions; power and
privilege and an applauding audience for the games they
play. Might not the mere nature of boys have done all, and

rather more than all, that needed doing in this direction without assistance?

But whatever the rationality of the design, I contend that it did not achieve its object. For the last thirty years or so England has been filled with a bitter, truculent, skeptical debunking, and cynical *intelligentsia*. A great many of them were at public schools, and I believe very few of them liked it. Those who defend the schools will, of course, say that these Prigs are the cases which the system failed to cure; they were not kicked, mocked, fagged, flogged, and humiliated enough. But surely it is equally possible that they are the products of the system? that they were not Prigs at all when they came to their schools but were made Prigs by their first year, as I was? For, really, that would be a very natural result. Where oppression does not completely and permanently break the spirit, has it not a natural tendency to produce retaliatory pride and contempt? We reimburse ourselves for cuffs and toil by a double dose of self-esteem. No one is more likely to be arrogant than a lately freed slave.

I write, of course, only to neutral readers. With the whole-hearted adherents of the system there is no arguing, for, as we have already seen, they have maxims and logic which the lay mind cannot apprehend. I have even heard them defend compulsory games on the ground that all boys "except a few rotters" like the games; they have to be compulsory because no compulsion is needed. (I wish I had never heard chaplains in the armed forces produce a similar argument in defense of the wicked institution of Church Parades.)

But the essential evil of public-school life, as I see it, did not lie either in the sufferings of the fags or in the privileged arrogance of the Bloods. These were symptoms of something more all-pervasive, something which, in the long run, did most harm to the boys who succeeded best at school and were happiest there. Spiritually speaking, the deadly thing was that school life was a life almost wholly dominated by the social struggle; to get on, to arrive, or, having reached the top, to remain there, was the absorbing preoccupation. It is often, of course, the preoccupation of adult life as well; but I have not yet seen any adult society in which the surrender to this impulse was so total. And from it, at school as in the world, all sorts of meanness flow; the sycophancy that courts those higher in the scale, the cultivation of those whom it is well to know, the speedy abandonment of friendships that will not help on the upward path, the readiness to join the cry against the unpopular, the secret motive in almost every action. The Wyvernians seem to me in retrospect to have been the least spontaneous, in that sense the least boyish, society I have ever known. It would perhaps not be too much to say that in some boys' lives everything was calculated to the great end of advancement. For this games were played; for this clothes, friends, amusements, and vices were chosen.

And that is why I cannot give pederasty anything like a first place among the evils of the Coll. There is much hypocrisy on this theme. People commonly talk as if every other evil were more tolerable than this. But why? Because those of us who do not share the vice feel for it a certain nausea, as we do, say, for necrophily? I think that of very little relevance to moral judgment. Because it produces permanent perversion? But there is very little evidence that it does. The Bloods would have preferred girls to boys if they could have come by them; when, at a later age, girls were obtainable, they probably took them. Is it then on Christian grounds? But how many of those who fulminate on the matter are in fact Christians? And what Christian, in a society so worldly and cruel as that of Wyvern, would pick out the carnal sins for special reprobation? Cruelty is surely more evil than lust and the World at least as dangerous as the Flesh. The real reason for all the pother is, in my opinion, neither Christian nor ethical. We attack this vice not because it is the worst but because it is, by adult standards, the most disreputable and unmentionable, and happens also to be a crime in English law. The World will lead you only to Hell; but sodomy may lead you to jail and create a scandal, and lose you your job. The World, to do it justice, seldom does that.

If those of us who have known a school like Wyvern dared to speak the truth, we should have to say that pederasty, however great an evil in itself, was, in that time and place, the only foothold or cranny left for certain good things. It was the only counterpoise to the social struggle; the one oasis (though green only with weeds and moist only with fetid water) in the burning desert of competitive ambition. In his unnatural love affairs, and perhaps only there, the Blood went a little out of himself, forgot for a few hours that he was One of the Most Important People There Are. It softens the picture. A perversion was the only chink left through which something spontaneous and uncalculating could creep in. Plato was right after all. Eros, turned upside down, blackened, distorted, and filthy, still bore the traces of his divinity.

What an answer, by the by, Wyvern was to those who derive all the ills of society from economics! For money had nothing to do with its class system. It was not (thank Heaven) the boys with threadbare coats who became Punts, nor the boys with plenty of pocket money who became Bloods. According to some theorists, therefore, it ought to have been entirely free from bourgeois vulgarities and iniquities. Yet I have never seen a community so competitive, so full of snobbery and flunkeyism, a ruling class so selfish and so class-conscious, or a proletariat so fawning, so lacking in all solidarity and sense of corporate honor. But perhaps one hardly needs to cite experience for a truth so obvious a priori. As Aristotle remarked, men do not become dictators in order to keep warm. If a ruling class has some other source of strength, why need it bother about money? Most of what it wants will be pressed upon it by emulous flatterers; the rest can be taken by force.

There were two blessings at Wyvern that wore no disguise; one of them was my form master, Smewgy as we called him. I spell the name so as to insure the right pronunciation—the first syllable should rhyme exactly with *Fugue*—though the Wyvernian spelling was "Smugy."

Except at Oldie's I had been fortunate in my teachers ever since I was born; but Smewgy was "beyond expectation, beyond hope." He was a gray-head with large spectacles and a wide mouth which combined to give him a froglike expression, but nothing could be less froglike than his voice. He was honey-tongued. Every verse he read turned into music on his lips: something midway between speech and song. It is not the only good way of reading verse, but it is the way to enchant boys; more dramatic and less rhythmical ways can be learned later. He first taught me the right sensuality of poetry, how it should be savored and mouthed in solitude. Of Milton's "Thrones, Dominations, Princedoms, Virtues, Powers" he said, "That line made me happy for a week." It was not the sort of thing I had heard anyone say before. Nor had I ever met before perfect courtesy in a teacher. It had nothing to do with softness; Smewgy could be very severe, but it was the severity of a judge, weighty and measured, without taunting—

> *He never yet no vileinye ne sayde*
> *In all his lyf unto no maner wight.*

He had a difficult team to drive, for our form consisted partly of youngsters, New Bugs with scholarships, starting there like myself, and partly of veterans who had arrived there at the end of their slow journey up the school. He made us a unity by his good manners. He always addressed us as "gentlemen" and the possibility of behaving otherwise seemed thus to be ruled out from the beginning; and in that room at least the distinction between fags and Bloods never raised its head. On a hot day, when he had given us permission to remove our coats, he asked our permission before removing his gown. Once for bad work I was sent by him to the Headmaster to be threatened and rated. The Headmaster misunderstood Smewgy's report and thought there had been some complaint about my manners. Afterward Smewgy got wind of the Head's actual words and at once corrected the mistake, drawing me aside and saying, "There has been some curious misunderstanding. I said nothing of the sort about you. You will have to be whipped if you don't do better at your Greek Grammar next week, but naturally that has nothing to do with your manners or mine." The idea that the tone of conversation between one gentleman and another should be altered by a flogging (any more than by a duel) was ridiculous. His manner was perfect: no familiarity, no hostility, no threadbare humor; mutual respect; decorum. "Never let us live with *amousia,*" was one of his favorite maxims: *amousia,* the absence of the Muses. And he knew, as Spenser knew, that courtesy was of the Muses.

Thus, even had he taught us nothing else, to be in Smewgy's form was to be in a measure ennobled. Amidst all the banal ambition and flashy splendors of school life he stood as a permanent reminder of things more gracious, more humane, larger and cooler. But his teaching, in the narrower sense, was equally good. He could enchant but he could also analyze. An idiom or a textual crux, once expounded by Smewgy, became clear as day. He made us feel that the scholar's demand for accuracy was not merely pedantic, still less an arbitrary moral discipline, but rather a niceness, a delicacy, to lack which argued "a gross and swainish disposition." I began to see that the reader who misses syntactical points in a poem is missing aesthetic points as well.

In those days a boy on the classical side officially did almost nothing but classics. I think this was wise; the greatest service we can do to education today is to teach fewer subjects. No one has time to do more than a very few things well before he is twenty, and when we force a boy to be a mediocrity in a dozen subjects we destroy his standards, perhaps for life. Smewgy taught us Latin and Greek, but everything else came in incidentally. The books I liked best under his teaching were Horace's Odes, Aeneid IV, and Euripides' *Bacchae*. I had always in one sense "liked" my classical work, but hitherto this had only been the pleasure that everyone feels in mastering a craft. Now I tasted the classics as poetry. Euripides' picture of Dionysus was closely linked in my mind with the whole mood of Mr. Stephens' *Crock of Gold*, which I had lately read for the first time with great excitement. Here was something very different from the Northernness. Pan and Dionysus lacked the cold, piercing appeal of Odin and Frey. A new quality entered my imagination: something Mediterranean and volcanic, the orgiastic drum beat. Orgiastic, but not, or not strongly, erotic. It was perhaps unconsciously connected with my growing hatred of the public school orthodoxies and conventions, my desire to break and tear it all.

The other undisguised blessing of the Coll was "the Gurney," the school library; not only because it was a library, but because it was sanctuary. As the Negro used to become free on touching English soil, so the meanest boy was "unfaggable" once he was inside the Gurney. It was not, of course, easy to get there. In the winter terms if you were not on the list for "Clubs" you had to go out for a run. In summer you could reach sanctuary of an afternoon only under favorable conditions. You might be put down for Clubs, and that excluded you. Or there might be either a House match or a Coll match which you were compelled to watch. Thirdly, and most probably, on your way to the Gurney you might be caught and fagged for the whole afternoon. But sometimes one succeeded in running the gauntlet of all these dangers; and then—the books, silence, leisure, the distant sound of bat and ball ("Oh the brave music of a *distant* drum"), bees buzzing at the open windows, and freedom. In the Gurney I found *Corpus Poeticum Boreale* and tried, vainly but happily, to hammer out the originals from the translation at the bottom of the page. There too I found Milton, and Yeats, and a book on Celtic mythology, which soon became, if not a rival, yet a humble companion, to Norse. That did me good; to enjoy two mythologies (or three, now that I had begun to love the Greek), fully aware of their differing flavors, is a balancing thing, and makes for catholicity. I felt keenly the difference between the stony and fiery sublimity of Asgard, the green, leafy, amorous, and elusive world of Cruachan and the Red Branch and Tir-nan-Og, the harder, more defiant, sun-bright beauty of Olympus. I began (presumably in the holidays) an epic on Cuchulain and another on Finn, in English hexameters and in fourteeners respectively. Luckily they were abandoned before these easy and vulgar metres had time to spoil my ear.

But the Northernness still came first and the only work I completed at this time was a tragedy, Norse in subject and Greek in form. It was called *Loki Bound* and was as classical as any Humanist could have desired, with Prologos, Parodos,

Epeisodia, Stasima, Exodos, Stichomythia, and (of course) one passage in trochaic *septenarii*—with rhyme. I never enjoyed anything more. The content is significant. My Loki was not merely malicious. He was against Odin because Odin had created a world though Loki had clearly warned him that this was a wanton cruelty. Why should creatures have the burden of existence forced on them without their consent? The main contrast in my play was between the sad wisdom of Loki and the brutal orthodoxy of Thor. Odin was partly sympathetic; he could at least see what Loki meant and there had been old friendship between those two before cosmic politics forced them apart. Thor was the real villain, Thor with his hammer and his threats, who was always egging Odin on against Loki and always complaining that Loki did not sufficiently respect the major gods; to which Loki replied

I pay respect to wisdom not to strength.

Thor was, in fact, the symbol of the Bloods; though I see that more clearly now than I did at the time. Loki was a projection of myself; he voiced that sense of priggish superiority whereby I was, unfortunately, beginning to compensate myself for my unhappiness.

The other feature in *Loki Bound* which may be worth commenting on is the pessimism. I was at this time living, like so many Atheists or Antitheists, in a whirl of contradictions. I maintained that God did not exist. I was also very angry with God for not existing. I was equally angry with Him for creating a world.

How far was this pessimism, this desire not to have been, sincere? Well, I must confess that this desire quite slipped out of my mind during the seconds when I was covered by the wild Earl's revolver. By the Chestertonian test, then, the test of *Manalive*, it was not sincere at all. But I am still not convinced by Chesterton's argument. It is true that when a pessimist's life is threatened he behaves like other men; his impulse to preserve life is stronger than his judgment that life is not worth preserving. But how does this prove that the judgment was insincere or even erroneous? A man's judgment that whisky is bad for him is not invalidated by the fact that when the bottle is at hand he finds desire stronger than reason and succumbs. Having once tasted life, we are subjected to the impulse of self-preservation. Life, in other words, is as habit-forming as cocaine. What then? If I still held creation to be "a great injustice" I should hold that this impulse to retain life aggravates the injustice. If it is bad to be forced to drink the potion, how does it mend matters that the potion turns out to be an addiction drug? Pessimism cannot be answered so. Thinking as I then thought about the universe, I was reasonable in condemning it. At the same time I now see that my view was closely connected with a certain lopsidedness of temperament. I had always been more violent in my negative than in my positive demands. Thus, in personal relations, I could forgive much neglect more easily than the least degree of what I regarded as interference. At table I could forgive much insipidity in my food more easily than the least suspicion of what seemed to me excessive or inappropriate seasoning. In the course of life I could put up with any amount of monotony far more patiently than even the smallest disturbance, bother, bustle, or what the Scotch call *kurfuffle*. Never at any age did I clamor to be amused; always and at all ages (where I dared) I hotly demanded not to be interrupted. The pessimism, or cowardice, which would prefer nonexistence itself to even the mildest unhappiness was thus merely the generalization of all these pusillanimous preferences. And it remains true that I have, almost all my life, been quite unable to feel that horror of nonentity, of annihilation, which, say, Dr. Johnson felt so strongly. I felt it for the first time only in 1947. But that was after I had long been reconverted and thus begun to know what life really is and what would have been lost by missing it.

VIII

RELEASE

As Fortune is wont, at her chosen hour,
Whether she sends us solace or sore,
The wight to whom she shows her power
Will find that he gets still more and more.

PEARL

A FEW chapters ago I warned the reader that the return of Joy had introduced into my life a duality which makes it difficult to narrate. Reading through what I have just written about Wyvern, I find myself exclaiming, "Lies, lies! This was really a period of ecstasy. It consisted chiefly of moments when you were too happy to speak, when the gods and heroes rioted through your head, when satyrs danced and Maenads roared on the mountains, when Brynhild and Sieglinde, Deirdre, Maeve and Helen were all about you, till sometimes you felt that it might break you with mere richness." And all that is true. There were more Leprechauns than fags in that House. I have seen the victories of Cuchulain more often than those of the first eleven. Was Borage the Head of the Coll? or was it Conachar MacNessa? And the world itself—can I have been unhappy, living in Paradise? What keen, tingling sunlight there was! The mere smells were enough to make a man tipsy—cut grass, dew-dabbled mosses, sweet pea, autumn woods, wood burning, peat, salt water. The sense ached. I was sick with desire; that sickness better than health. All this is true, but it does not make the other version a lie. I am telling a story of two lives. They have nothing to do with each other: oil and vinegar, a river running beside a canal, Jekyll and Hyde. Fix your eye on either and it claims to be the sole truth. When I remember my outer life I see clearly that the other is but momentary flashes, seconds of gold scattered in months of dross, each instantly swallowed up in the old, familiar, sordid, hopeless weariness. When I remember my inner life I see that everything mentioned in the last two chapters was merely a coarse curtain which at any moment might be drawn aside to reveal all the heavens I then knew. The same duality perplexes the story of my home life, to which I must now turn.

Once my brother had left Wyvern and I had gone to it, the classic period of our boyhood was at an end. Something not so good succeeded it, but this had long been prepared by slow development within the classic age itself. All began, as I have said, with the fact that our father was out of the house from nine in the morning till six at night. From the very first we built up for ourselves a life that excluded him. He on his part demanded a confidence even more boundless, perhaps, than a father usually, or wisely, demands. One instance of this, early in my life, had far-reaching effects. Once when I was at Oldie's and had just begun to try to live as a Christian I wrote out a set of rules for myself and put them in my pocket. On the first day of the holidays, noticing that my pockets bulged with all sorts of papers and that my coat was being pulled out of all shape, he plucked out the whole pile of rubbish and began to go through it. Boylike, I would have died rather than let him see my list of good resolutions. I managed to keep them out of his reach and get them into the fire. I do not see that either of us was to blame; but never from that moment until the hour of his death did I enter his house without first going through my own pockets and removing anything that I wished to keep private.

A habit of concealment was thus bred before I had anything guilty to conceal. By now I had plenty. And even what I had no wish to hide I could not tell. To have told him what Wyvern or even Chartres was really like would have been risky (he might write to the Headmaster) and intolerably embarrassing. It would also have been impossible; and here I must touch on one of his strangest characteristics.

My father—but these words, at the head of a paragraph, will carry the reader's mind inevitably to *Tristram Shandy*. On second thoughts I am content that they should. It is only in a Shandean spirit that my matter can be approached. I have to describe something as odd and whimsical as ever entered the brain of Sterne; and if I could, I would gladly lead you to the same affection for my father as you have for Tristram's. And now for the thing itself. You will have grasped that my father was no fool. He had even a streak of genius in him. At the same time he had—when seated in his own arm chair after a heavy midday dinner on an August afternoon with all the windows shut—more power of confusing an issue or taking up a fact wrongly than any man I have ever known. As a result it was impossible to drive into his head any of the realities of our school life, after which (neverthe-

less) he repeatedly enquired. The first and simplest barrier
to communication was that, having earnestly asked, he did
not "stay for an answer" or forgot it the moment it was
uttered. Some facts must have been asked for and told him,
on a moderate computation, once a week, and were received
by him each time as perfect novelties. But this was the simplest barrier. Far more often he retained something, but something very unlike what you had said. His mind so bubbled
over with humor, sentiment, and indignation that, long before he had understood or even listened to your words, some
accidental hint had set his imagination to work, he had produced his own version of the facts, and believed that he was
getting it from you. As he invariably got proper names wrong
(no name seemed to him less probable than another) his *textus
receptus* was often almost unrecognizable. Tell him that a
boy called Churchwood had caught a field mouse and kept it
as a pet, and a year, or ten years later, he would ask you, "Did
you ever hear what became of poor Chickweed who was so
afraid of the rats?" For his own version, once adopted, was in-
delible, and attempts to correct it only produced an incredulous "Hm! Well, that's not the story you *used* to tell." Sometimes, indeed, he took in the facts you had stated; but truth
fared none the better for that. What are facts without interpretation? It was axiomatic to my father (in theory) that
nothing was said or done from an obvious motive. Hence he
who in his real life was the most honorable and impulsive of
men, and the easiest victim that any knave or imposter could
hope to meet, became a positive Machiavel when he knitted
his brows and applied to the behavior of people he had never

seen the spectral and labyrinthine operation which he called "reading between the lines." Once embarked upon that, he might make his landfall anywhere in the wide world: and always with unshakable conviction. "I see it all"—"I understand it perfectly"—"It's as plain as a pikestaff," he would say; and then, as we soon learned, he would believe till his dying day in some deadly quarrel, some slight, some secret sorrow or some immensely complex machination, which was not only improbable but impossible. Dissent on our part was attributed, with kindly laughter, to our innocence, gullibility, and general ignorance of life. And besides all these confusions, there were the sheer *non sequiturs* when the ground seemed to open at one's feet. "Did Shakespeare spell his name with an e at the end?" asked my brother. "I believe," said I—but my father interrupted: "I very much doubt if he used the Italian calligraphy *at all*." A certain church in Belfast has both a Greek inscription over the door and a curious tower. "That church is a great landmark," said I, "I can pick it out from all sorts of places—even from the top of Cave Hill." "Such nonsense," said my father, "how could you make out Greek letters three or four miles away?"

One conversation, held several years later, may be recorded as a specimen of these continual cross-purposes. My brother had been speaking of a reunion dinner for the officers of the Nth Division which he had lately attended. "I suppose your friend Collins was there," said my father.

B.   Collins? Oh no. He wasn't in the Nth, you know.

F.   (After a pause.) Did these fellows not like Collins then?

B. I don't quite understand. What fellows?

F. The Johnnies that got up the dinner.

B. Oh no, not at all. It was nothing to do with liking or not liking. You see, it was a purely Divisional affair. There'd be no question of asking anyone who hadn't been in the Nth.

F. (After a long pause.) Hm! Well, I'm sure poor Collins was very much hurt.

There are situations in which the very genius of Filial Piety would find it difficult not to let some sign of impatience escape him.

I would not commit the sin of Ham. Nor would I, as historian, reduce a complex character to a false simplicity. The man who, in his armchair, sometimes appeared not so much incapable of understanding anything as determined to misunderstand everything, was formidable in the police court and, I presume, efficient in his office. He was a humorist, even on occasion, a wit. When he was dying, the pretty nurse, rallying him, said, "What an old pessimist you are! You're just like my father." "I suppose," replied her patient, "he has *several* daughters."

The hours my father spent at home were thus hours of perplexity for us boys. After an evening of the sort of conversation I have been describing one felt as if one's head were spinning like a top. His presence put an end to all our innocent as well as to all our forbidden occupations. It is a hard thing—nay, a wicked thing—when a man is felt to be an intruder in his own house. And yet, as Johnson said, "Sensation is sensation." I am sure it was not his fault, I believe much of it was ours; what is certain is that I increasingly found it oppressive to be with him. One of his most amiable qualities helped to make it so. I have said before that he "conned no state"; except during his Philippics he treated us as equals. The theory was that we lived together more like three brothers than like a father and two sons. That, I say, was the theory. But of course it was not and could not be so; indeed ought not to have been so. That relation cannot really exist between schoolboys and a middle-aged man of overwhelming personality and of habits utterly unlike theirs. And the pretense that it does ends by putting a curious strain on the juniors. Chesterton has laid his finger on the weak point of all such factitious equality: "If a boy's aunts are his pals, will it not soon follow that a boy needs no pals but his aunts?" That was not, of course, the question for us; we wanted no pals. But we did want liberty, if only liberty to walk about the house. And my father's theory that we were three boys together actually meant that while he was at home we were as closely bound to his presence as if the three of us had been chained together; and all our habits were frustrated. Thus if my father came home unexpectedly at midday, having allowed himself an extra half-holiday, he might, if it were summer, find us with chairs and books in the garden. An austere parent, of the formal school, would have gone in to his own adult occupations. Not so my father. Sitting in the garden? An excellent idea. But would not all three of us be better on the summer seat? Thither, after he had assumed one of his "light spring overcoats," we would go. (I do not know how many overcoats he had; I am still wearing two of them.) After

sitting for a few minutes, thus clad, on a shadeless seat where
the noonday sun was blistering the paint, he not unnaturally
began to perspire. "I don't know what you two think," he
would say, "but I'm finding this almost *too* hot. What about
moving indoors?" That meant an adjournment to the study,
where even the smallest chink of open window was rather
grudgingly allowed. I say "allowed," but there was no question of authority. In theory, everything was decided by the
general Will. "Liberty Hall, boys, Liberty Hall," as he delighted to quote. "What time would you like lunch?" But we
knew only too well that the meal which would otherwise
have been at one had already been shifted, in obedience to his
lifelong preference, to two or even two-thirty; and that the
cold meats which we liked had already been withdrawn in
favor of the only food our father ever voluntarily ate—hot
butcher's meat, boiled, stewed or roast . . . and this to be
eaten in mid-afternoon in a dining room that faced south. For
the whole of the rest of the day, whether sitting or walking,
we were inseparable; and the speech (you see that it could
hardly be called conversation), the speech with its cross-
purposes, with its tone (inevitably) always set by him, continued intermittently till bedtime. I should be worse than a
dog if I blamed my lonely father for thus desiring the friendship of his sons; or even if the miserable return I made him
did not to this day lie heavy on my conscience. But "sensation
is sensation." It was extraordinarily tiring. And in my own
contributions to these endless talks—which were indeed too
adult for me, too anecdotal, too prevailingly jocular—I was
increasingly aware of an artificiality. The anecdotes were, in-

deed, admirable in their kind: business stories, Mahaffy stories (many of which I found attached to Jowett at Oxford), stories of ingenious swindles, social blunders, police-court "drunks." But I was acting when I responded to them. Drollery, whimsicality, the kind of humor that borders on the fantastic, was my line. I had to act. My father's geniality and my own furtive disobediences both helped to drive me into hypocrisy. I could not "be myself" while he was at home. God forgive me, I thought Monday morning, when he went back to his work, the brightest jewel in the week.

Such was the situation which developed during the classic period. Now, when I had gone to Wyvern and my brother to a tutor to prepare for Sandhurst, there came a change. My brother had liked Wyvern as much as I loathed it. There were many reasons for this: his more adaptable temper, his face which bore no such smack-inviting signature as mine, but most of all the fact that he had gone there straight from Oldie's and I from preparatory school where I had been happy. No school in England but would have appeared a heaven on earth after Oldie's. Thus in one of his first letters from Wyvern my brother communicated the startling fact that you could really eat as much (or as little) as you wanted at table. To a boy fresh from the school at Belsen, this alone would have outweighed almost everything else. But by the time I went to Wyvern I had learned to take decent feeding for granted. And now a terrible thing happened. My reaction to Wyvern was perhaps the first great disappointment my brother had ever experienced. Loving the place as he did, he had looked forward to the days when this too could be shared between us—an *idem sentire* about Wyvern succeeding an *idem sentire* about Boxen. Instead he heard, from me, blasphemies against all his gods; from Wyvern, that his young brother looked like becoming a Coll Punt. The immemorial league between us was strained, all but broken.

All this was cruelly complicated by the fact that relations between my father and my brother were never before or since so bad as at this time; and Wyvern was behind that too. My brother's reports had grown worse and worse; and the tutor to whom he had now been sent confirmed them to the extent of saying that he seemed to have learned almost nothing at school. Nor was that all. Sentences savagely underlined in my father's copy of *The Lanchester Tradition* reveal his thoughts. They are passages about a certain glazed insolence, an elaborate, heartless flippancy, which the reforming Headmaster in that story encountered in the Bloods of the school he wished to reform. That was how my father envisaged my brother at this period: flippant, languid, emptied of the intellectual interests which had appeared in his earlier boyhood, immovable, indifferent to all real values, and urgent in his demand for a motor bicycle.

It was, of course, to turn us into public-school boys that my father had originally sent us to Wyvern; the finished product appalled him. It is a familiar tragicomedy and you can study it in Lockhart; Scott labored hard to make his son a hussar, but when the actual hussar was presented to him, Scott sometimes forgot the illusion of being an aristocrat and became once more a respectable Edinburgh lawyer with strong views about Puppyism. So in our family. Mispronunciation was one of my father's favorite rhetorical weapons. He now always sounded the first syllable of Wyvern wrongly. I can still hear him growl, "Wyvernian affectation." In proportion as my brother's tone became languid and urbanely weary, so my father's voice became more richly and energetically Irish, and all manner of strange music from his boyhood in Cork and Dublin forced its way up through the more recent Belfastian crust.

During these miserable debates I occupied a most unfortunate position. To have been on my father's side and against my brother I should have had to unmake myself; it was a state of parties outside my whole philosophy of domestic politics. It was all very disagreeable.

Yet out of this "unpleasantness" (a favorite word of my father's) there sprang what I still reckon, by merely natural standards, the most fortunate thing that ever happened to me. The tutor (in Surrey) to whom my brother had been sent was one of my father's oldest friends. He had been headmaster of Lurgan when my father was a boy there. In a surprisingly short time he so rebuilt and extended the ruins of my brother's education that he not only passed into Sandhurst but was placed among those very few candidates at the top of the list who received prize cadetships. I do not think my father ever did justice to my brother's achievement; it came at a time when the gulf between them was too wide, and when they were friends again it had become ancient history. But he saw very clearly what it proved about the exceptional powers of his teacher. At the same time, he was almost as sick as I of the very name of Wyvern. And I never ceased, by letter and by word of mouth, to beg that I might be taken away. All these factors urged him to the decision which he now made. Might it not after all be best to give me my desire? to have done with school for good and send me also to Surrey to read for the University with Mr. Kirkpatrick? He did not form this plan without much doubt and hesitation. He did his best to put all the risks before me: the dangers of solitude, the sudden change from the life and bustle of a great school (which change I might not like so much as I anticipated), the possibly deadening effect of living with only an old man and his old wife for company. Should I really be happy with no companions of my own age? I tried to look very grave at these questions. But it was all imposture. My heart laughed. Happy without other boys? Happy without toothache, without chilblains, happy without pebbles in my shoes? And so the arrangement was made. If it had had nothing else to recommend it, the mere thought, "Never, never, never, shall I have to play games again," was enough to transport me. If you want to know how I felt, imagine your own feelings on waking one morning to find that income tax or unrequited love had somehow vanished from the world.

I should be sorry if I were understood to think, or if I encouraged any reader in thinking, that this invincible dislike of doing things with a bat or a ball were other than a misfortune. Not, indeed, that I allow to games any of the moral and almost mystical virtues which schoolmasters claim for them; they seem to me to lead to ambition, jealousy, and embittered partisan feeling, quite as often as to anything else. Yet not to like them is a misfortune, because it cuts you off from companionship with many excellent people who can be approached in no other way. A misfortune, not a vice; for it is involuntary. I had tried to like games and failed. That impulse had been left out of my make-up; I was to games, as the proverb has it, like an ass to the harp.

It is a curious truth, noticed by many writers, that good fortune is nearly always followed by more good fortune, and bad, by more bad. About the same time that my father decided to send me to Mr. Kirkpatrick, another great good came to me. Many chapters ago I mentioned a boy who lived near us and who had tried, quite unsuccessfully, to make friends with my brother and myself. His name was Arthur and he was my brother's exact contemporary; he and I had been at Campbell together though we never met. I think it was shortly before the beginning of my last term at Wyvern that I received a message saying that Arthur was in bed, convalescent, and would welcome a visit. I can't remember what led me to accept this invitation, but for some reason I did.

I found Arthur sitting up in bed. On the table beside him lay a copy of *Myths of the Norsemen.*

"Do *you* like that?" said I.

"Do *you* like that?" said he.

Next moment the book was in our hands, our heads were bent close together, we were pointing, quoting, talking—soon almost shouting—discovering in a torrent of questions that we liked not only the same thing, but the same parts of it and in the same way; that both knew the stab of Joy and that, for both, the arrow was shot from the North. Many thousands of people have had the experience of finding the first friend, and it is none the less a wonder; as great a wonder (*pace* the novelists) as first love, or even a greater. I had been so far from thinking such a friend possible that I had never even longed for one; no more than I longed to be King of England. If I had found that Arthur had independently built up an exact replica of the Boxonian world I should not really have been much more surprised. Nothing, I suspect, is more astonishing in any man's life than the discovery that there do exist people very, very like himself.

During my last few weeks at Wyvern strange stories began to appear in the papers, for this was the summer of 1914. I remember how a friend and I puzzled over a column that bore the headline "Can England keep out of it?" "Keep out of it?" said he, "I don't see how she can get into it." Memory paints the last hours of that term in slightly apocalyptic colors, and perhaps memory lies. Or perhaps for me it was apocalyptic enough to know that I was leaving, to see all those hated things for the last time; yet not simply (at that moment) to hate them. There is a "rumness," a ghostliness, about even a Windsor chair when it says, "You will not see me again." Early in the holidays we declared war. My brother, then on leave from Sandhurst, was recalled. Some weeks later I went to Mr. Kirkpatrick at Great Bookham in Surrey.

IX

THE GREAT KNOCK

You will often meet with characters in nature so extravagant that a discreet poet would not venture to set them upon the stage.

LORD CHESTERFIELD

O_N A September day, having crossed to Liverpool and reached London, I made my way to Waterloo and ran down to Great Bookham. I had been told that Surrey was "suburban," and the landscape that actually flitted past the windows astonished me. I saw steep little hills, watered valleys, and wooded commons which ranked by my Wyvernian and Irish standards as forest; bracken everywhere; a world of red and russet and yellowish greens. Even the sprinkling of suburban villas (much rarer then than now) delighted me. These timbered and red-tiled houses, embosomed in trees, were wholly unlike the stuccoed monstrosities which formed the suburbs of Belfast. Where I had expected gravel drives and iron gates and interminable laurels and monkey puzzlers, I saw crooked paths running up or down hill from wicket gates, between fruit trees and birches. By a severer taste than mine these houses would all be mocked perhaps; yet I cannot help thinking that those who designed them and their gardens achieved their object, which was to suggest Happiness. They filled me with a desire for that domesticity which, in its full development, I had never known; they set one thinking of tea trays.

At Bookham I was met by my new teacher—"Kirk" or "Knock" or the Great Knock as my father, my brother, and I all called him. We had heard about him all our lives and I therefore had a very clear impression of what I was in for. I came prepared to endure a perpetual lukewarm shower bath of sentimentality. That was the price I was ready to pay for the infinite blessedness of escaping school; but a heavy price. One story of my father's, in particular, gave me the most embarrassing forebodings. He had loved to tell how once at Lurgan, when he was in some kind of trouble or difficulty, the Old Knock, or the dear Old Knock, had drawn him aside and there "quietly and naturally" slid his arm round him and rubbed his dear old whiskers against my father's youthful cheek and whispered a few words of comfort. . . . And here was Bookham at last, and there was the arch-sentimentalist himself waiting to meet me.

He was over six feet tall, very shabbily dressed (like a gardener, I thought), lean as a rake, and immensely muscular. His wrinkled face seemed to consist entirely of muscles, so far as it was visible; for he wore mustache and side whiskers with a clean-shaven chin like the Emperor Franz Joseph. The whiskers, you will understand, concerned me very much at that moment. My cheek already tingled in anticipation. Would he begin at once? There would be tears for certain; perhaps worse things. It is one of my lifelong weaknesses that I never could endure the embrace or kiss of my own sex. (An unmanly weakness, by the way; Aeneas, Beowulf, Roland, Launcelot, Johnson, and Nelson knew nothing of it.)

Apparently, however, the old man was holding his fire. We shook hands, and though his grip was like iron pincers it was not lingering. A few minutes later we were walking away from the station.

"You are now," said Kirk, "proceeding along the principal artery between Great and Little Bookham."

I stole a glance at him. Was this geographical exordium a heavy joke? Or was he trying to conceal his emotions? His face, however, showed only an inflexible gravity. I began to "make conversation" in the deplorable manner which I had acquired at those evening parties and indeed found increasingly necessary to use with my father. I said I was surprised at the "scenery" of Surrey; it was much "wilder" than I had expected.

"Stop!" shouted Kirk with a suddenness that made me jump. "What do you mean by wildness and what grounds had you for not expecting it?"

I replied I don't know what, still "making conversation." As answer after answer was torn to shreds it at last dawned upon me that he really wanted to know. He was not making conversation, nor joking, nor snubbing me; he wanted to know. I was stung into attempting a real answer. A few passes sufficed to show that I had no clear and distinct idea corresponding to the word "wildness," and that, in so far as I had any idea at all, "wildness" was a singularly inept word. "Do you not see, then," concluded the Great Knock, "that your remark was meaningless?" I prepared to sulk a little, assuming that the subject would now be dropped. Never was I more mistaken in my life. Having analyzed my terms, Kirk was proceeding to deal with my proposition as a whole. On what had I based (but he pronounced it *baized*) my expectations about the Flora and Geology of Surrey? Was it maps, or photographs, or books? I could produce none. It had, heaven help me, never occurred to me that what I called my thoughts needed to be "baized" on anything. Kirk once more drew a conclusion—without the slightest sign of emotion, but equally without the slightest concession to what I thought good manners: "Do you not see, then, that you had no right to have any opinion whatever on the subject?"

By this time our acquaintance had lasted about three and a half minutes; but the tone set by this first conversation was preserved without a single break during all the years I spent at Bookham. Anything more grotesquely unlike the "dear Old Knock" of my father's reminiscences could not be conceived. Knowing my father's invariable intention of veracity and also knowing what strange transformations every truth underwent when once it entered his mind, I am sure he did not mean to deceive us. But if Kirk at any time of his life took a boy aside and there "quietly and naturally" rubbed the boy's face with his whiskers, I shall as easily believe that he sometimes varied the treatment by quietly and naturally standing on his venerable and egg-bald head.

If ever a man came near to being a purely logical entity, that man was Kirk. Born a little later, he would have been a Logical Positivist. The idea that human beings should exercise their vocal organs for any purpose except that of communicating or discovering truth was to him preposterous. The most casual remark was taken as a summons to disputation. I soon came to know the differing values of his three openings. The loud cry of "Stop!" was flung in to arrest a torrent of verbiage which could not be endured a moment longer; not because it fretted his patience (he never thought of that) but because it was wasting time, darkening counsel. The hastier and quieter "Excuse!" (*i.e.*, "Excuse me") ushered in a correction or distinction merely parenthetical and betokened that, thus set right, your remark might still, without absurdity, be allowed to reach completion. The most encouraging of all was, "I hear you." This meant that your remark was significant and only required refutation; it had risen to the dignity of error. Refutation (when we got so far) always followed the same lines. Had I read this? Had I studied that? Had I any statistical evidence? Had I any evidence in my own experience? And so to the almost inevitable conclusion, "Do you not see then that you had no right, etc."

Some boys would not have liked it; to me it was red beef and strong beer. I had taken it for granted that my leisure hours at Bookham would be passed in "grown-up conversation." And that, as you know already, I had no taste for. In my experience it meant conversation about politics, money, deaths, and digestion. I assumed that a taste for it, as for eating mustard or reading newspapers, would develop in me when I grew older (so far, all three expectations have been disappointed). The only two kinds of talk I wanted were the almost purely imaginative and the almost purely rational; such talk as I had about Boxen with my brother or about Valhalla with Arthur, on the one hand, or such talk as I had had with my uncle Gussie about astronomy on the other. I could never have gone far in any science because on the path of every science the lion Mathematics lies in wait for you. Even in Mathematics, whatever could be done by mere reasoning (as in simple geometry) I did with delight; but the moment calculation came in I was helpless. I grasped the principles but my answers were always wrong. Yet though I could never have been a scientist, I had scientific as well as imaginative impulses, and I loved ratiocination. Kirk excited and satisfied one side of me. Here was talk that was really about something. Here was a man who thought not about you but about what you said. No doubt I snorted and bridled a little at some of my tossings; but, taking it all in all, I loved the treatment. After being knocked down sufficiently often I began to know a few guards and blows, and to put on intellectual muscle. In the end, unless I flatter myself, I became a not contemptible sparring partner. It was a great day when the man who had so long been engaged in exposing my vagueness at last cautioned me against the dangers of excessive subtlety.

If Kirk's ruthless dialectic had been merely a pedagogic instrument I might have resented it. But he knew no other way of talking. No age or sex was spared the elenchus. It was a continuous astonishment to him that anyone should not desire to be clarified or corrected. When a very dignified neighbor, in the course of a Sunday call, observed with an air of finality, "Well, well, Mr. Kirkpatrick, it takes all sorts to make a world. You are a Liberal and I am a Conservative; we naturally look at the facts from different angles," Kirk replied, "What do you mean? Are you asking me to picture Liberals and Conservatives playing peep-bo at a rectangular Fact from opposite sides of a table?" If an unwary visitor, hoping to waive a subject, observed, "Of course, I know opinions differ—" Kirk would raise both his hands and exclaim, "Good heavens! I have no *opinions* on any subject whatsoever." A favorite maxim was, "You can have enlightenment for ninepence but you prefer ignorance." The commonest metaphors would be questioned till some bitter truth had been forced from its hiding place. "These fiendish German atrocities—" "But are not fiends a figment of the imagination?"—"Very well, then; these brutal atrocities—" "But none of the brutes does anything of the kind!"—"Well, what am I to call them?" "Is it not plain that we must call them simply *Human?*" What excited his supreme contempt was the conversation of other Headmasters, which he had sometimes had to endure at conferences when he himself was Head of Lurgan. "They would come and ask me, 'What attitude do you adopt to a boy who does so-and-so?' Good Heavens! As if I ever adopted an attitude to anybody or anything!" Sometimes, but rarely, he was driven to irony. On such occasions his voice became even weightier than usual and only the distention of his nostrils betrayed the secret to those who knew him. It was in such fashion that he produced his *dictum*, "The Master of Balliol is one of the most important beings in the universe."

It will be imagined that Mrs. Kirkpatrick led a somewhat uneasy life: witness the occasion on which her husband by some strange error found himself in the drawing room at the beginning of what his lady had intended to be a bridge party. About half an hour later she was observed to leave the room with a remarkable expression on her face; and many hours later still the Great Knock was discovered sitting on a stool in the midst of seven elderly ladies ("ful drery was hire chere") begging them to clarify their terms.

I have said that he was almost wholly logical; but not quite. He had been a Presbyterian and was now an Atheist. He spent Sunday, as he spent most of his time on weekdays, working in his garden. But one curious trait from his Presbyterian youth survived. He always, on Sundays, gardened in a different, and slightly more respectable, suit. An Ulster Scot may come to disbelieve in God, but not to wear his weekday clothes on the Sabbath.

Having said that he was an Atheist, I hasten to add that he was a "Rationalist" of the old, high and dry nineteenth-century type. For Atheism has come down in the world since those days, and mixed itself with politics and learned to dabble in dirt. The anonymous donor who now sends me anti-God magazines hopes, no doubt, to hurt the Christian in me; he really hurts the ex-Atheist. I am ashamed that my old mates and (which matters much more) Kirk's old mates should have sunk to what they are now. It was different then; even McCabe wrote like a man. At the time when I knew him, the fuel of Kirk's Atheism was chiefly of the anthropological and pessimistic kind. He was great on *The Golden Bough* and Schopenhauer.

The reader will remember that my own Atheism and Pessimism were fully formed before I went to Bookham. What I got there was merely fresh ammunition for the defense of a position already chosen. Even this I got indirectly from the tone of his mind or independently from reading his books. He never attacked religion in my presence. It is the sort of fact that no one would infer from an outside knowledge of my life, but it is a fact.

I arrived at Gastons (so the Knock's house was called) on a Saturday, and he announced that we would begin Homer on Monday. I explained that I had never read a word in any dialect but the Attic, assuming that when he knew this he would approach Homer through some preliminary lessons on the Epic language. He replied merely with a sound very frequent in his conversation which I can only spell "Huh." I found this rather disquieting; and I woke on Monday saying to myself, "Now for Homer. Golly!" The name struck awe into my soul. At nine o'clock we sat down to work in the little upstairs study which soon became so familiar to me. It contained a sofa (on which we sat side by side when he was working with me), a table and chair (which I used when I was alone), a bookcase, a gas stove, and a framed photograph of Mr. Gladstone. We opened our books at *Iliad*, Book I. Without a word of introduction Knock read aloud the first twenty lines or so in the "new" pronunciation, which I had never heard before. Like Smewgy, he was a chanter; less mellow in voice, yet full gutturals and rolling r's and more varied vowels seemed to suit the Bronze Age epic as well as Smewgy's honey tongue had suited Horace. For Kirk, even after years of residence in England, spoke the purest Ulster.

He then translated, with a few, a very few explanations, about a hundred lines. I had never seen a classical author taken in such large gulps before. When he had finished he handed me over Crusius' *Lexicon* and, having told me to go through again as much as I could of what he had done, left the room. It seems an odd method of teaching, but it worked. At first I could travel only a very short way along the trail he had blazed, but every day I could travel further. Presently I could travel the whole way. Then I could go a line or two beyond his furthest North. Then it became a kind of game to see how far beyond. He appeared at this stage to value speed more than absolute accuracy. The great gain was that I very soon became able to understand a great deal without (even mentally) translating it; I was beginning to think in Greek. That is the great Rubicon to cross in learning any language. Those in whom the Greek word lives only while they are hunting for it in the lexicon, and who then substitute the English word for it, are not reading the Greek at all; they are only solving a puzzle. The very formula, "*Naus* means a ship," is wrong. *Naus* and *ship* both mean a thing, they do not mean one another. Behind *Naus*, as behind *navis* or *naca*, we want to have a picture of a dark, slender mass with sail or oars, climbing the ridges, with no officious English word intruding.

We now settled into a routine which has ever since served in my mind as an archetype, so that what I still mean when I speak of a "normal" day (and lament that normal days are so rare) is a day of the Bookham pattern. For if I could please myself I would always live as I lived there. I would choose always

to breakfast at exactly eight and to be at my desk by nine, there
to read or write till one. If a cup of good tea or coffee could
be brought me about eleven, so much the better. A step or so
out of doors for a pint of beer would not do quite so well;
for a man does not want to drink alone and if you meet a
friend in the taproom the break is likely to be extended beyond its ten minutes. At one precisely lunch should be on the
table; and by two at the latest I would be on the road. Not,
except at rare intervals, with a friend. Walking and talking
are two very great pleasures, but it is a mistake to combine
them. Our own noise blots out the sounds and silences of the
outdoor world; and talking leads almost inevitably to smoking, and then farewell to nature as far as one of our senses
is concerned. The only friend to walk with is one (such as I
found, during the holidays, in Arthur) who so exactly shares
your taste for each mood of the countryside that a glance, a
halt, or at most a nudge, is enough to assure us that the pleasure is shared. The return from the walk, and the arrival of
tea, should be exactly coincident, and not later than a quarter
past four. Tea should be taken in solitude, as I took it at Bookham on those (happily numerous) occasions when Mrs. Kirkpatrick was out; the Knock himself disdained this meal. For
eating and reading are two pleasures that combine admirably.
Of course not all books are suitable for mealtime reading.
It would be a kind of blasphemy to read poetry at table.
What one wants is a gossipy, formless book which can be
opened anywhere. The ones I learned so to use at Bookham
were Boswell, and a translation of Herodotus, and Lang's
History of English Literature. Tristram Shandy, Elia and the

Anatomy of Melancholy are all good for the same purpose. At five a man should be at work again, and at it till seven. Then, at the evening meal and after, comes the time for talk, or, failing that, for lighter reading; and unless you are making a night of it with your cronies (and at Bookham I had none) there is no reason why you should ever be in bed later than eleven. But when is a man to write his letters? You forget that I am describing the happy life I led with Kirk or the ideal life I would live now if I could. And it is an essential of the happy life that a man would have almost no mail and never dread the postman's knock. In those blessed days I received, and answered, only two letters a week; one from my father, which was a matter of duty, and one from Arthur which was the high light of the week, for we poured out to each other on paper all the delight that was intoxicating us both. Letters from my brother, now on active service, were longer and rarer, and so were my replies.

Such is my ideal, and such then (almost) was the reality, of "settled, calm, Epicurean life." It is no doubt for my own good that I have been so generally prevented from leading it, for it is a life almost entirely selfish. Selfish, not self-centered: for in such a life my mind would be directed toward a thousand things, not one of which is myself. The distinction is not unimportant. One of the happiest men and most pleasing companions I have ever known was intensely selfish. On the other hand I have known people capable of real sacrifice whose lives were nevertheless a misery to themselves and to others, because self-concern and self-pity filled all their thoughts. Either condition will destroy the soul in the end.

But till the end, give me the man who takes the best of everything (even at my expense) and then talks of other things, rather than the man who serves me and talks of himself, and whose very kindnesses are a continual reproach, a continual demand for pity, gratitude, and admiration.

Kirk did not, of course, make me read nothing but Homer. The Two Great Bores (Demosthenes and Cicero) could not be avoided. There were (oh glory!) Lucretius, Catullus, Tacitus, Herodotus. There was Virgil, for whom I still had no true taste. There were Greek and Latin compositions. (It is a strange thing that I have contrived to reach my late fifties without ever reading one word of Caesar.) There were Euripides, Sophocles, Aeschylus. In the evenings there was French with Mrs. Kirkpatrick, treated much as her husband treated Homer. We got through a great many good novels in this way and I was soon buying French books on my own. I had hoped there would be English essays, but whether because he felt he could not endure mine or because he soon guessed that I was already only too proficient in that art (which he almost certainly despised) Kirk never set me one. For the first week or so he gave me directions about my English reading, but when he discovered that, left to myself, I was not likely to waste my time, he gave me absolute freedom. Later in my career we branched out into German and Italian. Here his methods were the same. After the very briefest contact with Grammars and Exercises I was plunged into *Faust* and the *Inferno*. In Italian we succeeded. In German I have little doubt that we should equally have succeeded if I had stayed with him a little longer. But I left too soon and my German has remained all my life that of a schoolboy. Whenever I have set about rectifying this, some other and more urgent task has always interrupted me.

But Homer came first. Day after day and month after month we drove gloriously onward, tearing the whole *Achilleid* out of the *Iliad* and tossing the rest on one side, and then reading the *Odyssey* entire, till the music of the thing and the clear, bitter brightness that lives in almost every formula had become part of me. Of course my appreciation was very romanticized—the appreciation of a boy soaked in William Morris. But this slight error saved me from that far deeper error of "classicism" with which the Humanists have hoodwinked half the world. I cannot therefore deeply regret the days when I called Circe a "wise-wife" and every marriage a "high-tide." That has all burned itself out and left no snuff, and I can now enjoy the *Odyssey* in a maturer way. The wanderings mean as much as ever they did; the great moment of "eucatastrophe" (as Professor Tolkien would call it) when Odysseus strips off his rags and bends the bow, means more; and perhaps what now pleases me best of all is those exquisite, Charlotte M. Yonge families at Pylos and elsewhere. How rightly Sir Maurice Powicke says, "There have been civilised people in all ages." And let us add, "In all ages they have been surrounded by barbarism."

Meanwhile, on afternoons and on Sundays, Surrey lay open to me. County Down in the holidays and Surrey in the term— it was an excellent contrast. Perhaps, since their beauties were such that even a fool could not force them into competition, this cured me once and for all of the pernicious tendency to compare and to prefer—an operation that does little good even when we are dealing with works of art and endless harm when we are dealing with nature. Total surrender is the first step toward the fruition of either. Shut your mouth; open your eyes and ears. Take in what is there and give no thought to what might have been there or what is somewhere else. That can come later, if it must come at all. (And notice here how the true training for anything whatever that is good always prefigures and, if submitted to, will always help us in, the true training for the Christian life. That is a school where they can always use your previous work whatever subject it was on.) What delighted me in Surrey was its intricacy. My Irish walks commanded large horizons and the general lie of land and sea could be taken in at a glance; I will try to speak of them later. But in Surrey the contours were so tortuous, the little valleys so narrow, there was so much timber, so many villages concealed in woods or hollows, so many field paths, sunk lanes, dingles, copses, such an unpredictable variety of cottage, farmhouse, villa, and country seat, that the whole thing could never lie clearly in my mind, and to walk in it daily gave one the same sort of pleasure that there is in the labyrinthine complexity of Malory or the *Faerie Queene*. Even where the prospect was tolerably open, as when I sat looking down on the Leatherhead and Dorking valley from Polesdan Lacey, it always lacked the classic comprehensibility of the Wyvern landscape. The valley twisted away southward into another valley, a train thudded past invisible in a wooded cutting, the opposite ridge concealed its bays and promontories. This, even on a summer morning. But I remember more dearly autumn afternoons in bottoms that lay intensely silent under old and great trees, and especially the moment, near Friday Street, when our party (that time I was not alone) suddenly discovered, from recognizing a curiously shaped stump, that we had traveled round in a circle for the last half-hour; or one frosty sunset over the Hog's Back at Guildford. On a Saturday afternoon in winter, when nose and fingers might be pinched enough to give an added relish to the anticipation of tea and fireside, and the whole week-end's reading lay ahead, I suppose I reached as much happiness as is ever to be reached on earth. And especially if there were some new, long-coveted book awaiting me.

For I had forgotten. When I spoke of the post I forgot to tell you that it brought parcels as well as letters. Every man of my age has had in his youth one blessing for which our juniors may well envy him: we grew up in a world of cheap and abundant books. Your *Everyman* was then a bare shilling, and, what is more, always in stock; your *World's Classic*, *Muses' Library*, *Home University Library*, *Temple Classic*, Nelson's French series, Bohn, and Longman's Pocket Library, at proportionate prices. All the money I could spare went in postal orders to Messrs. Denny of the Strand. No days, even at Bookham, were happier than those on which the afternoon post brought me a neat little parcel in dark gray paper. Milton, Spenser, Malory, *The High History of the Holy Grail*, the *Laxdale Saga*, Ronsard, Chénier, Voltaire, *Beowulf* and *Gawain and the Green Knight* (both in translations), Apuleius, the *Kalevala*, Herrick, Walton, Sir John Mandeville, Sidney's *Arcadia*, and nearly all of Morris, came volume by volume into my hands. Some of my purchases proved disappointments and some went beyond my hopes, but the undoing of the parcel always remained a delicious moment. On my rare visits to London I looked at Messrs. Denny in the Strand with a kind of awe; so much pleasure had come from it.

Smewgy and Kirk were my two greatest teachers. Roughly, one might say (in medieval language) that Smewgy taught me Grammar and Rhetoric and Kirk taught me Dialectic. Each had, and gave me, what the other lacked. Kirk had none of Smewgy's graciousness or delicacy, and Smewgy had less humor than Kirk. It was a saturnine humor. Indeed he was very like Saturn—not the dispossessed King of Italian legend, but grim old Cronos, Father Time himself with scythe and hourglass. The bitterest, and also funniest, things came out when he had risen abruptly from table (always before the rest of us) and stood ferreting in a villainous old tobacco jar on the mantelpiece for the dottles of former pipes which it was his frugal habit to use again. My debt to him is very great, my reverence to this day undiminished.

X

FORTUNE'S SMILE

The fields, the floods, the heavens, with one consent
Did seeme to laugh on me, and favour mine intent.

SPENSER

AT THE same time that I exchanged Wyvern for Bookham
I also exchanged my brother for Arthur as my chief companion. My brother, as you know, was serving in France.
From 1914 to 1916, which is the Bookham period, he becomes
a figure that at rare intervals appears unpredicted on leave, in
all the glory of a young officer, with what then seemed un-
limited wealth at his command, and whisks me off to Ireland.
Luxuries hitherto unknown to me, such as first-class railway
carriages and sleeping cars, glorify these journeys. You will
understand that I had been crossing the Irish sea six times a
year since I was nine. My brother's leaves now often added
journeys extraordinary. That is why my memory is stored
with ship's-side images to a degree unusual for such an un-
traveled man. I have only to close my eyes to see if I choose,
and sometimes whether I choose or no, the phosphorescence
of a ship's wash, the mast unmoving against the stars though
the water is rushing past us, the long salmon-colored rifts of
dawn or sunset on the horizon of cold gray-green water, or
the astonishing behavior of land as you approach it, the
promontories that walk out to meet you, the complex move-

ments and final disappearance of the mountains further inland.

These leaves were of course a great delight. The strains that had been developing (thanks to Wyvern) before my brother went to France were forgotten. There was a tacit determination on both sides to revive, for the short time allowed us, the classic period of our boyhood. As my brother was in the R.A.S.C., which in those days was reckoned a safe place to be, we did not feel that degree of anxiety about him which most families were suffering at this time. There may have been more anxiety in the unconscious than came out in fully waking thought. That, at least, would explain an experience I had, certainly once, and perhaps more often; not a belief, nor quite a dream, but an impression, a mental image, a haunting, which on a bitter winter night at Bookham represented my brother hanging about the garden and calling —or rather trying to call, but as in Virgil's Hell *inceptus clamor frustratur hiantem*, a bat's cry is all that comes. There hung over this image an atmosphere which I dislike as much as any I ever breathed, a blend of the macabre and the weakly, wretchedly, hopelessly pathetic—the dreary miasma of the Pagan Hades.

Though my friendship with Arthur began from an identity of taste on a particular point, we were sufficiently different to help one another. His home life was almost the opposite of mine. His parents were members of the Plymouth Brothers, and he was the youngest of a large family; his home, nevertheless, was almost as silent as ours was noisy. He was at this time working in the business of one of his brothers, but his health was delicate and after an illness or two he was withdrawn from it. He was a man of more than one talent: a pianist and, in hope, a composer, and also a painter. One of our earliest schemes was that he should make an operatic score for *Loki Bound*—a project which, of course, after an extremely short and happy life, died a painless death. In literature he influenced me more, or more permanently, than I did him. His great defect was that he cared very little for verse. Something I did to mend this, but less than I wished. He, on the other hand, side by side with his love for myth and marvel, which I fully shared, had another taste which I lacked till I met him and with which, to my great good, he infected me for life. This was the taste for what he called "the good, solid, old books," the classic English novelists. It is astonishing how I had avoided them before I met Arthur. I had been persuaded by my father to read *The Newcomes* when I was rather too young for it and never tried Thackeray again till I was at Oxford. He is still antipathetic to me, not because he preaches but because he preaches badly. Dickens I looked upon with a feeling of horror, engendered by long poring over the illustrations before I had learned to read. I still think them depraved. Here, as in Walt Disney, it is not the ugliness of the ugly figures but the simpering dolls intended for our sympathy which really betray the secret (not that Walt Disney is not far superior to the illustrators of Dickens). Of Scott I knew only a few of the medieval, that is, the weakest, novels. Under Arthur's influence I read at this time all the best Waverleys, all the Brontës, and all the Jane Austens. They provided an admirable complement to my more fantastic reading, and each was the more enjoyed for its contrast to the other. The very qualities which had previously deterred me from such books Arthur taught me to see as their charm. What I would have called their "stodginess" or "ordinariness" he called "Homeliness"—a key word in his imagination. He did not mean merely Domesticity, though that came into it. He meant the rooted quality which attaches them to all our simple experiences, to weather, food, the family, the neighborhood. He could get endless enjoyment out of the opening sentence of *Jane Eyre*, or that other opening sentence in one of Hans Andersen's stories, "How it did rain, to be sure." The mere word "beck" in the Brontës was a feast to him; and so were the schoolroom and kitchen scenes. This love of the "Homely" was not confined to literature; he looked for it in out-of-door scenes as well and taught me to do the same.

Hitherto my feelings for nature had been too narrowly romantic. I attended almost entirely to what I thought awe-inspiring, or wild, or eerie, and above all to distance. Hence mountains and clouds were my especial delight; the sky was, and still is, to me one of the principal elements in any landscape, and long before I had seen them all named and sorted out in *Modern Painters* I was very attentive to the different qualities, and different heights, of the cirrus, the cumulus, and the raincloud. As for the Earth, the country I grew up in had everything to encourage a romantic bent, had indeed done so ever since I first looked at the unattainable Green Hills through the nursery window. For the reader who knows those parts it will be enough to say that my main haunt was the Holywood Hills—the irregular polygon you would have described if you drew a line from Stormont to Comber, from Comber to Newtownards, from Newtownards to Scrabo, from Scrabo to Craigantlet, from Craigantlet to Holywood, and thence through Knocknagonney back to Stormont. How to suggest it all to a foreigner I hardly know.

First of all, it is by Southern English standards bleak. The woods, for we have a few, are of small trees, rowan and birch and small fir. The fields are small, divided by ditches with ragged sea-nipped hedges on top of them. There is a good deal of gorse and many outcroppings of rock. Small abandoned quarries, filled with cold-looking water, are surprisingly numerous. There is nearly always a wind whistling through the grass. Where you see a man plowing there will be gulls following him and pecking at the furrow. There are no field paths or rights of way, but that does not matter for everyone knows you—or if they do not know you, they know your kind and understand that you will shut gates and not walk over crops. Mushrooms are still felt to be common property, like the air. The soil has none of the rich chocolate or ocher you find in parts of England: it is pale—what Dyson calls "the ancient, bitter earth." But the grass is soft, rich, and sweet, and the cottages, always whitewashed and single storied and roofed with blue slate, light up the whole landscape.

Although these hills are not very high, the expanse seen from them is huge and various. Stand at the northeastern extremity where the slopes go steeply down to Holywood. Beneath you is the whole expanse of the Lough. The Antrim coast twists sharply to the north and out of sight; green, and humble in comparison, Down curves away southward. Between the two the Lough merges into the sea, and if you look carefully on a good day you can even see Scotland, phantomlike on the horizon. Now come further to the south and west. Take your stand at the isolated cottage which is visible from my father's house and overlooks our whole suburb, and which everyone calls the Shepherd's Hut, though we are not really a shepherd country. You are still looking down on the Lough, but its mouth and the sea are now hidden by the shoulder you have just come from, and it might (for all you see) be a landlocked lake. And here we come to one of those great contrasts which have bitten deeply into my mind—Niflheim and Asgard, Britain and Logres, Handramit and Harandra, air and ether, the low world and the high. Your horizon from here is the Antrim Mountains, probably a uniform mass of grayish blue, though if it is a sunny day you may just trace on the Cave Hill the distinction between the green slopes that climb twothirds of the way to the summit and the cliff wall that perpendicularly accomplishes the rest. That is one beauty; and here where you stand is another, quite different and even more dearly loved—sunlight and grass and dew, crowing cocks and gaggling ducks. In between them, on the flat floor of the Valley at your feet, a forest of factory chimneys, gantries, and giant cranes rising out of a welter of mist, lies Belfast. Noises come up from it continually, whining and screeching of trams, clatter of horse traffic on uneven sets, and, dominating all else, the continual throb and stammer of the great shipyards. And because we have heard this all our lives it does not, for us, violate the peace of the hilltop; rather, it emphasizes it, enriches the contrast, sharpens the dualism. Down in that "smoke and stir" is the hated office to which Arthur, less fortunate than I, must return tomorrow: for it is only one of his rare holidays that allows us to stand here together on a weekday morning. And down there too are the barefoot old women, the drunken men stumbling in and out of the "spirit grocers" (Ireland's horrible substitute for the kindly English "pub"), the straining, overdriven horses, the hard-faced rich women—all the world which Alberich created when he cursed love and twisted the gold into a ring.

Now step a little way—only two fields and across a lane and up to the top of the bank on the far side—and you will see, looking south with a little east in it, a different world. And having seen it, blame me if you can for being a romantic. For here is the thing itself, utterly irresistible, the way to the world's end, the land of longing, the breaking and blessing of hearts. You are looking across what may be called, in a certain sense, the plain of Down, and seeing beyond it the Mourne Mountains.

It was K.—that is, Cousin Quartus' second daughter, the Valkyrie—who first expounded to me what this plain of Down is really like. Here is the recipe for imagining it. Take a number of medium-sized potatoes and lay them down (one layer of them only) in a flat-bottomed tin basin. Now shake loose earth over them till the potatoes themselves, but not the shape of them, is hidden; and of course the crevices between them will now be depressions of earth. Now magnify the whole thing till those crevices are large enough to conceal each its stream and its huddle of trees. And then, for coloring, change your brown earth into the checkered pattern of fields, always small fields (a couple of acres each), with all their normal variety of crop, grass, and plow. You have now got a picture of the "plain" of Down, which is a plain only in the sense that if you were a very large giant you would regard it as level but very ill to walk on—like cobbles. And now remember that every cottage is white. The whole expanse laughs with these little white dots; it is like nothing so much as the assembly of white foam caps when a fresh breeze is on a summer sea. And the roads are white too; there is no tarmac yet. And because the whole country is a turbulent democracy of little hills, these roads shoot in every direction, disappearing and reappearing. But you must not spread over this landscape your hard English sunlight; make it paler, make it softer, blur the edges of the white cumuli, cover it with watery gleams, deepening it, making all unsubstantial. And beyond all this, so remote that they seem fantastically abrupt, at the very limit of your vision, imagine the mountains. They are no stragglers. They are steep and compact and pointed and toothed and jagged. They seem to have nothing to do with the little hills and cottages that divide you from them. And sometimes they are blue, sometimes violet; but quite often they look transparent—as if huge sheets of gauze had been cut out into mountainous shapes and hung up there, so that you could see through them the light of the invisible sea at their backs.

I number it among my blessings that my father had no car, while yet most of my friends had, and sometimes took me for a drive. This meant that all these distant objects could be visited just enough to clothe them with memories and not impossible desires, while yet they remained ordinarily as inaccessible as the Moon. The deadly power of rushing about wherever I pleased had not been given me. I measured distances by the standard of man, man walking on his two feet, not by the standard of the internal combustion engine. I had not been allowed to deflower the very idea of distance; in return I possessed "infinite riches" in what would have been to motorists "a little room." The truest and most horrible claim made for modern transport is that it "annihilates space." It does. It annihilates one of the most glorious gifts we have been given. It is a vile inflation which lowers the value of distance, so that a modern boy travels a hundred miles with less sense of liberation and pilgrimage and adventure than his grandfather got from traveling ten. Of course if a man hates space and wants it to be annihilated, that is another matter. Why not creep into his coffin at once? There is little enough space there.

Such were my outdoor delights before I met Arthur, and all these he shared and confirmed. And in his search for the Homely he taught me to see other things as well. But for him I should never have known the beauty of the ordinary vegetables that we destine to the pot. "Drills," he used to say. "Just ordinary drills of cabbages—what can be better?" And he was right. Often he recalled my eyes from the horizon just to look through a hole in a hedge, to see nothing more than a farmyard in its mid-morning solitude, and perhaps a gray cat squeezing its way under a barn door, or a bent old woman with a wrinkled, motherly face coming back with an empty bucket from the pigsty. But best of all we liked it when the

Homely and the unhomely met in sharp juxtaposition; if a little kitchen garden ran steeply up a narrowing enclave of fertile ground surrounded by outcroppings and furze, or some shivering quarry pool under a moonrise could be seen on our left, and on our right the smoking chimney and lamp-lit window of a cottage that was just settling down for the night.

Meanwhile, on the Continent, the unskilled butchery of the first German War went on. As it did so and as I began to foresee that it would probably last till I reached military age, I was compelled to make a decision which the law had taken out of the hands of English boys of my own age; for in Ireland we had no conscription. I did not much plume myself even then for deciding to serve, but I did feel that the decision absolved me from taking any further notice of the war. For Arthur, whose heart hopelessly disqualified him, there was no such question. Accordingly I put the war on one side to a degree which some people will think shameful and some incredible. Others will call it a flight from reality. I maintain that it was rather a treaty with reality, the fixing of a frontier. I said to my country, in effect, "You shall have me on a certain date, not before. I will die in your wars if need be, but till then I shall live my own life. You may have my body, but not my mind. I will take part in battles but not read about them." If this attitude needs excusing I must say that a boy who is unhappy at school inevitably learns the habit of keeping the future in its place; if once he began to allow infiltrations from the coming term into the present holidays he would despair. Also, the Hamilton in me was always on guard against the Lewis; I had seen enough of the self-torturing temperament.

No doubt, even if the attitude was right, the quality in me which made it so easy to adopt is somewhat repellent. Yet, even so, I can hardly regret having escaped the appalling waste of time and spirit which would have been involved in reading the war news or taking more than an artificial and formal part in conversations about the war. To read without military knowledge or good maps accounts of fighting which were distorted before they reached the Divisional general and further distorted before they left him and then "written up" out of all recognition by journalists, to strive to master what will be contradicted the next day, to fear and hope intensely on shaky evidence, is surely an ill use of the mind. Even in peacetime I think those are very wrong who say that school-boys should be encouraged to read the newspapers. Nearly all that a boy reads there in his teens will be known before he is twenty to have been false in emphasis and interpretation, if not in fact as well, and most of it will have lost all impor-tance. Most of what he remembers he will therefore have to unlearn; and he will probably have acquired an incurable taste for vulgarity and sensationalism and the fatal habit of fluttering from paragraph to paragraph to learn how an actress has been divorced in California, a train derailed in France, and quadruplets born in New Zealand.

I was now happier than I had ever been. All the sting had been drawn from the beginning of term. Yet the homecoming at its end remained almost as joyful as before. The holidays grew better and better. Our grown-up friends, and especially my cousins at Mountbracken, now seemed less grown up—for one's immediate elders grow downward or backward to meet one at that age. There were many merry meetings, much good talk. I discovered that other people besides Arthur loved books that I loved. The horrible old "social functions," the dances, were at an end, for my father now allowed me to refuse the invitations. All my engagements were now pleasant ones, within a small circle of people who were all intermarried, or very old neighbors, or (the women anyway) old school fellows. I am shy of mentioning them. Of Mountbracken I have had to speak because the story of my life could not be told without it; beyond that I hesitate to go. Praise of one's friends is near impertinence. I cannot tell you here of Janie M. nor of her mother, nor of Bill and Mrs. Bill. In novels, provincial-suburban society is usually painted gray to black. I have not found it so. I think we Strandtown and Belmont people had among us as much kindness, wit, beauty, and taste as any circle of the same size that I have ever known.

At home the real separation and apparent cordiality between my father and myself continued. Every holidays I came back from Kirk with my thoughts and my speech a little clearer, and this made it progressively less possible to have any real conversation with my father. I was far too young and raw to appreciate the other side of the account, to weigh the rich (if vague) fertility, the generosity and humor of my father's mind against the dryness, the rather death-like lucidity, of Kirk's. With the cruelty of youth I allowed myself to be irritated by traits in my father which, in other elderly men, I have since regarded as lovable foibles. There were so many unbridgeable misunderstandings. Once I received a letter from my brother in my father's presence which he immediately demanded to see. He objected to some expressions in it about a third person. In defense of them I pleaded that they had not been addressed to him. "What nonsense!" answered my father. "He knew you would show me the letter, and intended you to show me the letter." In reality, as I well knew, my brother had foolishly gambled on the chance that it would arrive when my father was out. But this my father could not conceive. He was not overriding by authority a claim to privacy which he disallowed; he could not imagine anyone making such a claim.

My relations to my father help to explain (I am not suggesting that they excuse) one of the worst acts of my life. I allowed myself to be prepared for confirmation, and confirmed, and to make my first Communion, in total disbelief, acting a part, eating and drinking my own condemnation. As Johnson points out, where courage is not, no other virtue can survive except by accident. Cowardice drove me into hypocrisy and hypocrisy into blasphemy. It is true that I did not and could not then know the real nature of the thing I was doing: but I knew very well that I was acting a lie with the greatest possible solemnity. It seemed to me impossible to tell my father my real views. Not that he would have stormed and thundered like the traditional orthodox parent. On the contrary, he would (at first) have responded with the greatest kindness. "Let's talk the whole thing over," he would have said. But it would have been quite impossible to drive into his head my real position. The thread would have been lost almost at once, and the answer implicit in all the quotations, anecdotes, and reminiscences which would have poured over me would have been one I then valued not a straw—the beauty of the Authorized Version, the beauty of the Christian tradition and sentiment and character. And later, when this failed, when I still tried to make my exact points clear, there would have been anger between us, thunder from him and a thin, peevish rattle from me. Nor could the subject, once raised, ever have been dropped again. All this, of course, ought to have been dared rather than the thing I did. But at the time it seemed to me impossible. The Syrian captain was forgiven for bowing in the house of Rimmon. I am one of many who have bowed in the house of the real God when I believed Him to be no more than Rimmon.

During the week ends and evenings I was closely tethered to my father and felt this something of a hardship, since these were the times when Arthur was most often accessible. My weekdays continued to supply me with a full ration of solitude. I had, to be sure, the society of Tim, who ought to have been mentioned far sooner. Tim was our dog. He may hold a record for longevity among Irish terriers since he was already with us when I was at Oldie's and did not die till 1922. But Tim's society did not amount to much. It had long since been agreed between him and me that he should not be expected to accompany me on walks. I went a good deal further than he liked, for his shape was already that of a bolster, or even a barrel, on four legs. Also, I went to places where other dogs might be met; and though Tim was no coward (I have seen him fight like a demon on his home ground) he hated dogs.

In his walking days he had been known, on seeing a dog far ahead, to disappear behind the hedge and re-emerge a hundred yards later. His mind had been formed during our schooldays and he had perhaps learned his attitude to other dogs from our attitude to other boys. By now he and I were less like master and dog than like two friendly visitors in the same hotel. We met constantly, passed the time of day, and parted with much esteem to follow our own paths. I think he had one friend of his own species, a neighboring red setter; a very respectable, middle-aged dog. Perhaps a good influence; for poor Tim, though I loved him, was the most undisciplined, unaccomplished, and dissipated-looking creature that ever went on four legs. He never exactly obeyed you; he sometimes agreed with you.

The long hours in the empty house passed delightfully in reading and writing. I was in the midst of the Romantics now. There was a humility in me (as a reader) at that time which I shall never recapture. Some poems I could not enjoy as well as others. It never occurred to me that these might be the inferior ones; I merely thought that I was getting tired of my author or was not in the right mood. The *longueurs* of Endymion I attributed wholly to myself. The "swoony" element in Keats' sensuality (as when Porphyro grows "faint") I tried hard to like, and failed. I thought—though I have forgotten why—that Shelley must be better than Keats and was sorry I liked him less. But my great author at this period was William Morris. I had met him first in quotation in books on Norse Mythology; that led me to *Sigurd the Volsung*. I did not really like this as much as I tried to, and I think I now know why: the metre does not satisfy my ear. But then, in Arthur's bookcase, I found *The Well at the World's End*. I looked—I read chapter headings—I dipped—and next day I was off into town to buy a copy of my own. Like so many new steps it appeared to be partly a revival—"Knights in Armor" returning from a very early period of my childhood. After that I read all the Morris I could get, *Jason, The Earthly Paradise*, the prose romances. The growth of the new delight is marked by my sudden realization, almost with a sense of disloyalty, that the letters WILLIAM MORRIS were coming to have at least as potent a magic in them as WAGNER.

One other thing that Arthur taught me was to love the bodies of books. I had always respected them. My brother and I might cut up stepladders without scruple; to have thumb-marked or dog's-eared a book would have filled us with shame. But Arthur did not merely respect, he was enamored; and soon, I too. The set up of the page, the feel and smell of the paper, the differing sounds that different papers make as you turn the leaves, became sensuous delights. This revealed to me a flaw in Kirk. How often have I shuddered when he took a new classical text of mine in his gardener's hands, bent back the boards till they creaked, and left his sign on every page.

"Yes, I remember," said my father. "That was old Knock's one fault."

"A bad one," said I.

"An all but unforgivable one," said my father.

XI

CHECK

When bale is at highest, boote is at next.

THE HISTORY of Joy, since it came riding back to me on huge waves of Wagnerian music and Norse and Celtic mythology several chapters ago, must now be brought up to date.

I have already hinted how my first delight in Valhalla and Valkyries began to turn itself imperceptibly into a scholar's interest in them. I got about as far as a boy who knew no old Germanic language could get. I could have faced a pretty stiff examination in my subject. I would have laughed at popular bunglers who confused the late mythological Sagas with the classic Sagas, or the Prose with the Verse Edda, or even, more scandalously, Edda with Saga. I knew my way about the Eddaic cosmos, could locate each of the roots of the Ash and knew who ran up and down it. And only very gradually did I realize that all this was something quite different from the original Joy. And I went on adding detail to detail, progressing toward the moment when "I should know most and should least enjoy." Finally I woke from building the temple to find that the God had flown. Of course I did not put it that way. I would have said simply that I didn't get

165

the old thrill. I was in the Wordsworthian predicament, lamenting that "a glory" had passed away.

Thence arose the fatal determination to recover the old thrill, and at last the moment when I was compelled to realize that all such efforts were failures. I had no lure to which the bird would come. And now, notice my blindness. At that very moment there arose the memory of a place and time at which I had tasted the lost Joy with unusual fullness. It had been a particular hill walk on a morning of white mist. The other volumes of the *Ring* (*The Rheingold* and *The Valkyrie*) had just arrived as a Christmas present from my father, and the thought of all the reading before me, mixed with the coldness and loneliness of the hillside, the drops of moisture on every branch, and the distant murmur of the concealed town, had produced a longing (yet it was also fruition) which had flowed over from the mind and seemed to involve the whole body. That walk I now remembered. It seemed to me that I had tasted heaven then. If only such a moment could return! But what I never realized was that it had returned—that the remembering of that walk was itself a new experience of just the same kind. True, it was desire, not possession. But then what I had felt on the walk had also been desire, and only possession in so far as that kind of desire is itself desirable, is the fullest possession we can know on earth; or rather, because the very nature of Joy makes nonsense of our common distinction between having and wanting. There, to have is to want and to want is to have. Thus, the very moment when I longed to be so stabbed again, was itself again such a stabbing. The Desirable which had once alighted on

Valhalla was now alighting on a particular moment of my own past; and I would not recognize him there because, being an idolater and a formalist, I insisted that he ought to appear in the temple I had built him; not knowing that he cares only for temples building and not at all for temples built. Wordsworth, I believe, made this mistake all his life. I am sure that all that sense of the loss of vanished vision which fills *The Prelude* was itself vision of the same kind, if only he could have believed it.

In my scheme of thought it is not blasphemous to compare the error which I was making with that error which the angel at the Sepulchre rebuked when he said to the women, "Why seek ye the living among the dead? He is not here, He is risen." The comparison is of course between something of infinite moment and something very small; like comparison between the Sun and the Sun's reflection in a dewdrop. Indeed, in my view, very like it, for I do not think the resemblance between the Christian and the merely imaginative experience is accidental. I think that all things, in their way, reflect heavenly truth, the imagination not least. "Reflect" is the important word. This lower life of the imagination is not[1] a beginning of, nor a step toward, the higher life of the spirit, merely an image. In me, at any rate, it contained no element either of belief or of ethics; however far pursued, it would never have made me either wiser or better. But it still had, at however many removes, the shape of the reality it reflected.

If nothing else suggests this resemblance it is at least sug-

---

[1] *I.e.*, not necessarily and by its own nature. God can cause it to be such a beginning.

gested by the fact that we can make exactly the same mistakes on both levels. You will remember how, as a schoolboy, I had destroyed my religious life by a vicious subjectivism which made "realizations" the aim of prayer; turning away from God to seek states of mind, and trying to produce those states of mind by "maistry." With unbelievable folly I now proceeded to make exactly the same blunder in my imaginative life; or rather the same pair of blunders. The first was made at the very moment when I formulated the complaint that the "old thrill" was becoming rarer and rarer. For by that complaint I smuggled in the assumption that what I wanted was a "thrill," a state of my own mind. And there lies the deadly error. Only when your whole attention and desire are fixed on something else—whether a distant mountain, or the past, or the gods of Asgard—does the "thrill" arise. It is a by-product. Its very existence presupposes that you desire not it but something other and outer. If by any perverse askesis or the use of any drug it could be produced from within, it would at once be seen to be of no value. For take away the object, and what, after all, would be left?—a whirl of images, a fluttering sensation in the diaphragm, a momentary abstraction. And who could want that? This, I say, is the first and deadly error, which appears on every level of life and is equally deadly on all, turning religion into a self-caressing luxury and love into auto-eroticism. And the second error is, having thus falsely made a state of mind your aim, to attempt to produce it. From the fading of the Northernness I ought to have drawn the conclusion that the Object, the Desirable, was further away, more external, less subjective, than even such a comparatively public and external thing as a system of mythology—had, in fact, only shone through that system. Instead, I concluded that it was a mood or state within myself which might turn up in any context. To "get it again" became my constant endeavor; while reading every poem, hearing every piece of music, going for every walk, I stood anxious sentinel at my own mind to watch whether the blessed moment was beginning and to endeavor to retain it if it did. Because I was still young and the whole world of beauty was opening before me, my own officious obstructions were often swept aside and, startled into self-forgetfulness, I again tasted Joy. But far more often I frightened it away by my greedy impatience to snare it, and, even when it came, instantly destroyed it by introspection, and at all times vulgarized it by my false assumption about its nature.

One thing, however, I learned, which has since saved me from many popular confusions of mind. I came to know by experience that it is not a disguise of sexual desire. Those who think that if adolescents were all provided with suitable mistresses we should soon hear no more of "immortal longings" are certainly wrong. I learned this mistake to be a mistake by the simple, if discreditable, process of repeatedly making it. From the Northernness one could not easily have slid into erotic fantasies without noticing the difference; but when the world of Morris became the frequent medium of Joy, this transition became possible. It was quite easy to think that one desired those forests for the sake of their female inhabitants, the garden of Hesperus for the sake of his daughters, Hylas' river for the river nymphs. I repeatedly followed that path

—to the end. And at the end one found pleasure; which immediately resulted in the discovery that pleasure (whether that pleasure or any other) was not what you had been looking for. No moral question was involved; I was at this time as nearly nonmoral on that subject as a human creature can be. The frustration did not consist in finding a "lower" pleasure instead of a "higher." It was the irrelevance of the conclusion that marred it. The hounds had changed scent. One had caught the wrong quarry. You might as well offer a mutton chop to a man who is dying of thirst as offer sexual pleasure to the desire I am speaking of. I did not recoil from the erotic conclusion with chaste horror, exclaiming, "Not that!" My feelings could rather have been expressed in the words, "Quite. I see. But haven't we wandered from the real point?" Joy is not a substitute for sex; sex is very often a substitute for Joy. I sometimes wonder whether all pleasures are not substitutes for Joy.

Such, then, was the state of my imaginative life; over against it stood the life of my intellect. The two hemispheres of my mind were in the sharpest contrast. On the one side a many-islanded sea of poetry and myth; on the other a glib and shallow "rationalism." Nearly all that I loved I believed to be imaginary; nearly all that I believed to be real I thought grim and meaningless. The exceptions were certain people (whom I loved and believed to be real) and nature herself. That is, nature as she appeared to the senses. I chewed endlessly on the problem: "How can it be so beautiful and also so cruel, wasteful and futile?" Hence at this time I could almost have said with Santayana, "All that is good is imaginary;

all that is real is evil." In one sense nothing less like a "flight from reality" could be conceived. I was so far from wishful thinking that I hardly thought anything true unless it contradicted my wishes.

Hardly, but not quite. For there was one way in which the world, as Kirk's rationalism taught me to see it, gratified my wishes. It might be grim and deadly but at least it was free from the Christian God. Some people (not all) will find it hard to understand why this seemed to me such an overwhelming advantage. But you must take into account both my history and my temperament. The period of faith which I had lived through at Oldie's had contained a good deal of fear. And by now, looking back on that fear, and egged on by Shaw and Voltaire and Lucretius with his *Tantum religio*, I greatly exaggerated that element in my memory and forgot the many other elements which had been combined with it. At all costs I was anxious that those full-moonlit nights in the dormitory should never come again. I was also, as you may remember, one whose negative demands were more violent than his positive, far more eager to escape pain than to achieve happiness, and feeling it something of an outrage that I had been created without my own permission. To such a craven the materialist's universe had the enormous attraction that it offered you limited liabilities. No strictly infinite disaster could overtake you in it. Death ended all. And if ever finite disasters proved greater than one wished to bear, suicide would always be possible. The horror of the Christian universe was that it had no door marked *Exit*. It was also perhaps not unimportant that the externals of Christianity made no appeal to my sense of beauty. Oriental imagery and style largely repelled me; and for the rest, Christianity was mainly associated for me with ugly architecture, ugly music, and bad poetry. Wyvern Priory and Milton's verse were almost the only points at which Christianity and beauty had overlapped in my experience. But, of course, what mattered most of all was my deep-seated hatred of authority, my monstrous individualism, my lawlessness. No word in my vocabulary expressed deeper hatred than the word *Interference*. But Christianity placed at the center what then seemed to me a transcendental Interferer. If its picture were true then no sort of "treaty with reality" could ever be possible. There was no region even in the innermost depth of one's soul (nay, there least of all) which one could surround with a barbed wire fence and guard with a notice No Admittance. And that was what I wanted; some area, however small, of which I could say to all other beings, "This is my business and mine only."

In this respect, and this only at first, I may have been guilty of wishful thinking. Almost certainly I was. The materialist conception would not have seemed so immensely probable to me if it had not favored at least one of my wishes. But the difficulty of explaining even a boy's thought entirely in terms of his wishes is that on such large questions as these he always has wishes on both sides. Any conception of reality which a sane mind can admit must favor some of its wishes and frustrate others. The materialistic universe had one great, negative attraction to offer me. It had no other. And this had to be accepted; one had to look out on a meaningless dance of atoms (remember, I was reading Lucretius), to realize that all the apparent beauty was a subjective phosphorescence, and to relegate everything one valued to the world of mirage. That price I tried loyally to pay. For I had learned something from Kirk about the honor of the intellect and the shame of voluntary inconsistency. And, of course, I exulted with youthful and vulgar pride in what I though my enlightenment. In argument with Arthur I was a very swashbuckler. Most of it, as I now see, was incredibly crude and silly. I was in that state of mind in which a boy thinks it extremely telling to call God *Jahveh* and Jesus *Yeshua*.

Looking back on my life now, I am astonished that I did not progress into the opposite orthodoxy—did not become a Leftist, Atheist, satiric Intellectual of the type we all know so well. All the conditions seem to be present. I had hated my public school. I hated whatever I knew or imagined of the British Empire. And though I took very little notice of Morris's socialism (there were too many things in him that interested me far more), continual reading of Shaw had brought it about that such embryonic political opinions as I had were vaguely socialistic. Ruskin had helped me in the same direction. My lifelong fear of sentimentalism ought to have qualified me to become a vigorous "debunker." It is true that I hated the Collective as much as any man can hate anything; but I certainly did not then realize its relations to socialism. I suppose that my Romanticism was destined to divide me from the orthodox Intellectuals as soon as I met them; and also that a mind so little sanguine as mine about the future and about common action could only with great difficulty be made revolutionary.

Such, then, was my position: to care for almost nothing but the gods and heroes, the garden of the Hesperides, Launcelot and the Grail, and to believe in nothing but atoms and evolution and military service. At times the strain was severe, but I think this was a wholesome severity. Nor do I believe that the intermittent wavering in my materialistic "faith" (so to call it) which set in toward the end of the Bookham period would ever have arisen simply from my wishes. It came from another source.

Among all the poets whom I was reading at this time (I read *The Faerie Queene* and *The Earthly Paradise* entire) there was one who stood apart from the rest. Yeats was this poet. I had been reading him for a long time before I discovered the difference, and perhaps I should never have discovered it if I had not read his prose as well: things like *Rosa Alchemica* and *Per Amica Silentia Lunae*. The difference was that Yeats believed. His "ever living ones" were not merely feigned or merely desired. He really thought that there was a world of beings more or less like them, and that contact between that world and ours was possible. To put it quite plainly, he believed seriously in Magic. His later career as a poet has somewhat obscured that phase in popular estimates of him, but there is no doubt about the fact—as I learned when I met him some years later. Here was a pretty kettle of fish. You will understand that my rationalism was inevitably based on what I believed to be the findings of the sciences, and those findings, not being a scientist, I had to take on trust—in fact, on authority. Well, here was an opposite authority. If he had been a Christian I should have discounted his testimony, for I thought I had the Christians "placed" and disposed of forever. But I now learned that there were people, not traditionally orthodox, who nevertheless rejected the whole Materialist philosophy out of hand. And I was still very ingenuous. I had no conception of the amount of nonsense written and printed in the world. I regarded Yeats as a learned, responsible writer: what he said must be worthy of consideration. And after Yeats I plunged into Maeterlinck; quite innocently and naturally since everyone was reading him at that time and since I made a point of including a fair amount of French in my diet. In Maeterlinck I came up against Spiritualism, Theosophy, and Pantheism. Here once more was a responsible adult (and not a Christian) who believed in a world behind, or around, the material world. I must do myself the justice of saying that I did not give my assent categorically. But a drop of disturbing doubt fell into my Materialism. It was merely a "Perhaps." Perhaps (oh joy!) there was, after all, "something else"; and (oh reassurance!) perhaps it had nothing to do with Christian Theology. And as soon as I paused on that "Perhaps," inevitably all the old Occultist lore, and all the old excitement which the Matron of Chartres had innocently aroused in me, rose out of the past.

Now the fat was in the fire with a vengeance. Two things hitherto widely separated in my mind rushed together: the imaginative longing for Joy, or rather the longing which *was* Joy, and the ravenous, quasi-prurient desire for the Occult, the Preternatural as such. And with these there came (less welcome) some stirring of unease, some of the immemorial fear we have all known in the nursery, and (if we are honest) long after the nursery age. There is a kind of gravitation in the mind whereby good rushes to good and evil to evil. This mingled repulsion and desire drew toward them everything else in me that was bad. The idea that if there were Occult knowledge it was known to very few and scorned by the many became an added attraction: "we few," you will remember, was an evocative expression for me. That the means should be Magic—the most exquisitely unorthodox thing in the world, unorthodox both by Christian and by Rationalist standards —of course appealed to the rebel in me. I was already acquainted with the more depraved side of Romanticism; had read *Anactoria*, and Wilde, and pored upon Beardsley, not hitherto attracted, but making no moral judgment. Now I thought I began to see the point of it. In a word, you have already had in this story the World and the Flesh; now came the Devil. If there had been in the neighborhood some elder person who dabbled in dirt of the Magical kind (such have a good nose for potential disciples) I might now be a Satanist or a maniac.

In actual fact I was wonderfully protected, and this spiritual debauch had in the end one rather good result. I was protected, first, by ignorance and incapacity. Whether Magic were possible or not, I at any rate had no teacher to start me on the path. I was protected also by cowardice; the reawakened terrors of childhood might add a spice to my greed and curiosity as long as it was daylight. Alone, and in darkness, I used my best endeavors to become a strict Materialist again; not always with success. A "Perhaps" is quite enough for the nerves to work upon. But my best protection was the known nature of Joy. This ravenous desire to break the bounds, to tear the curtain, to be in the secret, revealed itself, more and more clearly the longer I indulged it, to be quite different from the longing that is Joy. Its coarse strength betrayed it. Slowly, and with many relapses, I came to see that the magical conclusion was just as irrelevant to Joy as the erotic conclusion has been. Once again one had changed scents. If circles and pentangles and the Tetragrammaton had been tried and had in fact raised, or seemed to raise, a spirit, that might have been—if a man's nerves could stand it—extremely interesting; but the real Desirable would have evaded one, the real Desire would have been left saying, "What is this to me?"

What I like about experience is that it is such an honest thing. You may take any number of wrong turnings; but keep your eyes open and you will not be allowed to go very far before the warning signs appear. You may have deceived yourself, but experience is not trying to deceive you. The universe rings true wherever you fairly test it.

The other results of my glance into the dark room were as follows. First, I now had both a fresh motive for wishing Materialism to be true and a decreased confidence that it was. The fresh motive came, as you have divined, from those fears which I had so wantonly stirred up from their sleeping place in the memories of childhood; behaving like a true Lewis who will not leave well alone. Every man who is afraid of spooks will have a reason for wishing to be a Materialist; that creed promises to exclude the bogies. As for my shaken confidence, it remained in the form of a "Perhaps," stripped of its directly and grossly magical "affect"—a pleasing possibility that the Universe might combine the snugness of Materialism here and now with . . . well, with I didn't know what; somewhere or something beyond, "the unimaginable lodge for solitary thinkings." This was very bad. I was beginning to try to have it both ways: to get the comforts both of a materialist and of a spiritual philosophy without the rigors of either. But the second result was better. I had learned a wholesome antipathy to everything occult and magical which was to stand me in good stead when, at Oxford, I came to meet Magicians, Spiritualists, and the like. Not that the ravenous lust was never to tempt me again but that I now knew it for a temptation. And above all, I now knew that Joy did not point in that direction.

You might sum up the gains of this whole period by saying that henceforward the Flesh and the Devil, though they could still tempt, could no longer offer me the supreme bribe. I had learned that it was not in their gift. And the World had never even pretended to have it.

And then, on top of this, in superabundance of mercy, came that event which I have already more than once attempted to describe in other books. I was in the habit of walking over to Leatherhead about once a week and sometimes taking the train back. In summer I did so chiefly because Leatherhead boasted a tiny swimming bath; better than nothing to me who had learned to swim almost before I can remember and who, till middle age and rheumatism crept upon me, was passionately fond of being in water. But I went in winter, too, to look for books and to get my hair cut. The evening that I now speak of was in October. I and one porter had the long, timbered platform of Leatherhead station to ourselves. It was getting just dark enough for the smoke of an engine to glow red on the underside with the reflection of the furnace. The hills beyond the Dorking Valley were of a blue so intense as to be nearly violet and the sky was green with frost. My ears tingled with the cold. The glorious week end of reading was before me. Turning to the bookstall, I picked out an Everyman in a dirty jacket, *Phantastes, a faerie Romance,* George MacDonald. Then the train came in. I can still remember the voice of the porter calling out the village names, Saxon and sweet as a nut— "Bookham, Effingham, Horsley train." That evening I began to read my new book.

The woodland journeyings in that story, the ghostly enemies, the ladies both good and evil, were close enough to my habitual imagery to lure me on without the perception of a change. It is as if I were carried sleeping across the frontier, or as if I had died in the old country and could never remember how I came alive in the new. For in one sense the new country was exactly like the old. I met there all that had already charmed me in Malory, Spenser, Morris, and Yeats. But in another sense all was changed. I did not yet know (and I was long in learning) the name of the new quality, the bright shadow, that rested on the travels of Anodos. I do now. It was Holiness. For the first time the song of the sirens sounded like the voice of my mother or my nurse. Here were old wives' tales; there was nothing to be proud of in enjoying them. It was as though the voice which had called to me from the world's end were now speaking at my side. It was with me in the room, or in my own body, or behind me. If it had once eluded me by its distance, it now eluded me by proximity—something too near to see, too plain to be understood, on this side of knowledge. It seemed to have been always with me; if I could ever have turned my head quick enough I should have seized it. Now for the first time I felt that it was out of reach not because of something I could not do but because of something I could not stop doing. If I could only leave off, let go, unmake myself, it would be there. Meanwhile, in this new region all the confusions that had hitherto perplexed my search for Joy were disarmed. There was no temptation to confuse the scenes of the tale with the light that rested upon them, or to suppose that they were put forward as realities, or even to dream that if they had been realities and I could reach the woods where Anodos journeyed I should thereby come a step nearer to my desire. Yet, at the same time, never had the wind of Joy blowing through any story been less separable from the story itself. Where the god and the *idolon* were most nearly one there was least danger of confounding them. Thus, when the great moments came I did not break away from the woods and cottages that I read of to seek some bodiless light shining beyond them, but gradually, with a swelling continuity (like the sun at mid-morning burning through a fog) I found the light shining on those woods and cottages, and then on my own past life, and on the quiet room where I sat and on my old teacher where he nodded above his little

Tacitus. For I now perceived that while the air of the new region made all my erotic and magical perversions of Joy look like sordid trumpery, it had no such disenchanting power over the bread upon the table or the coals in the grate. That was the marvel. Up till now each visitation of Joy had left the common world momentarily a desert—"The first touch of the earth went nigh to kill." Even when real clouds or trees had been the material of the vision, they had been so only by reminding me of another world; and I did not like the return to ours. But now I saw the bright shadow coming out of the book into the real world and resting there, transforming all common things and yet itself unchanged. Or, more accurately, I saw the common things drawn into the bright shadow. *Unde hoc mihi?* In the depth of my disgraces, in the then invincible ignorance of my intellect, all this was given me without asking, even without consent. That night my imagination was, in a certain sense, baptized; the rest of me, not unnaturally, took longer. I had not the faintest notion what I had let myself in for by buying *Phantastes.*

GUNS AND GOOD COMPANY

*La compagnie, de tant d'hommes vous plaist, nobles,
jeunes, actifs; la liberté de cette conversation sans art, et
une façon de vie masle et sans cérémonie.*

MONTAIGNE

THE OLD pattern began to repeat itself. The Bookham
days, like a longer and more glorious holidays, drew to
their end; a scholarship examination and, after that, the army,
loomed behind them like a grimmer term. The good time
had never been better than in its last months. I remember, in
particular, glorious hours of bathing in Donegal. It was surf
bathing: not the formal affair with boards that you have now,
but mere rough and tumble, in which the waves, the monstrous, emerald, deafening waves, are always the winner, and
it is at once a joke, a terror, and a joy to look over your shoulder and see (too late) one breaker of such sublime propor-
tions that you would have avoided him had you known he
was coming. But they gather themselves up, pre-eminent
above their fellows, as suddenly and unpredictably as a
revolution.

It was late in the winter term of 1916 that I went to Oxford to sit for my scholarship examination. Boys who have
faced this ordeal in peacetime will not easily imagine the indifference with which I went. This does not mean that I

underestimated the importance (in one sense) of succeeding. I knew very well by now that there was hardly any position in the world save that of a don in which I was fitted to earn a living, and that I was staking everything on a game in which few won and hundreds lost. As Kirk had said of me in a letter to my father (I did not, of course, see it till many years later), "You may make a writer or a scholar of him, but you'll not make anything else. You may make up your mind to *that*." And I knew this myself; sometimes it terrified me. What blunted the edge of it now was that whether I won a scholarship or no I should next year go into the army; and even a temper more sanguine than mine could feel in 1916 that an infantry subaltern would be insane to waste anxiety on anything so hypothetical as his postwar life. I once tried to explain this to my father; it was one of the attempts I often made (though doubtless less often than I ought) to break through the artificiality of our intercourse and admit him to my real life. It was a total failure. He replied at once with fatherly counsels about the necessity of hard work and concentration, the amount that he had already spent in educating me, the very moderate, nay negligible, assistance he would be able to give me in later life. Poor man! He misjudged me sadly if he thought that idleness at my book was among my many vices. And how, I asked myself, could he expect the winning or losing of a scholarship to lose none of its importance when life and death were the real issues? The truth is, I think, that while death (mine, his, everyone's) was often vividly present to him as a subject of anxiety and other emotions, it had no place in his mind as a sober, matter-of-fact contingency from which consequences could be drawn. At any rate the conversation was a failure. It shipwrecked on the old rock. His intense desire for my total confidence co-existed with an inability to listen (in any strict sense) to what I said. He could never empty, or silence, his own mind to make room for an alien thought.

My first taste of Oxford was comical enough. I had made no arrangements about quarters and, having no more luggage than I could carry in my hand, I sallied out of the railway station on foot to find either a lodging house or a cheap hotel; all agog for "dreaming spires" and "last enchantments." My first disappointment at what I saw could be dealt with. Towns always show their worst face to the railway. But as I walked on and on I became more bewildered. Could this succession of mean shops really be Oxford? But I still went on, always expecting the next turn to reveal the beauties, and reflecting that it was a much larger town than I had been led to suppose. Only when it became obvious that there was very little town left ahead of me, that I was, in fact, getting to open country, did I turn round and look. There, behind me, far away, never more beautiful since, was the fabled cluster of spires and towers. I had come out of the station on the wrong side and been all this time walking into what was even then the mean and sprawling suburb of Botley. I did not see to what extent this little adventure was an allegory of my whole life. I merely walked back to the station, somewhat footsore, took a hansom, and asked to be driven to "some place where I can get rooms for a week, please." The method, which I should now think hazardous, was a complete success, and I was soon at tea in comfortable lodgings. The house is still there, the first on the right as you turn into Mansfield Road out of Holywell. I shared the sitting room with another candidate, a man from Cardiff College, which he pronounced to be architecturally superior to anything in Oxford. His learning terrified me, but he was an agreeable man. I have never seen him since.

It was very cold and the next day snow began to fall, turning pinnacles into wedding-cake decorations. The examination was held in the Hall of Oriel, and we all wrote in greatcoats and mufflers and wearing at least our left-hand gloves. The Provost, old Phelps, gave out the papers. I remember very little about them, but I suppose I was outshone in pure classics by many of my rivals and succeeded on my general knowledge and dialectics. I had the impression that I was doing badly. Long years (or years that seemed long) with the Knock had cured me of my defensive Wyvernian priggery, and I no longer supposed other boys to be ignorant of what I knew. Thus the essay was on a quotation from Johnson. I had read several times the Boswellian conversation in which it occurred and was able to replace the whole question in that context; but I never thought that this (any more than a fairish knowledge of Schopenhauer) would gain me any particular credit. It was a blessed state to be in, but for the moment depressing. As I left the Hall after that essay I heard one candidate say to his friend, "I worked in all my stuff about Rousseau and the Social Contract." That struck dismay into my soul, for though I had dabbled (not to my good) in the *Confessions* I knew nothing of the *Contrat Social*. At the beginning of the morning a nice Harrovian had whispered to me, "I don't even know if it's Sam or Ben." In my innocence I explained to him that it was Sam and could not be Ben because Ben was spelled without an h. I did not think there could be any harm in giving away such information.

When I arrived home I told my father that I had almost certainly failed. It was an admission calculated to bring out all his tenderness and chivalry. The man who could not understand a boy's taking his own possible, or probable, death into account could very well understand a child's disappointment. Not a word was now heard of expenses and difficulties; nothing but consolation, reassurance and affection. Then, almost on Christmas Eve, we heard that "Univ" (University College) had elected me.

Though I was now a scholar of my College I still had to pass "Responsions," which involved elementary mathematics. To prepare for this I returned after Christmas for one last term with Kirk—a golden term, poignantly happy under the approaching shadow. At Easter I was handsomely plowed in Responsions, having been unable as usual to get my sums right. "Be more careful," was the advice that everyone gave me, but I found it useless. The more care I took the more mistakes I made; just as, to this day, the more anxiously I fair copy a piece of writing the more certain I am to make a ghastly clerical error in the very first line.

In spite of this I came into residence in the summer (Trinity) term of 1917; for the real object now was simply to enter the University Officers' Training Corps as my most promising route into the army. My first studies at Oxford, nevertheless, still had Responsions in view. I read algebra (devil take it!) with old Mr. Campbell of Hertford who turned out to be a friend of our dear friend Janie M. That I never passed Responsions is certain, but I cannot remember whether I again sat for it and was again plowed. The question became unimportant after the war, for a benevolent decree exempted ex-servicemen from taking it. Otherwise, no doubt, I should have had to abandon the idea of going to Oxford.

I was less than a term at Univ when my papers came through and I enlisted; and the conditions made it a most abnormal term. Half the College had been converted into a hospital and was in the hands of the R.A.M.C. In the remaining portion lived a tiny community of undergraduates—two of us not yet of military age, two unfit, one a Sinn-Feiner who would not fight for England, and a few other oddments which I never quite placed. We dined in the little lecture room which is now a passage between Common Room and Hall. Small though our numbers were (about eight) we were rather distinguished, for we included E. V. Gordon, afterward Professor of English at Manchester, and A. C. Ewing, the Cambridge philosopher; also that witty and kindly man, Theobald Butler, skilled in turning the most lurid limericks into Greek verse. I enjoyed myself greatly; but it bore little resemblance to normal undergraduate life and was for me an unsettled, excited, and generally useless period. Then came the army. By a remarkable turn of fate this did not mean removal from Oxford. I was drafted into a Cadet Battalion whose billet was Keble.

I passed through the ordinary course of training (a mild

affair in those days compared with that of the recent war)
and was commissioned as a Second Lieutenant in the Somer-
set Light Infantry, the old XIIIth Foot. I arrived in the front
line trenches on my nineteenth birthday (November 1917),
saw most of my service in the villages before Arras—Fam-
poux and Monchy—and was wounded at Mt. Bernenchon,
near Lillers, in April, 1918.

I am surprised that I did not dislike the army more. It
was, of course, detestable. But the words "of course" drew
the sting. That is where it differed from Wyvern. One did
not expect to like it. Nobody said you ought to like it. Nobody pretended to like it. Everyone you met took it for
granted that the whole thing was an odious necessity, a
ghastly interruption of rational life. And that made all the
difference. Straight tribulation is easier to bear than tribulation which advertises itself as pleasure. The one breeds cam-
araderie and even (when intense) a kind of love between the
fellow sufferers; the other, mutual distrust, cynicism, concealed and fretting resentment. And secondly, I found my
military elders and betters incomparably nicer than the Wyvern Bloods. This is no doubt because Thirty is naturally
kinder to Nineteen than Nineteen is to Thirteen: it is really
grown up and does not need to reassure itself. But I am inclined
to think that my face had altered. That "look" which I had so
often been told to "take off it" had apparently taken itself off
—perhaps when I read *Phantastes*. There is even some evidence that it had been succeeded by a look which excited
either pity or kindly amusement. Thus, on my very first night
in France, in a vast marquee or drill hall where about a hun-

dred officers were to sleep on plank beds, two middle-aged Canadians at once took charge of me and treated me, not like a son (that might have given offence) but like a long-lost friend. Blessings upon them! Once, too, in the Officers' Club at Arras where I was dining alone, and quite happy with my book and my wine (a bottle of Heidsieck then cost 8 francs, and a bottle of Perrier Jouet, 12) two immensely senior officers, all covered with ribbons and red tabs, came over to my table toward the end of the meal, and hailing me as "Sunny Jim" carried me off to their own for brandy and cigars. They weren't drunk either; nor did they make me drunk. It was pure good will. And though exceptional, this was not so very exceptional. There were nasty people in the army; but memory fills those months with pleasant, transitory contacts. Every few days one seemed to meet a scholar, an original, a poet, a cheery buffoon, a raconteur, or at the least a man of good will.

Some time in the middle of that winter I had the good luck to fall sick with what the troops called "trench fever" and the doctors P.U.O. (Pyrexia, unknown origin) and was sent for a wholly delightful three weeks to hospital at Le Tréport. Perhaps I ought to have mentioned before that I had had a weak chest ever since childhood and had very early learned to make a minor illness one of the pleasures of life, even in peacetime. Now, as an alternative to the trenches, a bed and a book were "very heaven." The hospital was a converted hotel and we were two in a room. My first week was marred by the fact that one of the night nurses was conducting a furious love affair with my roommate. I had too high a temperature to be embarrassed, but the human whisper is a very tedious and unmusical noise; especially at night. After that my fortune mended. The amorous man was sent elsewhere and replaced by a musical misogynist from Yorkshire, who on our second morning together said to me, "Eh, lad, if we make beds ourselves dom b——s won't stay in room so long" (or words to that effect). Accordingly, we made our own beds every day, and every day when the two V.A.D.'s looked in they said, "Oh, they've made their beds! Aren't these two good?" and rewarded us with their brightest smiles. I think they attributed our action to gallantry.

It was here that I first read a volume of Chesterton's essays. I had never heard of him and had no idea of what he stood for; nor can I quite understand why he made such an immediate conquest of me. It might have been expected that my pessimism, my atheism, and my hatred of sentiment would have made him to me the least congenial of all authors. It would almost seem that Providence, or some "second cause" of a very obscure kind, quite overrules our previous tastes when it decides to bring two minds together. Liking an author may be as involuntary and improbable as falling in love. I was by now a sufficiently experienced reader to distinguish liking from agreement. I did not need to accept what Chesterton said in order to enjoy it. His humor was of the kind which I like best—not "jokes" imbedded in the page like currants in a cake, still less (what I cannot endure), a general tone of flippancy and jocularity, but the humor which is not in any way separable from the argument but is rather (as Aristotle would say) the "bloom" on dialectic itself. The sword glitters not because the swordsman set out to make it glitter but because he is fighting for his life and therefore moving it very quickly. For the critics who think Chesterton frivolous or "paradoxical" I have to work hard to feel even pity; sympathy is out of the question. Moreover, strange as it may seem, I liked him for his goodness. I can attribute this taste to myself freely (even at that age) because it was a liking for goodness which had nothing to do with any attempt to be good myself. I have never felt the dislike of goodness which seems to be quite common in better men than me. "Smug" and "smugness" were terms of disapprobation which had never had a place in my critical vocabulary. I lacked the cynic's nose, the *odora canum vis* or bloodhound sensitivity for hypocrisy or Pharisaism. It was a matter of taste: I felt the "charm" of goodness as a man feels the charm of a woman he has no intention of marrying. It is, indeed, at that distance that its "charm" is most apparent.

In reading Chesterton, as in reading MacDonald, I did not know what I was letting myself in for. A young man who wishes to remain a sound Atheist cannot be too careful of his reading. There are traps everywhere—"Bibles laid open, millions of surprises," as Herbert says, "fine nets and stratagems." God is, if I may say it, very unscrupulous.

In my own battalion also I was assailed. Here I met one Johnson (on whom be peace) who would have been a life-long friend if he had not been killed. He was, like me, already a scholar of an Oxford college (Queen's) who hoped to take up his scholarship after the war, but a few years my senior and at that time in command of a company. In him I found dialectical sharpness such as I had hitherto known only in Kirk, but coupled with youth and whim and poetry. He was moving toward Theism and we had endless arguments on that and every other topic whenever we were out of the line. But it was not this that mattered. The important thing was that he was a man of conscience. I had hardly till now encountered principles in anyone so nearly of my own age and my own sort. The alarming thing was that he took them for granted. It crossed my mind for the first time since my apostasy that the severer virtues might have some relevance to one's own life. I say "the severer virtues" because I already had some notion of kindness and faithfulness to friends and generosity about money—as who has not till he meets the temptation which gives all their opposite vices new and more civil names? But it had not seriously occurred to me that people like ourselves, people like Johnson and me who wanted to know whether beauty was objective or how Aeschylus handled the reconciliation of Zeus and Prometheus, should be attempting strict veracity, chastity, or devotion to duty. I had taken it that they were not our subjects. There was no discussion between us on the point and I do not think he ever suspected the truth about me. I was at no pains to display it. If this is hypocrisy, then I must conclude that hypocrisy can do a man good. To be ashamed of what you were about to say, to pretend that something which you had meant seriously was only a joke—this is an ignoble part. But it is better than not to be ashamed at all. And the distinction between pretending you are better than you are and beginning to be better in reality is finer than moral sleuthhounds conceive. I was, in intention, concealing only a part: I accepted his principles at once, made no attempt internally to defend my own "unexamined life." When a boor first enters the society of courteous people what can he do, for a while, except imitate the motions? How can he learn except by imitation?

You will have divined that ours was a very nice battalion; a minority of good regulars ruling a pleasantly mixed population of promoted rankers (west country farmers, these), barristers, and university men. You could get as good talk there as anywhere. Perhaps the best of us all was our butt, Wallie. Wallie was a farmer, a Roman Catholic, a passionate soldier (the only man I met who really longed for fighting) and gullible to any degree by the rawest subaltern. The technique was to criticize the Yeomanry. Poor Wallie knew that it was the bravest, the most efficient, the hardest and cleanest corps that ever sat on horses. He knew all that inside, having learned it from an uncle in the Yeomanry when he was a child. But he could not get it out. He stammered and contradicted himself and always came at last to his trump card: "I wish my Uncle Ben was here to talk to you. Uncle Ben'd talk to you. He'd tell you." Mortals must not judge; but I doubt whether any man fought in France who was more likely to go straight to Heaven if he were killed. I would have been better employed cleaning his boots than laughing at him. I may add that I did not enjoy the short time I spent in the company he commanded. Wallie had a genuine passion for killing Germans and a complete disregard of his own or anyone else's safety. He was always striking out bright ideas at which the hair of us subalterns stood on end. Luckily he could be very easily dissuaded by any plausible argument that occurred to us. Such was his valor and innocence that he never for a moment suspected us of any but a military motive. He could never grasp the neighborly principles which, by the tacit agreement of the troops, were held to govern trench warfare, and to which I was introduced at once by my sergeant. I had suggested "pooping" a rifle grenade into a German post where we had seen heads moving. "Just as 'ee like, zir," said the sergeant, scratching his head, "but once 'ee start doing that kind of thing, 'ee'll get zummit back, zee?"

I must not paint the wartime army all gold. I met there both the World and the great goddess Nonsense. The world presented itself in a very ridiculous form on that night (my nineteenth birthday) when I first arrived "up the line." As I emerged from the shaft into the dugout and blinked in the candlelight I noticed that the Captain to whom I was reporting was a master whom I had liked more than I had respected at one of my schools. I ventured to claim acquaintance. He admitted in a low, hurried voice that he had once been a schoolmaster, and the topic was never raised between us again. The impact of the Great Goddess was even funnier, and I met it long before I had reached my own battalion. The troop train from Rouen—that interminable, twelve-mile-an-hour train, in which no two coaches were alike—left at about ten in the evening. Three other officers and I were allotted a compartment. There was no heating; for light we brought our own candles; for sanitation there were the windows. The journey would last about fifteen hours. It was freezing hard. In the tunnel just outside Rouen (all my generation remember it) there was a sudden wrenching and grating noise and one of our doors dropped off bodily into the dark. We sat with chattering teeth till the next stop, where the officer commanding the train came bustling up and demanded what we had done with our door. "It came off, sir," said we. "Don't talk nonsense," said he, "it wouldn't have come off if there hadn't been some horseplay!"—as if nothing were more natural than that four officers (being, of course, provided with screwdrivers) should begin a night journey in midwinter by removing the door of their carriage.

The war itself has been so often described by those who saw more of it than I that I shall here say little about it. Until the great German attack came in the Spring we had a pretty quiet time. Even then they attacked not us but the Canadians on our right, merely "keeping us quiet" by pouring shells into our line about three a minute all day. I think it was that day I noticed how a greater terror overcomes a less: a mouse that I met (and a poor shivering mouse it was, as I was a poor shivering man) made no attempt to run from me. Through the winter, weariness and water were our chief enemies. I have gone to sleep marching and woken again and found myself marching still. One walked in the trenches in thigh gum boots with water above the knee; one remembers the icy stream welling up inside the boot when you punctured it on concealed barbed wire. Familiarity both with the very old and the very recent dead confirmed that view of corpses which had been formed the moment I saw my dead mother. I came to know and pity and reverence the ordinary man: particularly dear Sergeant Ayres, who was (I suppose) killed by the same shell that wounded me. I was a futile officer (they gave commissions too easily then), a puppet moved about by him, and he turned this ridiculous and painful relation into something beautiful, became to me almost like a father. But for the rest, the war—the frights, the cold, the smell of H.E., the horribly smashed men still moving like half-crushed beetles, the sitting or standing corpses, the landscape of sheer earth without a blade of grass, the boots worn day and night till they seemed to grow to your feet— all this shows rarely and faintly in memory. It is too cut off from the rest of my experience and often seems to have happened to someone else. It is even in a way unimportant. One imaginative moment seems now to matter more than the realities that followed. It was the first bullet I heard—so far from me that it "whined" like a journalist's or a peacetime poet's bullet. At that moment there was something not exactly like fear, much less like indifference: a little quavering signal that said, "This is War. This is what Homer wrote about."

XIII

THE NEW LOOK

*This wall I was many a weary month in finishing, and
yet never thought myself safe till it was done.*

DEFOE, *Robinson Crusoe*

THE REST of my war experiences have little to do with this
story. How I "took" about sixty prisoners—that is, discovered to my great relief that the crowd of field-gray
figures who suddenly appeared from nowhere, all had their
hands up—is not worth telling, save as a joke. Did not Falstaff
"take" Sir Colville of the Dale? Nor does it concern the
reader to know how I got a sound "Blighty" from an English
shell, or how the exquisite Sister N. in the C.C.S. has ever
since embodied my idea of Artemis. Two things stand out.
One is the moment, just after I had been hit, when I found
(or thought I found) that I was not breathing and concluded
that this was death. I felt no fear and certainly no courage.
It did not seem to be an occasion for either. The proposition
"Here is a man dying" stood before my mind as dry, as fac-
tual, as unemotional as something in a textbook. It was not
even interesting. The fruit of this experience was that when,
some years later, I met Kant's distinction between the Nou-
menal and the Phenomenal self, it was more to me than an
abstraction. I had tasted it; I had proved that there was a fully
conscious "I" whose connections with the "me" of intro-

197

spection were loose and transitory. The other momentous experience was that of reading Bergson in a Convalescent Camp on Salisbury Plain. Intellectually this taught me to avoid the snares that lurk about the word *Nothing*. But it also had a revolutionary effect on my emotional outlook. Hitherto my whole bent had been toward things pale, remote, and evanescent; the water-color world of Morris, the leafy recesses of Malory,[1] the twilight of Yeats. The word "life" had for me pretty much the same associations it had for Shelley in *The Triumph of Life*. I would not have understood what Goethe meant by *des Lebens goldnes Baum*. Bergson showed me. He did not abolish my old loves, but he gave me a new one. From him I first learned to relish energy, fertility, and urgency; the resource, the triumphs, and even the insolence, of things that grow. I became capable of appreciating artists who would, I believe, have meant nothing to me before; all the resonant, dogmatic, flaming, unanswerable people like Beethoven, Titian (in his mythological pictures), Goethe, Dunbar, Pindar, Christopher Wren, and the more exultant Psalms.

I returned to Oxford—"demobbed"—in January 1919. But before I say anything of my life there I must warn the reader that one huge and complex episode will be omitted. I have no choice about this reticence. All I can or need say is that my earlier hostility to the emotions was very fully and variously avenged. But even were I free to tell the story, I doubt if it has much to do with the subject of the book.

[1] The iron in Malory, the tragedy of contrition, I did not yet at all perceive.

The first lifelong friend I made at Oxford was A. K. Hamilton Jenkin, since known for his books on Cornwall. He continued (what Arthur had begun) my education as a seeing, listening, smelling, receptive creature. Arthur had had his preference for the Homely. But Jenkin seemed to be able to enjoy everything; even ugliness. I learned from him that we should attempt a total surrender to whatever atmosphere was offering itself at the moment; in a squalid town to seek out those very places where its squalor rose to grimness and almost grandeur, on a dismal day to find the most dismal and dripping wood, on a windy day to seek the windiest ridge. There was no Betjemannic irony about it; only a serious, yet gleeful, determination to rub one's nose in the very quiddity of each thing, to rejoice in its being (so magnificently) what it was.

My next was Owen Barfield. There is a sense in which Arthur and Barfield are the types of every man's First Friend and Second Friend. The First is the *alter ego*, the man who first reveals to you that you are not alone in the world by turning out (beyond hope) to share all your most secret delights. There is nothing to be overcome in making him your friend; he and you join like raindrops on a window. But the Second Friend is the man who disagrees with you about everything. He is not so much the *alter ego* as the antiself. Of course he shares your interests; otherwise he would not become your friend at all. But he has approached them all at a different angle. He has read all the right books but has got the wrong thing out of every one. It is as if he spoke your language but mispronounced it. How can he be so nearly right and yet, invariably, just not right? He is as fascinating (and infuriating) as a woman. When you set out to correct his heresies, you find that he forsooth has decided to correct yours! And then you go at it, hammer and tongs, far into the night, night after night, or walking through fine country that neither gives a glance to, each learning the weight of the other's punches, and often more like mutually respectful enemies than friends. Actually (though it never seems so at the time) you modify one another's thought; out of this perpetual dogfight a community of mind and a deep affection emerge. But I think he changed me a good deal more than I him. Much of the thought which he afterward put into *Poetic Diction* had already become mine before that important little book appeared. It would be strange if it had not. He was of course not so learned then as he has since become; but the genius was already there.

Closely linked with Barfield of Wadham was his friend (and soon mine), A. C. Harwood of The House, later a pillar of Michael Hall, the Steinerite school at Kidbrooke. He was different from either of us; a wholly imperturbable man. Though poor (like most of us) and wholly without "prospects," he wore the expression of a nineteenth-century gentleman with something in the Funds. On a walking tour when the last light of a wet evening had just revealed some ghastly error in map-reading (probably his own) and the best hope was "Five miles to Mudham (if we could find it) and we *might* get beds there," he still wore that expression. In the heat of argument he wore it still. You would think that he, if anyone, would have been told to "take that look

off his face." But I don't believe he ever was. It was no
mask and came from no stupidity. He has been tried since by
all the usual sorrows and anxieties. He is the sole Horatio
known to me in this age of Hamlets; no "stop for Fortune's
finger."

There is one thing to be said about these and other friends
whom I made at Oxford. They were all, by decent Pagan
standards (much more, by so low a standard as mine),
"good." That is, they all, like my friend Johnson, believed,
and acted on the belief, that veracity, public spirit, chastity,
and sobriety were obligatory—"to be attempted," as the
examiners say, "by all candidates." Johnson had prepared me
to be influenced by them. I accepted their standards in principle and perhaps (this part I do not very well remember)
tried to act accordingly.

During my first two years at Oxford I was busily engaged
(apart from "doing Mods" and "beginning Greats") in assuming what we may call an intellectual "New Look." There
was to be no more pessimism, no more self-pity, no flirtations
with any idea of the supernatural, no romantic delusions. In
a word, like the heroine of *Northanger Abbey*, I formed the
resolution "of always judging and acting in future with the
greatest good sense." And good sense meant, for me at that
moment, a retreat, almost a panic-stricken flight, from all that
sort of romanticism which had hitherto been the chief concern of my life. Several causes operated together.

For one thing, I had recently come to know an old, dirty,
gabbling, tragic, Irish parson who had long since lost his
faith but retained his living. By the time I met him his only

interest was the search for evidence of "human survival." On this he read and talked incessantly, and, having a highly critical mind, could never satisfy himself. What was especially shocking was that the ravenous desire for personal immortality co-existed in him with (apparently) a total indifference to all that could, on a sane view, make immortality desirable. He was not seeking the Beatific Vision and did not even believe in God. He was not hoping for more time in which to purge and improve his own personality. He was not dreaming of reunion with dead friends or lovers; I never heard him speak with affection of anybody. All he wanted was the assurance that something he could call "himself" would, on almost any terms, last longer than his bodily life. So, at least, I thought. I was too young and hard to suspect that what secretly moved him was a thirst for the happiness which had been wholly denied him on earth. And his state of mind appeared to me the most contemptible I had ever encountered. Any thoughts or dreams which might lead one into that fierce monomania were, I decided, to be utterly shunned. The whole question of immortality became rather disgusting to me. I shut it out. All one's thought must be confined to

> the very world, which is the world
> Of all of us—the place where, in the end,
> We find our happiness, or not at all.

Secondly, it had been my chance to spend fourteen days, and most of the fourteen nights as well, in close contact with a man who was going mad. He was a man whom I had dearly loved, and well he deserved love. And now I helped to hold him while he kicked and wallowed on the floor, screaming out that devils were tearing him and that he was that moment falling down into Hell. And this man, as I well knew, had not kept the beaten track. He had flirted with Theosophy, Yoga, Spiritualism, Psychoanalysis, what not? Probably these things had in fact no connection with his insanity, for which (I believe) there were physical causes. But it did not seem so to me at the time. I thought I had seen a warning; it was to this, this raving on the floor, that all romantic longings and unearthly speculations led a man in the end—

> *Be not too wildly amorous of the far*
> *Nor lure thy fantasy to its utmost scope.*

Safety first, thought I: the beaten track, the approved road, the center of the road, the lights on. For some months after that nightmare fortnight, the words "ordinary" and "humdrum" summed up everything that appeared to me most desirable.

Thirdly, the new Psychology was at that time sweeping through us all. We did not swallow it whole (few people then did) but we were all influenced. What we were most concerned about was "Fantasy" or "wishful thinking." For (of course) we were all poets and critics and set a very great value on "Imagination" in some high Coleridgean sense, so that it became important to distinguish Imagination, not only (as Coleridge did) from Fancy, but also from Fantasy as the psychologists understand that term. Now what, I asked myself, were all my delectable mountains and western gardens but sheer Fantasies? Had they not revealed their true nature by luring me, time and again, into undisguisedly erotic reverie or the squalid nightmare of Magic? In reality, of course, as previous chapters have told, my own experience had repeatedly shown that these romantic images had never been more than a sort of flash, or even slag, thrown off by the occurrence of Joy, that those mountains and gardens had never been what I wanted but only symbols which professed themselves to be no more, and that every effort to treat them as the real Desirable soon honestly proved itself to be a failure. But now, busy with my New Look, I managed to forget this. Instead of repenting my idolatry I vilified the unoffending images on which I had lavished it. With the confidence of a boy I decided I had done with all that. No more Avalon, no more Hesperides. I had (this was very precisely the opposite of the truth) "seen through" them. And I was never going to be taken in again.

Finally, there was of course Bergson. Somehow or other (for it does not seem very clear when I reopen his books today) I found in him a refutation of the old haunting idea, Schopenhauer's idea, that the universe "might not have existed." In other words one Divine attribute, that of necessary existence, rose above my horizon. It was still, and long after, attached to the wrong subject; to the universe, not to God. But the mere attribute was itself of immense potency. When once one has dropped the absurd notion that reality is an arbitrary alternative to "nothing," one gives up being a pessimist (or even an optimist). There is no sense in blaming or praising the Whole, nor, indeed, in saying anything about it. Even if you persist in hurling Promethean or Hardyesque defiances at it, then, since you are part of it, it is only that same Whole which through you "quietly declaims the cursings of itself"—a futility which seems to me to vitiate Lord Russell's stirring essay on "The Worship of a Free Man." Cursings were as futile, and as immature, as dreams about the western garden. One must (like Carlyle's lady) "accept" the universe; totally, with no reservations, loyally. This sort of Stoical Monism was the philosophy of my New Look. And it gave me a great sense of peace. It was perhaps the nearest thing to a religious experience which I had had since my prep-school days. It ended (I hope forever) any idea of a treaty or compromise with reality. So much the perception of even one Divine attribute can do.

As for Joy, I labeled it "aesthetic experience" and talked much about it under that name and said it was very "valuable." But it came very seldom and when it came it didn't amount to much.

Those early days of the New Look were on the whole happy ones. Very gradually the sky changed. There came to be more unhappiness and anxiety in my own life; and Barfield was living through

> *that whole year of youth*
> *When life ached like an aching tooth.*

Our generation, the generation of the returned soldiers, began to pass. Oxford was full of new faces. Freshmen began to make historical allowances for our warped point of view. The problem of one's career loomed larger and grimmer.

It was then that a really dreadful thing (dreadful to me)

happened. First Harwood (still without changing his expression), and then Barfield, embraced the doctrines of Steiner and became Anthroposophists. I was hideously shocked. Everything that I had labored so hard to expel from my own life seemed to have flared up and met me in my best friends. Not only my best friends but those whom I would have thought safest; the one so immovable, the other brought up in a free-thinking family and so immune from all "superstition" that he had hardly heard of Christianity itself until he went to school. (The gospel first broke on Barfield in the form of a dictated list of Parables Peculiar to St. Matthew.) Not only in my seeming-safest friends but at a moment when we all had most need to stand together. And as I came to learn (so far as I ever have learned) what Steiner thought, my horror turned into disgust and resentment. For here, apparently, were all the abominations; none more abominable than those which had once attracted me. Here were gods, spirits, after-life and pre-existence, initiates, occult knowledge, meditation. "Why—damn it—it's *medieval*," I exclaimed; for I still had all the chronological snobbery of my period and used the names of earlier periods as terms of abuse. Here was everything which the New Look had been designed to exclude; everything that might lead one off the main road into those dark places where men wallow on the floor and scream that they are being dragged down into Hell. Of course it was all arrant nonsense. There was no danger of *my* being taken in. But then, the loneliness, the sense of being deserted.

Naturally, I attributed to my friends the same desires which, had I become an Anthroposophist, would have been operative in me. I thought they were falling under that ravenous, salt lust for the occult. I now see that, from the very first, all the evidence was against this. They were not that sort. Nor does Anthroposophy, so far as I can see, cater for that sort. There is a difficulty and (to me) a reassuring Germanic dullness about it which would soon deter those who were looking for thrills. Nor have I ever seen that it had a deleterious effect on the character of those who embraced it; I have once known it to have a very good one.

I say this, not because I ever came within a hundred miles of accepting the thing myself, but in common fairness, and also as a tardy amends for the many hard, unjust and bitter things I once said about it to my friends. For Barfield's conversion to Anthroposophy marked the beginning of what I can only describe as the Great War between him and me. It was never, thank God, a quarrel, though it could have become one in a moment if he had used to me anything like the violence I allowed myself to him. But it was an almost incessant disputation, sometimes by letter and sometimes face to face, which lasted for years. And this Great War was one of the turning points of my life.

Barfield never made me an Anthroposophist, but his counterattacks destroyed forever two elements in my own thought. In the first place he made short work of what I have called my "chronological snobbery," the uncritical acceptance of the intellectual climate common to our own age and the assumption that whatever has gone out of date is on that account discredited. You must find why it went out of date. Was it ever refuted (and if so by whom, where, and how conclusively) or did it merely die away as fashions do? If the latter, this tells us nothing about its truth or falsehood. From seeing this, one passes to the realization that our own age is also "a period," and certainly has, like all periods, its own characteristic illusions. They are likeliest to lurk in those widespread assumptions which are so ingrained in the age that no one dares to attack or feels it necessary to defend them. In the second place he convinced me that the positions we had hitherto held left no room for any satisfactory theory of knowledge. We had been, in the technical sense of the term, "realists"; that is, we accepted as rock-bottom reality the universe revealed by the senses. But at the same time we continued to make for certain phenomena of consciousness all the claims that really went with a theistic or idealistic view. We maintained that abstract thought (if obedient to logical rules) gave indisputable truth, that our moral judgment was "valid," and our aesthetic experience not merely pleasing but "valuable." The view was, I think, common at the time; it runs through Bridges' *Testament of Beauty*, the work of Gilbert Murray, and Lord Russell's "Worship of a Free Man." Barfield convinced me that it was inconsistent. If thought were a purely subjective event, these claims for it would have to be abandoned. If one kept (as rock-bottom reality) the universe of the senses, aided by instruments and co-ordinated so as to form "science," then one would have to go much further—as many have since gone—and adopt a Behavioristic theory of logic, ethics, and aesthetics. But such a theory was, and is, unbelievable to me. I am using the word "unbelievable," which many use to mean "improbable" or even "undesirable," in a quite literal sense. I mean that the act of believing what the behaviorist believes is one that my mind simply will not perform. I cannot force my thought into that shape any more than I can scratch my ear with my big toe or pour wine out of a bottle into the cavity at the base of that same bottle. It is as final as a physical impossibility. I was therefore compelled to give up realism. I had been trying to defend it ever since I began reading philosophy. Partly, no doubt, this was mere "cussedness." Idealism was then the dominant philosophy at Oxford and I was by nature "against Government." But partly, too, realism satisfied an emotional need. I wanted Nature to be quite independent of our observation; something other, indifferent, self-existing. (This went with the Jenkinian zest for rubbing one's nose in the mere quiddity.) But now, it seemed to me, I had to give that up. Unless I were to accept an unbelievable alternative, I must admit that mind was no late-come epiphenomenon; that the whole universe was, in the last resort, mental; that our logic was participation in a cosmic *Logos*.

It is astonishing (at this time of day) that I could regard this position as something quite distinct from Theism. I suspect there was some willful blindness. But there were in those days all sorts of blankets, insulators, and insurances which enabled one to get all the conveniences of Theism, without believing in God. The English Hegelians, writers like T. H. Green, Bradley, and Bosanquet (then mighty names), dealt in precisely such wares. The Absolute Mind—better still, the Absolute—was impersonal, or it knew itself (but not us?) only in us, and it was so absolute that it wasn't really much more like a mind than anything else. And anyway, the more muddled one got about it and the more contradictions one committed, the more this proved that our discursive thought moved only on the level of "Appearance," and "Reality" must be somewhere else. And where else but, of course, in the Absolute? There, not here, was "the fuller splendor" behind the "sensuous curtain." The emotion that went with all this was certainly religious. But this was a religion that cost nothing. We could talk religiously about the Absolute: but there was no danger of Its doing anything about us. It was "there"; safely and immovably "there." It would never come "here," never (to be blunt) make a nuisance of Itself. This quasi-religion was all a one-way street; all *eros* (as Dr. Nygren would say) steaming up, but no *agape* darting down. There was nothing to fear; better still, nothing to obey.

Yet there was one really wholesome element in it. The Absolute was "there," and that "there" contained the reconciliation of all contraries, the transcendence of all finitude, the hidden glory which was the only perfectly real thing there is. In fact, it had much of the quality of Heaven. But it was a Heaven none of us could ever get to. For we are appearances. To be "there" is, by definition, not to be we. All who embrace such a philosophy live, like Dante's virtuous Pagans, "in desire without hope." Or like Spinoza they so love their God as to be unable even to wish that He should love them in return. I should be very sorry not to have passed through that experience. I think it is more religious than many experiences that have been called Christian. What I learned from the Idealists (and still most strongly hold) is this maxim: it is more important that Heaven should exist than that any of us should reach it.

And so the great Angler played His fish and I never dreamed that the hook was in my tongue. But two great advances had been made. Bergson had showed me necessary existence; and from Idealism I had come one step nearer to understanding the words, "We give thanks to thee for thy great glory." The Norse gods had given me the first hint of it; but then I didn't believe in them, and I did believe (so far as one can believe an *Unding*) in the Absolute.

XIV

CHECKMATE

The one principle of hell is—"I am my own."
GEORGE MACDONALD

IN THE summer of 1922 I finished Greats. As there were no
philosophical posts going, or none that I could get, my
long-suffering father offered me a fourth year at Oxford
during which I read English so as to get a second string to my
bow. The Great War with Barfield had, I think, begun at
this time.

No sooner had I entered the English School than I went to
George Gordon's discussion class. And there I made a new
friend. The very first words he spoke marked him out from
the ten or twelve others who were present; a man after my
own heart, and that too at an age when the instantaneous
friendships of earlier youth were becoming rather rare
events. His name was Nevill Coghill. I soon had the shock of
discovering that he—clearly the most intelligent and best-
informed man in that class—was a Christian and a thoroughgoing supernaturalist. There were other traits that I liked
but found (for I was still very much a modern) oddly archaic; chivalry, honor, courtesy, "freedom," and "gentil-
lesse." One could imagine him fighting a duel. He spoke
much "ribaldry" but never "villeinye." Barfield was begin-

ning to overthrow my chronological snobbery; Coghill gave it another blow. Had something really dropped out of our lives? Was the archaic simply the civilized, and the modern simply the barbaric? It will seem strange to many of my critics who regard me as a typical *laudator temporis acti* that this question should have arisen so comparatively late in my life. But then the key to my books is Donne's maxim, "The heresies that men leave are hated most." The things I assert most vigorously are those that I resisted long and accepted late.

These disturbing factors in Coghill ranged themselves with a wider disturbance which was now threatening my whole earlier outlook. All the books were beginning to turn against me. Indeed, I must have been as blind as a bat not to have seen, long before, the ludicrous contradiction between my theory of life and my actual experiences as a reader. George MacDonald had done more to me than any other writer; of course it was a pity he had that bee in his bonnet about Christianity. He was good *in spite of it*. Chesterton had more sense than all the other moderns put together; bating, of course, his Christianity. Johnson was one of the few authors whom I felt I could trust utterly; curiously enough, he had the same kink. Spenser and Milton by a strange coincidence had it too. Even among ancient authors the same paradox was to be found. The most religious (Plato, Aeschylus, Virgil) were clearly those on whom I could really feed. On the other hand, those writers who did not suffer from religion and with whom in theory my sympathy ought to have been complete—Shaw and Wells and Mill and Gibbon and Voltaire—

all seemed a little thin; what as boys we called "tinny." It wasn't that I didn't like them. They were all (especially Gibbon) entertaining; but hardly more. There seemed to be no depth in them. They were too simple. The roughness and density of life did not appear in their books.

Now that I was reading more English, the paradox began to be aggravated. I was deeply moved by the *Dream of the Rood;* more deeply still by Langland: intoxicated (for a time) by Donne; deeply and lastingly satisfied by Thomas Browne. But the most alarming of all was George Herbert. Here was a man who seemed to me to excel all the authors I had ever read in conveying the very quality of life as we actually live it from moment to moment; but the wretched fellow, instead of doing it all directly, insisted on mediating it through what I would still have called "the Christian mythology." On the other hand most of the authors who might be claimed as precursors of modern enlightenment seemed to me very small beer and bored me cruelly. I thought Bacon (to speak frankly) a solemn, pretentious ass, yawned my way through Restoration Comedy, and, having manfully struggled on to the last line of *Don Juan,* wrote on the end leaf "Never again." The only non-Christians who seemed to me really to know anything were the Romantics; and a good many of them were dangerously tinged with something like religion, even at times with Christianity. The upshot of it all could nearly be expressed in a perversion of Roland's great line in the *Chanson—*

Christians are wrong, but all the rest are bores.

The natural step would have been to inquire a little more closely whether the Christians were, after all, wrong. But I did not take it. I thought I could explain their superiority without that hypothesis. Absurdly (yet many Absolute Idealists have shared this absurdity) I thought that "the Christian myth" conveyed to unphilosophic minds as much of the truth, that is of Absolute Idealism, as they were capable of grasping, and that even that much put them above the irreligious. Those who could not rise to the notion of the Absolute would come nearer to the truth by belief in "a God" than by disbelief. Those who could not understand how, as Reasoners, we participated in a timeless and therefore deathless world, would get a symbolic shadow of the truth by believing in a life after death. The implication—that something which I and most other undergraduates could master without extraordinary pains would have been too hard for Plato, Dante, Hooker, and Pascal—did not yet strike me as absurd. I hope this is because I never looked it squarely in the face.

As the plot quickens and thickens toward its end, I leave out more and more of such matters as would go into a full autobiography. My father's death, with all the fortitude (even playfulness) which he displayed in his last illness, does not really come into the story I am telling. My brother was at that time in Shanghai. Nor would it be relevant to tell in detail how I became a temporary lecturer at Univ for a year and was elected a fellow of Magdalen in 1925. The worst is that I must leave undescribed many men whom I love and to whom I am deeply in debt; G. H. Stevenson and E. F. Carritt, my tutors, the Fark (but who could paint him anyway?), and five great Magdalen men who enlarged my very idea of what a learned life should be—P. V. M. Benecke, C. C. J. Webb, J. A. Smith, F. E. Brightman, and C. T. Onions. Except for Oldie, I have always been blessed both in my official and my unofficial teachers. In my earlier years at Magdalen I inhabited a world where hardly anything I wanted to know needed to be found out by my own unaided efforts. One or other of these could always give you a clue. ("You'll find something about it in Alanus. . . ."—"Macrobius would be the man to try. . . ."—"Doesn't Comparetti mention it?" . . . "Have you looked for it in Du Cange?") I found, as always, that the ripest are kindest to the raw and the most studious have most time to spare. When I began teaching for the English Faculty, I made two other friends, both Christians (these queer people seemed now to pop up on every side) who were later to give me much help in getting over the last stile. They were H. V. V. Dyson (then of Reading) and J. R. R. Tolkien. Friendship with the latter marked the breakdown of two old prejudices. At my first coming into the world I had been (implicitly) warned never to trust a Papist, and at my first coming into the English Faculty (explicitly) never to trust a philologist. Tolkien was both.

Realism had been abandoned; the New Look was somewhat damaged; and chronological snobbery was seriously shaken. All over the board my pieces were in the most disadvantageous positions. Soon I could no longer cherish even the illusion that the initiative lay with me. My Adversary began to make His final moves.

The first Move annihilated the last remains of the New Look. I was suddenly impelled to reread (which was certainly no business of mine at the moment) the *Hippolytus* of Euripides. In one chorus all that world's end imagery which I had rejected when I assumed my New Look rose before me. I liked, but did not yield; I tried to patronize it. But next day I was overwhelmed. There was a transitional moment of delicious uneasiness, and then—instantaneously—the long inhibition was over, the dry desert lay behind, I was off once more into the land of longing, my heart at once broken and exalted as it had never been since the old days at Bookham. There was nothing whatever to do about it; no question of returning to the desert. I had simply been ordered—or, rather, compelled—to "take that look off my face." And never to resume it either.

The next Move was intellectual, and consolidated the first Move. I read in Alexander's *Space Time and Deity* his theory of "Enjoyment" and "Contemplation." These are technical terms in Alexander's philosophy; "Enjoyment" has nothing to do with pleasure, nor "Contemplation" with the contemplative life. When you see a table you "enjoy" the act of seeing and "contemplate" the table. Later, if you took up Optics and thought about Seeing itself, you would be contemplating the seeing and enjoying the thought. In bereavement you contemplate the beloved and the beloved's death and, in Alexander's sense, "enjoy" the loneliness and grief; but a psychologist, if he were considering you as a case of melancholia, would be contemplating your grief and enjoying psychology. We do not "think a thought" in the same sense in which we "think that Herodotus is unreliable." When we think a thought, "thought" is a cognate accusative (like "blow" in "strike a blow"). We enjoy the thought (that Herodotus is unreliable) and, in so doing, contemplate the unreliability of Herodotus.

I accepted this distinction at once and have ever since regarded it as an indispensable tool of thought. A moment later its consequences—for me quite catastrophic—began to appear. It seemed to me self-evident that one essential property of love, hate, fear, hope, or desire was attention to their object. To cease thinking about or attending to the woman is, so far, to cease loving; to cease thinking about or attending to the dreaded thing is, so far, to cease being afraid. But to attend to your own love or fear is to cease attending to the loved or dreaded object. In other words the enjoyment and the contemplation of our inner activities are incompatible. You cannot hope and also think about hoping at the same moment; for in hope we look to hope's object and we interrupt this by (so to speak) turning round to look at the hope itself. Of course the two activities can and do alternate with great rapidity; but they are distinct and incompatible. This was not merely a logical result of Alexander's analysis, but could be verified in daily and hourly experience. The surest means of disarming an anger or a lust was to turn your attention from the girl or the insult and start examining the passion itself. The surest way of spoiling a pleasure was to start examining your satisfaction. But if so, it followed that all introspection is in one respect misleading. In introspection we try to look "inside ourselves" and see what is going on.

But nearly everything that was going on a moment before is stopped by the very act of our turning to look at it. Unfortunately this does not mean that introspection finds nothing. On the contrary, it finds precisely what is left behind by the suspension of all our normal activities; and what is left behind is mainly mental images and physical sensations. The great error is to mistake this mere sediment or track or by-product for the activities themselves. That is how men may come to believe that thought is only unspoken words, or the appreciation of poetry only a collection of mental pictures, when these in reality are what the thought or the appreciation, when interrupted, leave behind—like the swell at sea, working after the wind has dropped. Not, of course, that these activities, before we stopped them by introspection, were unconscious. We do not love, fear, or think without knowing it. Instead of the twofold division into Conscious and Unconscious, we need a threefold division: the Unconscious, the Enjoyed, and the Contemplated.

This discovery flashed a new light back on my whole life. I saw that all my waitings and watchings for Joy, all my vain hopes to find some mental content on which I could, so to speak, lay my finger and say, "This is it," had been a futile attempt to contemplate the enjoyed. All that such watching and waiting ever *could* find would be either an image (Asgard, the Western Garden, or what not) or a quiver in the diaphragm. I should never have to bother again about these images or sensations. I knew now that they were merely the mental track left by the passage of Joy—not the wave but the wave's imprint on the sand. The inherent dialectic of desire itself had in a way already shown me this; for all images and sensations, if idolatrously mistaken for Joy itself, soon honestly confessed themselves inadequate. All said, in the last resort, "It is not I. I am only a reminder. Look! Look! What do I remind you of?"

So far, so good. But it is at the next step that awe overtakes me. There was no doubt that Joy was a desire (and, in so far as it was also simultaneously a good, it was also a kind of love). But a desire is turned not to itself but to its object. Not only that, but it owes all its character to its object. Erotic love is not like desire for food, nay, a love for one woman differs from a love for another woman in the very same way and the very same degree as the two women differ from one another. Even our desire for one wine differs in tone from our desire for another. Our intellectual desire (curiosity) to know the true answer to a question is quite different from our desire to find that one answer, rather than another, is true. The form of the desired is in the desire. It is the object which makes the desire harsh or sweet, coarse or choice, "high" or "low." It is the object that makes the desire itself desirable or hateful. I perceived (and this was a wonder of wonders) that just as I had been wrong in supposing that I really desired the Garden of the Hesperides, so also I had been equally wrong in supposing that I desired Joy itself. Joy itself, considered simply as an event in my own mind, turned out to be of no value at all. All the value lay in that of which Joy was the desiring. And that object, quite clearly, was no state of my own mind or body at all. In a way, I had proved this by elimination. I had tried everything in my own mind and body; as it were, asking myself, "Is it this you want? Is it this?" Last of all I had asked if Joy itself was what I wanted; and, labelling it "aesthetic experience," had pretended I could answer Yes. But that answer too had broken down. Inexorably Joy proclaimed, "You want—I myself am your want of—something other, outside, not you nor any state of you." I did not yet ask, Who is the desired? only What is it? But this brought me already into the region of awe, for I thus understood that in deepest solitude there is a road right out of the self, a commerce with something which, by refusing to identify itself with any object of the senses, or anything whereof we have biological or social need, or anything imagined, or any state of our own minds, proclaims itself sheerly objective. Far more objective than bodies, for it is not, like them, clothed in our senses; the naked Other, imageless (though our imagination salutes it with a hundred images), unknown, undefined, desired.

That was the second Move; equivalent, perhaps, to the loss of one's last remaining bishop. The third Move did not seem to me dangerous at the time. It consisted merely in linking up this new *éclaircissement* about Joy with my idealistic philosophy. I saw that Joy, as I now understood it, would fit in. We mortals, seen as the sciences see us and as we commonly see one another, are mere "appearances." But appearances of the Absolute. In so far as we really are at all (which isn't saying much) we have, so to speak, a root in the Absolute, which is the utter reality. And that is why we experience Joy: we yearn, rightly, for that unity which we can never reach except by ceasing to be the separate phenomenal beings called "we." Joy was not a deception. Its visitations were rather the moments of clearest consciousness we had, when we became aware of our fragmentary and phantasmal nature and ached for that impossible reunion which would annihilate us or that self-contradictory waking which would reveal, not that we had had, but that we *were*, a dream. This seemed quite satisfactory intellectually. Even emotionally too; for it matters more that Heaven should exist than that we should ever get there. What I did not notice was that I had passed an important milestone. Up till now my thoughts had been centrifugal; now the centripetal movement had begun. Considerations arising from quite different parts of my experience were beginning to come together with a click. This new dovetailing of my desire-life with my philosophy foreshadowed the day, now fast approaching, when I should be forced to take my "philosophy" more seriously than I ever intended. I did not foresee this. I was like a man who has lost "merely a pawn" and never dreams that this (in that state of the game) means mate in a few moves.

The fourth Move was more alarming. I was now teaching philosophy (I suspect very badly) as well as English. And my watered Hegelianism wouldn't serve for tutorial purposes.[1] A tutor must make things clear. Now the Absolute cannot be made clear. Do you mean Nobody-knows-what, or do you mean a superhuman mind and therefore (we may as well admit) a Person? After all, did Hegel and Bradley and all the rest of them ever do more than add

[1] Not, of course, that I thought it a tutor's business to make converts to his own philosophy. But I found I needed a position of my own as a basis from which to criticize my pupils' essays.

mystifications to the simple, workable, theistic idealism of Berkeley? I thought not. And didn't Berkeley's "God" do all the same work as the Absolute, with the added advantage that we had at least some notion of what we meant by Him? I thought He did. So I was driven back into something like Berkeleyanism; but Berkeleyanism with a few top dressings of my own. I distinguished this philosophical "God" very sharply (or so I said) from "the God of popular religion." There was, I explained, no possibility of being in a personal relation with Him. For I thought He projected us as a dramatist projects his characters, and I could no more "meet" Him, than Hamlet could meet Shakespeare. I didn't call Him "God" either; I called Him "Spirit." One fights for one's remaining comforts.

Then I read Chesterton's *Everlasting Man* and for the first time saw the whole Christian outline of history set out in a form that seemed to me to make sense. Somehow I contrived not to be too badly shaken. You will remember that I already thought Chesterton the most sensible man alive "apart from his Christianity." Now, I veritably believe, I thought—I didn't of course *say;* words would have revealed the nonsense —that Christianity itself was very sensible "apart from its Christianity." But I hardly remember, for I had not long finished *The Everlasting Man* when something far more alarming happened to me. Early in 1926 the hardest boiled of all the atheists I ever knew sat in my room on the other side of the fire and remarked that the evidence for the historicity of the Gospels was really surprisingly good. "Rum thing," he went on. "All that stuff of Frazer's about the Dying God.

Rum thing. It almost looks as if it had really happened once."
To understand the shattering impact of it, you would need to
know the man (who has certainly never since shown any interest in Christianity). If he, the cynic of cynics, the toughest
of the toughs, were not—as I would still have put it—"safe,"
where could I turn? Was there then no escape?

The odd thing was that before God closed in on me, I was
in fact offered what now appears a moment of wholly free
choice. In a sense. I was going up Headington Hill on the top
of a bus. Without words and (I think) almost without
images, a fact about myself was somehow presented to me. I
became aware that I was holding something at bay, or shutting something out. Or, if you like, that I was wearing some
stiff clothing, like corsets, or even a suit of armor, as if I were
a lobster. I felt myself being, there and then, given a free
choice. I could open the door or keep it shut; I could unbuckle the armor or keep it on. Neither choice was presented
as a duty; no threat or promise was attached to either, though
I knew that to open the door or to take off the corslet meant
the incalculable. The choice appeared to be momentous but
it was also strangely unemotional. I was moved by no desires
or fears. In a sense I was not moved by anything. I chose to
open, to unbuckle, to loosen the rein. I say, "I chose," yet it
did not really seem possible to do the opposite. On the other
hand, I was aware of no motives. You could argue that I was
not a free agent, but I am more inclined to think that this
came nearer to being a perfectly free act than most that I
have ever done. Necessity may not be the opposite of freedom, and perhaps a man is most free when, instead of produc-

ing motives, he could only say, "I am what I do." Then came the repercussion on the imaginative level. I felt as if I were a man of snow at long last beginning to melt. The melting was starting in my back—drip-drip and presently trickle-trickle. I rather disliked the feeling.

The fox had been dislodged from Hegelian Wood and was now running in the open, "with all the wo in the world," bedraggled and weary, hounds barely a field behind. And nearly everyone was now (one way or another) in the pack; Plato, Dante, MacDonald, Herbert, Barfield, Tolkien, Dyson, Joy itself. Everyone and everything had joined the other side. Even my own pupil Griffiths—now Dom Bede Griffiths— though not yet himself a believer, did his share. Once, when he and Barfield were lunching in my room, I happened to refer to philosophy as "a subject." "It wasn't a *subject* to Plato," said Barfield, "it was a way." The quiet but fervent agreement of Griffiths, and the quick glance of understanding between these two, revealed to me my own frivolity. Enough had been thought, and said, and felt, and imagined. It was about time that something should be done.

For of course there had long been an ethic (theoretically) attached to my Idealism. I thought the business of us finite and half-unreal souls was to multiply the consciousness of Spirit by seeing the world from different positions while yet remaining qualitatively the same as Spirit; to be tied to a particular time and place and set of circumstances, yet there to will and think as Spirit itself does. This was hard; for the very act whereby Spirit projected souls and a world gave those souls different and competitive interests, so that there was a temptation to selfishness. But I thought each of us had it in his power to discount the emotional perspective produced by his own particular selfhood, just as we discount the optical perspective produced by our position in space. To prefer my own happiness to my neighbor's was like thinking that the nearest telegraph post was really the largest. The way to recover, and act upon, this universal and objective vision was daily and hourly to remember our true nature, to reascend or return into that Spirit which, in so far as we really were at all, we still were. Yes; but I now felt I had better try to do it. I faced at last (in MacDonald's words) "some thing to be neither more nor less nor other than *done*." An attempt at complete virtue must be made.

Really, a young Atheist cannot guard his faith too carefully. Dangers lie in wait for him on every side. You must not do, you must not even try to do, the will of the Father unless you are prepared to "know of the doctrine." All my acts, desires, and thoughts were to be brought into harmony with universal Spirit. For the first time I examined myself with a seriously practical purpose. And there I found what appalled me; a zoo of lusts, a bedlam of ambitions, a nursery of fears, a harem of fondled hatreds. My name was legion.

Of course I could do nothing—I could not last out one hour—without continual conscious recourse to what I called Spirit. But the fine, philosophical distinction between this and what ordinary people call "prayer to God" breaks down as soon as you start doing it in earnest. Idealism can be talked, and even felt; it cannot be lived. It became patently absurd to go on thinking of "Spirit" as either ignorant of, or passive to, my approaches. Even if my own philosophy were true, how could the initiative lie on my side? My own analogy, as I now first perceived, suggested the opposite: if Shakespeare and Hamlet could ever meet, it must be Shakespeare's doing.[1] Hamlet could initiate nothing. Perhaps, even now, my Absolute Spirit still differed in some way from the God of religion. The real issue was not, or not yet, there. The real terror was that if you seriously believed in even such a "God" or "Spirit" as I admitted, a wholly new situation developed. As the dry bones shook and came together in that dreadful valley of Ezekiel's, so now a philosophical theorem, cerebrally entertained, began to stir and heave and throw off its grave-cloths, and stood upright and became a living presence. I was to be allowed to play at philosophy no longer. It might, as I say, still be true that my "Spirit" differed in some way from "the God of popular religion." My Adversary waived the point. It sank into utter unimportance. He would not argue about it. He only said, "I am the Lord"; "I am that I am"; "I am."

People who are naturally religious find difficulty in understanding the horror of such a revelation. Amiable agnostics will talk cheerfully about "man's search for God." To me, as I then was, they might as well have talked about the mouse's search for the cat. The best image of my predicament is the meeting of Mime and Wotan in the first act of *Siegfried; hier brauch' ich nicht Spärer noch Späher, Einsam will ich.* . . .

[1] *I.e.,* Shakespeare could, in principle, make himself appear as Author within the play, and write a dialogue between Hamlet and himself. The "Shakespeare" within the play would of course be at once Shakespeare and one of Shakespeare's creatures. It would bear some analogy to Incarnation.

(I've no use for spies and snoopers. I would be private. . . .)

Remember, I had always wanted, above all things, not to be "interfered with." I had wanted (mad wish) "to call my soul my own." I had been far more anxious to avoid suffering than to achieve delight. I had always aimed at limited liabilities. The supernatural itself had been to me, first, an illicit dram, and then, as by a drunkard's reaction, nauseous. Even my recent attempt to live my philosophy had secretly (I now knew) been hedged round by all sorts of reservations. I had pretty well known that my ideal of virtue would never be allowed to lead me into anything intolerably painful; I would be "reasonable." But now what had been an ideal became a command; and what might not be expected of one? Doubtless, by definition, God was Reason itself. But would He also be "reasonable" in that other, more comfortable, sense? Not the slightest assurance on that score was offered me. Total surrender, the absolute leap in the dark, were demanded. The reality with which no treaty can be made was upon me. The demand was not even "All or nothing." I think that stage had been passed, on the bus top when I unbuckled my armor and the snowman started to melt. Now, the demand was simply "All."

You must picture me alone in that room in Magdalen, night after night, feeling, whenever my mind lifted even for a second from my work, the steady, unrelenting approach of Him whom I so earnestly desired not to meet. That which I greatly feared had at last come upon me. In the Trinity Term of 1929 I gave in, and admitted that God was God, and knelt and prayed: perhaps, that night, the most dejected and reluctant convert in all England. I did not then see what is now the most shining and obvious thing; the Divine humility which will accept a convert even on such terms. The Prodigal Son at least walked home on his own feet. But who can duly adore that Love which will open the high gates to a prodigal who is brought in kicking, struggling, resentful, and darting his eyes in every direction for a chance of escape? The words *compelle intrare*, compel them to come in, have been so abused by wicked men that we shudder at them; but, properly understood, they plumb the depth of the Divine mercy. The hardness of God is kinder than the softness of men, and His compulsion is our liberation.

XV

THE BEGINNING

Aliud est de silvestri cacumine videre patriam pacis
. . . et aliud tenere viam illuc ducentem.

ST. AUGUSTINE, *Confessions*, VII, xxi

For it is one thing to see the land of peace from a
wooded ridge . . . and another to tread the road that
leads to it.

IT MUST be understood that the conversion recorded in the last chapter was only to Theism, pure and simple, not to Christianity. I knew nothing yet about the Incarnation. The God to whom I surrendered was sheerly nonhuman.

It may be asked whether my terror was at all relieved by the thought that I was now approaching the source from which those arrows of Joy had been shot at me ever since childhood. Not in the least. No slightest hint was vouchsafed me that there ever had been or ever would be any connection between God and Joy. If anything, it was the reverse. I had hoped that the heart of reality might be of such a kind that we can best symbolize it as a place; instead, I found it to be a Person. For all I knew, the total rejection of what I called Joy might be one of the demands, might be the very first demand, He would make upon me. There was no strain of music from within, no smell of eternal orchards at the threshold, when I was dragged through the doorway. No kind of desire was present at all.

My conversion involved as yet no belief in a future life. I now number it among my greatest mercies that I was permitted for several months, perhaps for a year, to know God and to attempt obedience without even raising that question. My training was like that of the Jews, to whom He revealed Himself centuries before there was a whisper of anything better (or worse) beyond the grave than shadowy and featureless *Sheol*. And I did not dream even of that. There are men, far better men than I, who have made immortality almost the central doctrine of their religion; but for my own part I have never seen how a preoccupation with that subject at the outset could fail to corrupt the whole thing. I had been brought up to believe that goodness was goodness only if it were disinterested, and that any hope of reward or fear of punishment contaminated the will. If I was wrong in this (the question is really much more complicated than I then perceived) my error was most tenderly allowed for. I was afraid that threats or promises would demoralize me; no threats or promises were made. The commands were inexorable, but they were backed by no "sanctions." God was to be obeyed simply because he was God. Long since, through the gods of Asgard, and later through the notion of the Absolute, He had taught me how a thing can be revered not for what it can do to us but for what it is in itself. That is why, though it was a terror, it was no surprise to learn that God is to be obeyed because of what He is in Himself. If you ask why we should obey God, in the last resort the answer is, "I am." To know

God is to know that our obedience is due to Him. In His nature His sovereignty *de jure* is revealed.

Of course, as I have said, the matter is more complicated than that. The primal and necessary Being, the Creator, has sovereignty *de facto* as well as *de jure*. He has the power as well as the kingdom and the glory. But the *de jure* sovereignty was made known to me before the power, the right before the might. And for this I am thankful. I think it is well, even now, sometimes to say to ourselves, "God is such that if (*per impossibile*) his power could vanish and His other attributes remain, so that the supreme right were forever robbed of the supreme might, we should still owe Him precisely the same kind and degree of allegiance as we now do." On the other hand, while it is true to say that God's own nature is the real sanction of His commands, yet to understand this must, in the end, lead us to the conclusion that union with that Nature is bliss and separation from it horror. Thus Heaven and Hell come in. But it may well be that to think much of either except in this context of thought, to hypostatize them as if they had a substantial meaning apart from the presence or absence of God, corrupts the doctrine of both and corrupts us while we so think of them.

The last stage in my story, the transition from mere Theism to Christianity, is the one on which I am now least informed. Since it is also the most recent, this ignorance may seem strange. I think there are two reasons. One is that as we grow older we remember the more distant past better than what is nearer. But the other is, I believe, that one of the first results of my Theistic conversion was a marked decrease (and high time, as all readers of this book will agree) in the fussy attentiveness which I had so long paid to the progress of my own opinions and the states of my own mind. For many healthy extroverts self-examination first begins with conversion. For me it was almost the other way round. Self-examination did of course continue. But it was (I suppose, for I cannot quite remember) at stated intervals, and for a practical purpose; a duty, a discipline, an uncomfortable thing, no longer a hobby or a habit. To believe and to pray were the beginning of extroversion. I had been, as they say, "taken out of myself." If Theism had done nothing else for me, I should still be thankful that it cured me of the time-wasting and foolish practice of keeping a diary. (Even for autobiographical purposes a diary is nothing like so useful as I had hoped. You put down each day what you think important; but of course you cannot each day see what will prove to have been important in the long run.[1])

As soon as I became a Theist I started attending my parish church on Sundays and my college chapel on weekdays; not because I believed in Christianity, nor because I thought the difference between it and simple Theism a small one, but because I thought one ought to "fly one's flag" by some unmistakable overt sign. I was acting in obedience to a (perhaps mistaken) sense of honor. The idea of churchmanship was to me wholly unattractive. I was not in the least anticlerical, but

[1] The only real good I got from keeping a diary was that it taught me a just appreciation of Boswell's amazing genius. I tried very hard to reproduce conversations, in some of which very amusing and striking people had taken part. But none of these people came to life in the diary at all. Obviously something quite different from mere accurate reporting went to the presentation of Boswell's Langton, Beauclerk, Wilkes, and the rest.

I was deeply antiecclesiastical. That curates and archdeacons and churchwardens should exist was admirable. They gratified my Jenkinian love of everything which has its own strong flavor. And (apart from Oldie) I had been fortunate in my clerical acquaintances; especially in Adam Fox, the Dean of Divinity at Magdalen, and in Arthur Barton (later Archbishop of Dublin) who had been our Rector at home in Ireland. (He, by the by, had once suffered under Oldie at Belsen. Speaking of Oldie's death, I had said to him, "Well, we shan't see *him* again." "You mean," he answered with a grim smile, "we *hope* we shan't.") But though I liked clergymen as I liked bears, I had as little wish to be in the Church as in the zoo. It was, to begin with, a kind of collective; a wearisome "get-together" affair. I couldn't yet see how a concern of that sort should have anything to do with one's spiritual life. To me, religion ought to have been a matter of good men praying alone and meeting by twos and threes to talk of spiritual matters. And then the fussy, time-wasting botheration of it all! the bells, the crowds, the umbrellas, the notices, the bustle, the perpetual arranging and organizing. Hymns were (and are) extremely disagreeable to me. Of all musical instruments I liked (and like) the organ least. I have, too, a sort of spiritual *gaucherie* which makes me unapt to participate in any rite.

Thus my churchgoing was a merely symbolical and provisional practice. If it in fact helped to move me in the Christian direction, I was and am unaware of this. My chief companion on this stage of the road was Griffiths, with whom I kept up a copious correspondence. Both now believed in

God, and were ready to hear more of Him from any source, Pagan or Christian. In my mind (I cannot now answer for his and he has told his own story admirably in *The Golden String*) the perplexing multiplicity of "religions" began to sort itself out. The real clue had been put into my hand by that hard-boiled Atheist when he said, "Rum thing, all that about the Dying God. Seems to have really happened once"; by him and by Barfield's encouragement of a more respectful, if not more delighted, attitude to Pagan myth. The question was no longer to find the one simply true religion among a thousand religions simply false. It was rather, "Where has religion reached its true maturity? Where, if anywhere, have the hints of all Paganism been fulfilled?" With the irreligious I was no longer concerned; their view of life was henceforth out of court. As against them, the whole mass of those who had worshiped—all who had danced and sung and sacrificed and trembled and adored—were clearly right. But the intellect and the conscience, as well as the orgy and the ritual, must be our guide. There could be no question of going back to primitive, untheologized and unmoralized, Paganism. The God whom I had at last acknowledged was one, and was righteous. Paganism had been only the childhood of religion, or only a prophetic dream. Where was the thing full grown? or where was the awakening? (*The Everlasting Man* was helping me here.) There were really only two answers possible: either in Hinduism or in Christianity. Everything else was either a preparation for, or else (in the French sense) a *vulgarization* of, these. Whatever you could find elsewhere you could find better in one of these. But Hinduism seemed to have two disqualifications. For one thing, it appeared to be not so much a moralized and philosophical maturity of Paganism as a mere oil-and-water coexistence of philosophy side by side with Paganism unpurged; the Brahmin meditating in the forest, and, in the village a few miles away, temple prostitution, *sati*, cruelty, monstrosity. And secondly, there was no such historical claim as in Christianity. I was by now too experienced in literary criticism to regard the Gospels as myths. They had not the mythical taste. And yet the very matter which they set down in their artless, historical fashion—those narrow, unattractive Jews, too blind to the mythical wealth of the Pagan world around them—was precisely the matter of the great myths. If ever a myth had become fact, had been incarnated, it would be just like this. And nothing else in all literature was just like this. Myths were like it in one way. Histories were like it in another. But nothing was simply like it. And no person was like the Person it depicted; as real, as recognizable, through all that depth of time, as Plato's Socrates or Boswell's Johnson (ten times more so than Eckermann's Goethe or Lockhart's Scott), yet also numinous, lit by a light from beyond the world, a god. But if a god—we are no longer polytheists—then not a god, but God. Here and here only in all time the myth must have become fact; the Word, flesh; God, Man. This is not "a religion," nor "a philosophy." It is the summing up and actuality of them all.

As I have said, I speak of this last transition less certainly than of any which went before it, and it may be that in the preceding paragraph I have mixed thoughts that came later. But I can hardly be wrong about the main lines. Of one thing

I am sure. As I drew near the conclusion, I felt a resistance almost as strong as my previous resistance to Theism. As strong, but shorter-lived, for I understood it better. Every step I had taken, from the Absolute to "Spirit" and from "Spirit" to "God," had been a step toward the more concrete, the more imminent, the more compulsive. At each step one had less chance "to call one's soul one's own." To accept the Incarnation was a further step in the same direction. It brings God nearer, or near in a new way. And this, I found, was something I had not wanted. But to recognize the ground for my evasion was of course to recognize both its shame and its futility. I know very well when, but hardly how, the final step was taken. I was driven to Whipsnade one sunny morning. When we set out I did not believe that Jesus Christ is the Son of God, and when we reached the zoo I did. Yet I had not exactly spent the journey in thought. Nor in great emotion. "Emotional" is perhaps the last word we can apply to some of the most important events. It was more like when a man, after long sleep, still lying motionless in bed, becomes aware that he is now awake. And it was, like that moment on top of the bus, ambiguous. Freedom, or necessity? Or do they differ at their maximum? At that maximum a man is what he does; there is nothing of him left over or outside the act. As for what we commonly call Will, and what we commonly call Emotion, I fancy these usually talk too loud, protest too much, to be quite believed, and we have a secret suspicion that the great passion or the iron resolution is partly a put-up job.

They have spoiled Whipsnade since then. Wallaby Wood,

with the birds singing overhead and the bluebells underfoot and the Wallabies hopping all round one, was almost Eden come again.

But what, in conclusion, of Joy? for that, after all, is what the story has mainly been about. To tell you the truth, the subject has lost nearly all interest for me since I became a Christian. I cannot, indeed, complain, like Wordsworth, that the visionary gleam has passed away. I believe (if the thing were at all worth recording) that the old stab, the old bitter-sweet, has come to me as often and as sharply since my con-version as at any time of my life whatever. But I now know that the experience, considered as a state of my own mind, had never had the kind of importance I once gave it. It was valuable only as a pointer to something other and outer. While that other was in doubt, the pointer naturally loomed large in my thoughts. When we are lost in the woods the sight of a signpost is a great matter. He who first sees it cries, "Look!" The whole party gathers round and stares. But when we have found the road and are passing signposts every few miles, we shall not stop and stare. They will encourage us and we shall be grateful to the authority that set them up. But we shall not stop and stare, or not much; not on this road, though their pillars are of silver and their lettering of gold. "We would be at Jerusalem."

Not, of course, that I don't often catch myself stopping to stare at roadside objects of even less importance.